SOMATIC CELL GENETICS

SOMATIC CELL GENETICS

Fourth Macy Conference on Genetics

Edited by
ROBERT S. KROOTH, M. D.

Ann Arbor: The University of Michigan Press

PREFACE

Substantial progress appears to have been made during the last five years in the genetic study of cultured mammalian cells. The reasons for the increased activity in this field seem, at least to me, to fall into two categories.

First, on the technical level a great many events have made mammalian cell culture an easier and more repeatable experimental technique than it formerly was. I list the following (in arbitrary order) as among the most important:

1. The availability of antibiotics for use in cell culture media.
2. The availability of reliably pure biochemicals.
3. The clarification of the nutritional requirements of cultured mammalian cells.
4. The development of techniques that virtually always work for the initiation of human and other mammalian cell strains.
5. The development of techniques for an adequate visualization of the chromosomes of cultured mammalian cells.

Second, on the intellectual level, the striking advances that have been made in microbial genetics since World War II have led almost everyone to wonder whether analogous phenomena may also occur in cultures of mammalian cells.

Much of the progress that has been made is reported in this Fourth Macy Conference on Genetics. Although I have called this book *Somatic Cell Genetics,* most of it is devoted to but one aspect of the subject: Studies on cultured mammalian cells. Chapter I explores mammalian chromosomal genetics—this field was made possible by the fifth technical event I referred to above. The work here deals mainly with studies designed to show an association between the karyotype of a donor, or of a cell, and his or its phenotype. Chapter II deals with the phenotypic markers that have been used in cell culture to distinguish genetically disparate cells. In the second part of this chapter, experiments analogous to some of those performed in microbial genetics are reported.

The Preface published with the previous Macy Conferences on Genetics (and written by Dr. W. J. Schull) is also included here, following this one. It describes the history, purpose, and some of the editorial problems of these conferences. My own interpretation of the editor's role is that he is supposed to be only a collator. I have, therefore, left the documentation of statements, the citation of appropriate literature, etc., entirely to the individual participants. I have also permitted some revisions. It is difficult to enforce on one's colleagues restrictions that one would not wish to impose on oneself. In the main, however, this book is an accurate and nearly verbatim account of the conference.

ROBERT S. KROOTH

THE MACY CONFERENCES ON GENETICS

Somewhat over twenty years ago, the Josiah Macy, Jr. Foundation initiated a series of regularly scheduled conferences directed toward challenging problems in medicine and health. With time, firm but not immutable ground rules have been evolved for the conduct of these sessions. Thus, each conference group is to meet annually for a period of five or more years. Twenty-five persons, selected to represent a multi-discipline approach, are to participate in a meeting. These individuals are termed conference members if they have been selected to participate in a single meeting.

The purpose of each conference is the promotion of communication, the exchange of ideas. To this end, an informal give-and-take among the participants, members and guests, is encouraged. Structure and continuity are given the discussion by a leader whose function is to present some of the more interesting aspects of the problem under discussion. The participants are enjoined to interrupt this presentation with questions, criticisms, and comment. At their best, the interruptions lay bare the birth and maturation of an idea, and form, therefore, an essential part of the lessons to be gained from the conference process. To share these lessons as widely as possible, an edited transcript of the meeting is published. These transactions, which attempt to retain the spontaneity of the discussion, have aroused considerable interest and criticism. Comments range from an enthusiasm for, to a total rejection of, the personalized approach. Criticism, in the words of Frank Fremont-Smith, for many years the guardian of these conferences, "has been directed primarily to editorial permissiveness which has allowed in the final text, in some instances, too many questions, remarks, or comments which, although perhaps useful during a heated discussion, seem out of context and interrupt the sequence of thought." Clearly, not all critics recognize the narrowness of the path between spontaneity, on the one hand, and editorial permissiveness, on the other, nor the challenges which confront the editor.

WILLIAM J. SCHULL

CONTENTS

PARTICIPANTS

Fourth Josiah Macy, Jr. Conference on Genetics

October 15–17, 1962

Princeton, New Jersey

MEMBERS

Chairman:
Dr. James V. Neel
Department of Human Genetics
University of Michigan
Medical School
Ann Arbor, Michigan

Dr. Kimball G. Atwood
Department of Microbiology
University of Illinois
Urbana, Illinois

Dr. Alexander Gordon Bearn
Rockefeller Institute
New York, New York

*Dr. Charles W. Cotterman
Department of Medical Genetics
University of Wisconsin
Medical School
Madison, Wisconsin

Dr. James F. Crow
Department of Medical Genetics
University of Wisconsin
Medical School
Madison, Wisconsin

*Dr. H. Bentley Glass
Department of Biology
Johns Hopkins University
Baltimore, Maryland

*Absent

*Dr. Joshua Lederberg
Department of Genetics
Stanford University
School of Medicine
Palo Alto, California

Dr. Victor A. McKusick
Department of Medicine
Johns Hopkins University
School of Medicine
Baltimore, Maryland

Dr. Arno G. Motulsky
Department of Medicine
University of Washington
School of Medicine
Seattle, Washington

Dr. William J. Schull
Department of Human Genetics
University of Michigan
Medical School
Ann Arbor, Michigan

Dr. Arthur G. Steinberg
Department of Biology
Western Reserve University
Cleveland, Ohio

Dr. Curt Stern
Department of Zoology
University of California
Berkeley, California

GUESTS

Dr. Klaus E. Bayreuther
Division of Biology
California Institute of Technology
Pasadena, California

Dr. Rupert E. Billingham
The Wistar Institute
Philadelphia, Pennsylvania

Dr. Ernest H. Y. Chu
Biology Division
Oak Ridge National Laboratory
Oak Ridge, Tennessee

Dr. Robert DeMars
Department of Medical Genetics
University of Wisconsin
Medical School
Madison, Wisconsin

Dr. Harry S. Eagle
Department of Cell Biology
Albert Einstein College of Medicine
New York, New York

Prof. Boris Ephrussi
Department of Developmental Biology
Western Reserve University
Cleveland, Ohio

Dr. Stanley M. Gartler
Depts. of Medicine and Genetics
University of Washington
School of Medicine
Seattle, Washington

Dr. Leonard A. Herzenberg
Department of Genetics
Stanford University
School of Medicine
Palo Alto, California

Dr. Hilary Koprowski
The Wistar Institute
Philadelphia, Pennsylvania

Dr. Robert S. Krooth
Department of Human Genetics
University of Michigan
Medical School
Ann Arbor, Michigan

Dr. Jerome Lejeune
Institut de Progenèse
Faculté de Médecine
Paris, France

Dr. Klaus Patau
Department of Medical Genetics
University of Wisconsin
Medical School
Madison, Wisconsin

Dr. James Renwick
Department of Genetics
University of Glasgow
Glasgow, Scotland

Dr. Waclaw Szybalski
McArdle Laboratory
University of Wisconsin
Madison, Wisconsin

FROM THE FOUNDATION

Dr. Willard C. Rappleye, President

STENOTYPIST

Miss Edna Meininger

CHAPTER I: HUMAN CHROMOSOMAL GENETICS

The Study of Gross Chromosomal Abnormalities
by Dr. Jerome Lejeune

Neel: Dr. Jerome Lejeune is going to open the discussion for this Fourth Macy Conference. I should warn you, Dr. Lejeune, that you should not assume an extensive background on the part of your audience and, if you attempt to, you may find yourself summarily halted.

Lejeune: The main difficulty with human chromosomes is that, first, before looking at any abnormality, we have to be sure that we can recognize the chromosomes themselves. It may seem a little childish here to come back to the human karyotype in its normal form, but I just suppose it is necessary that we first recognize what is normal before saying something is abnormal.

Figure 1 shows the 47 chromosomes of a mongol boy, and Figure 2 shows the karyotype, according to the Denver classification.

The main problem is not so much to distinguish the big and the small chromosome, because, for example, nobody would have difficulty in finding the big acrocentrics and the small acrocentrics and so on, but the difficulty is whether we are really entiled to give a number, as set forth in the Denver agreement, to every one of the medium-sized chromosomes.

The problem has been mainly surreptitiously discussed, and I suppose that Dr. Patau will talk about it in a few moments. We wanted to know whether, really, the medium-sized chromosomes were different pairs, or if some of them were in the tetraploid state in our species. What we did was to plot the length of each element and the position of its centromere on 50 male cells and on 50 female cells. The centromere index was calculated as the ratio between the short arm and the total length of the element; that is, the distance, expressed as percent of the total length of the chromosome, of the centromere from that end of the chromosome which is closest to the centromere.

Figure 3 shows the results. In this figure there are 1550 points,

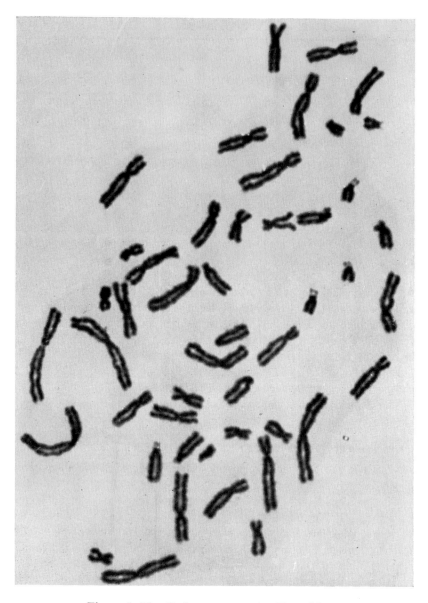

Figure 1. The 47 chromosomes of a Mongol boy.

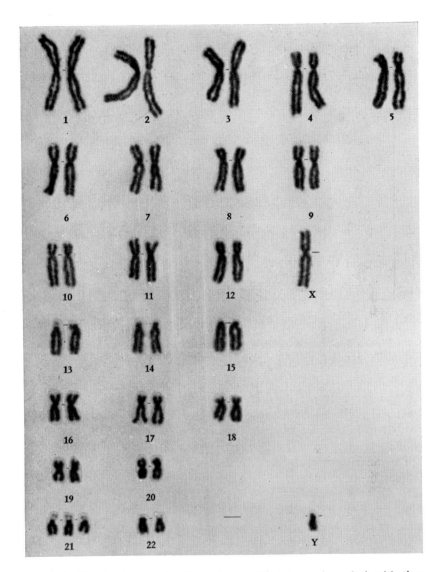

Figure 2. The karyotype of a Mongol boy. The trisomy is typical, with three satellited chromosomes. Faint satellites are seen in one of the 22 chromosomes.

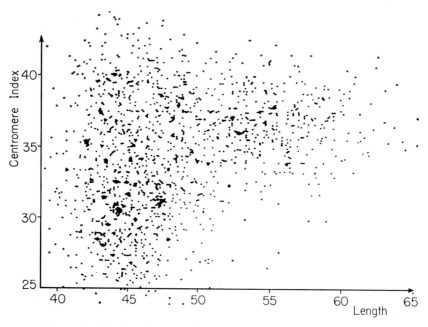

Figure 3. Plotting of the medium-sized pairs of 50 male and 50 female cells, according to relative length and centromere index.

representing only the medium-sized chromosomes, and each point is located by the measurements on only one chromosome. What we wanted to know was whether this showed a consistent pattern, that is, if some pairs were lying in some particular point of the plane.

The difficulty is that there are two errors: one in the actual size of the chromosome as seen in the microscope, which is subject to technical difficulties, such as spreading and tension inside the nucleus, and so on; and the other difficulty is that the measurements have to be made in pictures and are not very accurate. In order to know if there was a pattern here, a mathematical approach could be used, calculating any local concentration for any given area of the plane. But that is very cumbersome, and I could not do that, so what we did was just an optical trick.

Figure 4 will show us the result, which was to outfocus the projection so that instead of one point, we get a big circle for each point. I am sorry this does not show so well in the figure. There are points of concentration, which show much better when the light is not so bright.

Figure 4. Out-of-focus picture of the plot given in Figure 3.

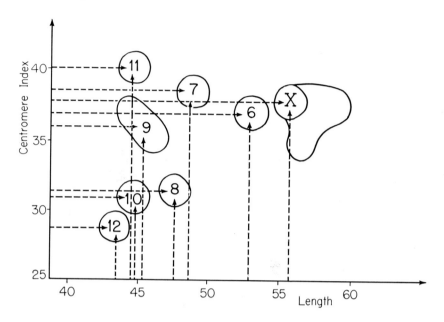

Figure 5. Diagram of the points of concentration and the corresponding chromosome numbers (Denver system).

Figure 5 shows us a diagram which is drawn from Figure 4, and shows where these points are. According to the Denver agreement, we have to put the chromosomes in order, beginning with the biggest one, and going on to the smallest one. The abscissa indicates the length of the chromosome, and the centromere index is indicated on the ordinate.

The problem was, afterward, to detect where the X chromosome was, and, to do this, we had to use a trick which probably is not perfectly justified, but we could not find another way which was better. The trick was to have a mean length for every cell; that is, for the medium-sized chromosome, we added the lengths to get the sum, which is the length of 15 chromosomes and of 16 chromosomes contained respectively in each male and female cell. We have a mean length for 50 male cells, and we have a mean length for 50 female cells. Now, if we assume that the difference between the two means is due to the presence of one X in the male and two X's in the female, it comes out that the difference is 0.56. For the centromere position, we did the same calculation; that is, the centromere index being, for

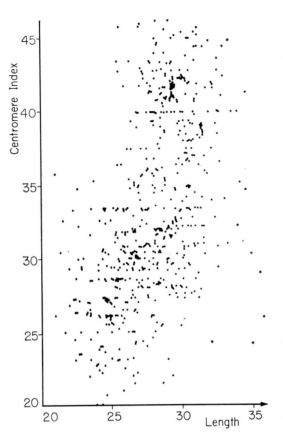

Figure 6. Scatter diagram of measurements on chromosomes in the 16 to 18 group. See Figure 3 for complete legend.

example, 0.33 in a given chromosome, we add up all the chromosomes of one cell, and then we get a mean sum for all the 50 female cells; in this way we get a total of centromere indices for each of 50 female cells and for each of 50 male cells.

If we consider that the centromere is a kind of weight, the difference is related to the position of the centromere of the X, and it turns out that the difference is 0.38.

Returning to Figure 5, we can locate the position corresponding to (38, 56), shown by dotted lines and arrows. This position is an area

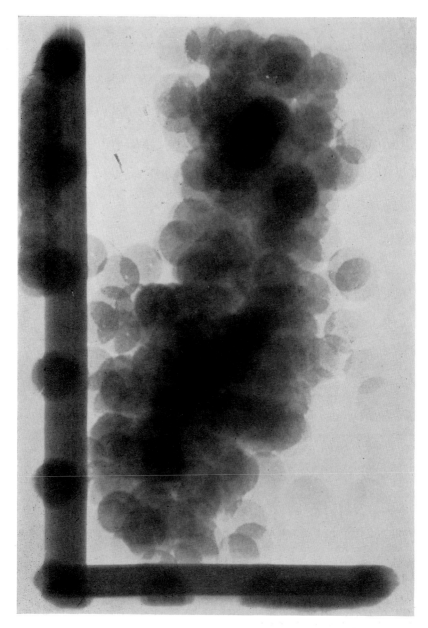

Figure 7. Out-of-focus picture of the plot given in Figure 6.

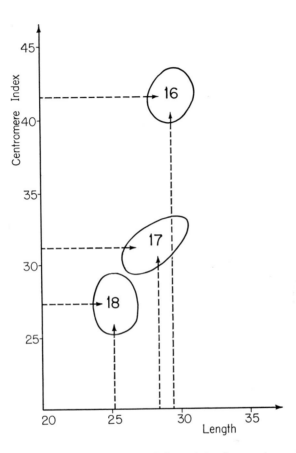

Figure 8. Diagram of the points of concentration, with the corresponding chromosome numbers. (Denver system).

representing one of the biggest chromosomes, not a distal centromere;
so, without any bias about matching, we come to the conclusion that
the big area, which exhibited a greater variation than areas representing the other chromosomes, is the X chromosome. The remaining
chromosomes were numbered by their length, as shown in Figure 5.
It turns out that three pairs are entirely different from the others,
those which are seen toward the bottom left-hand corner, and the
others can be recognized at least statistically. Now, the problem of
distinguishing among these chromosomes in every cell is more dif-

ficult, but I suppose the interesting part of this is to show that the numbering does represent a true thing. When we are building a karyotype, if we put chromosome 6 in the place where chromosome 7 should be, we are doing it wrong, but saying that one 6 is missing is probably allowed by this kind of data.

I will go very fast with the other slides, which deal with other groups of chromosomes, to show the technique used.

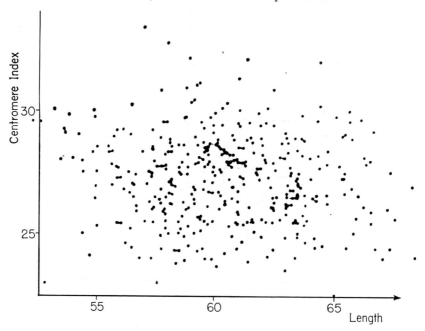

Figure 9. Scatter diagram of measurements on chromosomes. See Figure 3 for complete legend.

Figure 6 is the same plot for the groups 16 to 18, and Figure 7 shows that chromosome 16 makes a very nice dot in the top; that is, it is bigger and it has a rather medium centromere. Chromosome 17 is more in the middle, and 18 is quite at the bottom of the picture.

Figure 8 is just a diagrammatic representation of the dots.

Figure 9 shows the most difficult pair, the 4 and 5, which are quite hard to distinguish.

Figure 10, the outfocused picture, shows two points of concentration, and Figure 11 allows the conclusion that one of these chromosomes is

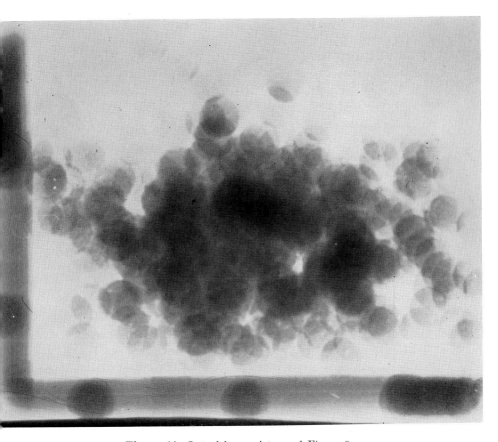

Figure 10. Out-of-focus picture of Figure 9.

bigger than the other, and the bigger one has a centromere which is a little more distal than the other one. This is, of course, a theoretical fact, which does represent what is probably the chromosome when it is not too much disturbed by the treatment, but it helps in establishing the karyotype because you play with two variables, after you have taken this information, instead of just playing with the length. You also take care of the centromere. It turns out that we could make many corrections in our previously established karyotypes, after knowing these few data which I wanted to present.

Neel: In view of the blood that has been spilled over this issue of ability to recognize individual chromosomes, I am amazed that Jerome got this far without interruption. Is there at this point somebody who would like to challenge him?

Patau: There is one question, of course; that is, to what extent can you exclude that these points or areas of concentration represent random accumulations? I realize the terrific amount of work that you have put into this, and I won't suggest that you do the whole thing all over, but, if you did, would you get the same areas of concentration

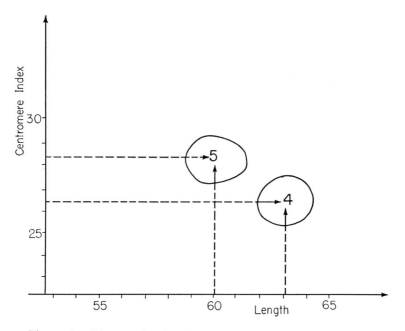

Figure 11. Diagram showing the probable concentration points with the corresponding chromosome numbers (Denver system).

that you have here? Have you made an attempt? Perhaps, it would be feasible to superimpose a grid and count the number of points per square, let's say, in the middle of your diagram, and see whether they agree with the Poisson distribution or show significant differences. When you scatter points at random, you also get accumulations. The question is: to what extent are your accumulations significantly nonrandom?

Lejeune: The relative confidence we have in this technique is based on two points. The first is that you get eight points, which is not, obviously, the solution which would occur if they were entirely randomly distributed, because you are dealing with eight pairs of chromosomes.

Steinberg: I wonder whether you have shown your photos to someone who did not know anything about what you have done and asked him about how many points were present? It seems to me, particularly in one of the later slides, where you had two points, I saw three or four, and Jim [Renwick] here also seemed to see more points. Maybe, these are the effects of last night, but we saw more points. [Laughter]

Lejeune: We can come back to the slide, if you wish.

Ephrussi: May I ask a purely technical question? Is your amount of outfocusing constant?

Lejeune: Yes, in all these pictures.

Ephrussi: It seems to me, if it were not, then the number of points and overlaps would be a function of the amount of outfocusing.

Lejeune: I have tried that repeatedly, and it does not change the number of points you get. We tried. The outfocusing is very simple.

Ephrussi: Is it always the same?

Lejeune: Well, the number of points are.

Ephrussi: No, no, the amount of outfocusing; is that the same every time or not?

Lejeune: Yes, every time. For given negatives, the outfocus used does not change the number of congruent points you do get. With very small outfocus, you get small diffraction pictures, and so they are not as nice as when they are bigger. But the number of points, so defined, does not change.

Now, if we could go back to Figure 3 again, just after the karyotype, we will see the points themselves, and you will see that there is evidence of concentration without any blurred picture.

Renwick: I think we might be more persuaded if, short of doing it all over again as Dr. Patau suggests, you could split up the data into two equal halves, at random, say, the first half that you did and the second half, and see whether you get the same readings for your coordinates to each point.

Lejeune: The evidence is that we have made those karyotypes progressively, and so we could calculate in each karyotype, for each pair of chromosomes the mean length and the mean position of the centromere. After pairing the chromosomes in each cell as well as we could, we determined for each chromosome pair, the length and centromere index. The points you get for chromosome 6, X, etc., are very close to the points you get in the outfocused picture. I have the tables here which I could show you, and the fit is quite satisfactory, in the sense that the arithmetic mean which you get just by counting the karyotypes themselves, made by a pairing method, comes inside, sometimes on the top and sometimes on the bottom of, the diffraction circle for each pair. It is quite unbelievable that this would occur if it were a random process.

Neel: Can we go back to that particular Rohrschach?

Patau: That is exactly what I wanted to say. The splitting up at random of your data into two groups should show it. If you get, with fifty nuclei—

Lejeune: You can see (Fig. 3), without any outfocused picture, there are numerous dots of concentration. This is not an optical trick. The optical trick is that it gives you an image of integration, of the concentration, because two different diffraction pictures will, in fact, give a dot in between, so it gives a mean effect of the concentration. But if there were not some dots, you would not get these diffraction images, if they were not in the negative before.

Renwick: I think it is not the optical trick on which we are commenting, but it is the ability to distinguish these blobs, to distinguish two of these blobs.

Patau: You have 50 nuclei here?

Lejeune: Yes.

Patau: If you took at random 25 nuclei and applied the same procedure and did the same with the second random sample, then you should certainly get a similar pattern, if this is not merely a chance effect. You should get a similar pattern because, after all, reducing your sample by a factor of 2 reduces the accuracy by only a factor of about 1.4, so if this pattern is correct, you should still get very much the same pattern with half the sample.

Lejeune: Well, we have done that in the middle of the thing, and that is the same type of pattern. But I have not taken a picture of it. The pattern was found at 25 cells, and the others were just increasing the evidence of the pattern.

Patau: I will accept that; probably some of these accumulations are significant, but are they all? I am, frankly, still a bit skeptical, because if you scatter points at random, they are never evenly distributed. They can't be. There must be at least the density variation of a Poisson distribution.

Lejeune: Well, if they are not evenly distributed, it means there is a correlation between the centromere and the length, and, if there is no correlation between the centromere and the length, in 1500 points, you should not see any concentration.

Patau: Oh, yes, by pure chance.

Lejeune: Not by pure chance, in a thousand, in 1500. We are not dealing with a small number of points.

Patau: No, but in any given area, the number is not so large, so a chance effect certainly comes in. As to the pairing off, Muldal and Ockey (30) published measurements on the seagull, on the 6 to 12 group, and gave a frequency distribution for each chromosome. They paired them off, and when you compute from them—I wonder if we could project a 3 × 5 slide?

Herzenberg: Could someone explain to some of us who are more naive what this is all leading to? This has been going on for several years, I understand, and I don't quite see what it is leading to from the point of being able to identify individual chromosomes from the particular cell or in a particular individual, since it seems as though it boils down to a statistical method of some sort, to be able to identify the chromosomes.

Lejeune: No, the very point was that we have to know if we are entitled to suppose that each pair differs from the others. If they are really the same, now, any matching is without any meaning.

Herzenberg: But we know there are differences. The question is—

Lejeune: Well, we do not have any information about their genetic difference.

Herzenberg: No, I know there are different pairs of chromosomes, and to be able to identify a specific visual object with a particular linkage group would, obviously, be very useful. But if you cannot do this in individual cases, I don't see the point of your being able to prove that, in the whole population, we do indeed have differences, statistical differences, between different chromosomes in large numbers of individuals.

Lejeune: This gives us, not an accuracy, but a measurement of the error. For example, we are sure that in every good cell we can split the medium-sized chromosomes into two classes, those which have a distal centromere and the others, which have a median centromere. In every good cell you can do that without any error.

It reminds us that we have three pairs of chromosomes, which we will call, according to the Denver classification, the 8, the 10, and the

12; in between, you can mix individuals. But, at least, if we found a trisomy for a medium-sized chromosome, we would establish fairly well whether it is one of those three or one of the others.

To go a little further would require another technique of chromosome study, that is, the optical observation cannot go further than that. But at least we have proved, or I suppose it is quite proved, that we can do the splitting of the medium sized in two different categories, according to the position of the centromere.

Herzenberg: Is there an argument about that? I didn't think there had been, for some long period of time; not if there were two groups; but the argument was whether you could pick out individual chromosomes within that group in a particular individual and assign a number to them.

Patau: Well, with a statistical approach would the principle be quite sufficient? Assume, for instance, you find in a female mosaic, with 46 and 45 chromosomes, that the missing chromosome belongs to the C group. The question is, is this coincidental? Did the abortion take place for some reason not connected with chromosomes, and was it possibly just an XO?

If the statistical method works and if you have enough slides, you could then find out whether it is the X or an autosome that is missing. I think, therefore, a reliable statistical method would be of great practical importance in cytogenetics, for evaluating situations that are at present ambiguous. I think the search with the statistical method is very worth while.

Szybalski: May I ask a question? Are the slides you have shown us, Dr. Lejeune, of one individual or of a group of individuals?

Lejeune: No, there are 50 cells, coming from 45 individuals.

Szybalski: What happens if you do the same analysis on a single individual? Do the points sharpen one way or another?

Lejeune: We had quite some concern about that, but we wanted to take our best karyotypes and so we selected the best of our collection, but we had to mix different individuals. I agree that it would be wise to do this again, taking just one individual and having a hundred cells from him, but the time it takes is really enormous, and that is the reason why we used the data we had collected, instead of doing the job specifically on one particular individual and on another one and then comparing the two.

I must say that we have used the raw material which was at hand for the calculation. For one cell, it takes around two hours, just to measure the chromosomes and compute all the indices, once you have a nice picture.

Neel: Two hours?

Lejeune: Yes, around two hours per cell. Now, to plot correctly for the groups, it takes around ten hours, just to put the needles on the big board; so it is quite a long job. It can be done for one individual, of course, but it is really a big amount of work.

Patau: You are not likely to get, from one culture, 50 plates that are really ideal for measurements. You see, it requires that all the chromosomes show the chromatids clearly. If you have a twist of the chromatids near the centromere, the position of the centromere is unclear and your measurements do not mean very much. So you have to select for cells in which the chromosomes are well displayed, and you just don't have that many from any given culture.

Szybalski: Are these bone-marrow pictures?

Lejeune: No, all of them were tissue culture, mainly of fascia lata and some of skin. Most of them were fibrous tissue.

Szybalski: I wonder whether any data are available indicating whether there is a bigger spread in chromosomal length between individuals than in one individual?

Lejeune: That is really not available.

Neel: The crux here is that this was probably a retrospective study and, having all these preparations, Jerome then went back to them.

Lejeune: Yes, that is really true. I was just using the amount of information we had stored.

Patau: I would not expect that you would find significant differences between normal people. Of course, any one of us may have a translocation in the C group, but this is certainly a very rare event. If you have a number of persons, the odds are heavily that they all have essentially the same chromosomes in the C group. I think we have much more reason to worry about pure chance effects.

Herzenberg: Could you tell us, again, whether there is any experimental justification for this presumption? Perhaps, another species would be adequate, indicating that the difference in length of chromosomes in one individual, in many cells, shows the same distribution as in taking the same chromosomes in a variety of individuals.

Patau: All we can say concerns those chromosomes that can be definitely identified, such as the largest ones. In persons selected at random, and we need not stick to normal persons for that purpose— mongoloids or other trisomics are also usable—we virtually always find that homologous chromosomes look the same.

Furthermore, it seems quite clear by now that man is more sensitive to chromosomal imbalance than Drosophila, so that very minor additions of euchromatin would be quite detrimental. We can hardly expect that there is a great degree of chromosomal polymorphism in the population. There must be heavy selection against it. At any rate, with very special exceptions, there is no evidence of such polymorphisms in human populations. It does exist, I think everybody agrees by now, for the Y chromosome, and this variation appears to have usually no noticeable effect on the phenotype. An entirely normal fertile male, looking fully virile, may have a short or a large Y chromosome. Polymorphisms seem also to be common for the short arms of the 21 and 22, and I think that this explains part of the difficulties of identifying the mongolism chromosome. In some normal persons both chromosomes 21 are somewhat larger and have in particular a larger short arm than the chromosomes 22. In this case 21 and 22 are easily distinguished. In other normal persons there are three chromosomes with relatively large short arms, and one with a minute short arm, or three chromosomes with a small short arm and one with a much larger one. This polymorphism, I think, fits in with the fact that the carriers of translocation mongoloidism, who must be lacking the short arm of one acrocentric, seem to be entirely normal. This all suggests that these short arms are heterochromatic. When I say that there is probably very little polymorphism in the human population, I mean the euchromatin, and I would except not only the Y chromosome but also the short arms of the small acrocentrics and, by implication, the short arms of the medium-sized acrocentrics. But these are really very minute differences.

They are visible here only because you can roughly estimate the relative masses of two short arms by eyesight. But these are differences which would be way below the accuracy of your measurements when you have big chromosomes, arms of which are much thicker. If you took away from a chromosome of the C group as much mass as is contained in the short arm of the mongolism chromosome, this would amount to the loss of a minute fraction of a micron which could never be recognized by measurements.

I would take a high bet that if we could identify and measure accurately the individual chromosomes of the medium-sized group, we would find no significant differences between homologues in any of us, or at least in the great majority of us. I think, therefore, if Dr. Lejeune's results are open to discussion, it is not on the ground of differences between persons but, rather, on the ground of chance accumulation of points in his graph.

Bearn: Before you go on with that, could I ask one question? Is there clear evidence from family studies that the variation in the Y chromosome is inherited? How much of the variation could be random?

Patau: Well, in the case of a man who has a fairly large Y chromosome, we have found that a son of his also has a large Y chromosome. I am sure you would find that.

Lejeune: A big Y has been described in a mongoloid and his father.

Chu: May I add a few small points, to supplement what has been said by the previous speakers, before you go on? Dr. Herzenberg raised the question about why we are interested in distinguishing individual chromosomes of a species. For a given species, we have no reason to expect that all chromosomes should look alike or should look different. The mouse karyotype is a good example of very similar chromosomes in the set. The human chromosomes are much better in the sense that most, if not all, chromosomes can be individually recognized. The prospect of eventual cytological mapping of human chromosomes depends on our ability to identify individual chromosomes.

Dr. Szybalski asked whether Lejeune's chromosome data were collected from one individual or from several individuals. I want to add that it is important to examine chromosomes from different tissues of the same individual. In several insects, the chromosome pattern appears to differ among tissues and during development. For mammalian chromosomes, our present techniques do not allow us to tell the difference, although it may indeed exist.

Concerning the chromosome polymorphism in human populations, I agree with Dr. Patau about the Y chromosome. I would also like to add that chromosome 16 may be polymorphic. There are reports that certain people have one large and one small chromosome 16. One distinct example is Dr. C. E. Ford himself. He is, of course, a perfectly normal person, we know.

Lejeune: He is not normal; he is outstanding! [Laughter]

Patau: A clear difference between two 16's is, in our experience, rare. At any rate, this is still a small chromosome compared with the C chromosomes, and it is now known that it has a secondary constriction (38), which quite likely means that there is a heterochromatic region of not negligible size. If there should be some polymorphism for 16, this may be of little genetic consequence. I don't mean to say that any heterochromatic section is entirely without genetic function. We know that the Y carries at least one male-determining factor, and even though distal parts of the Y are sometimes missing, they probably are genetically not entirely inconsequential; if they were, they would presumably have been lost long ago, so there is probably a slight selective pressure favoring the normal-sized Y, but this selective pressure seems to be small, or there would not be so much variation. Possibly, a similar situation might exist in a heterochromatic region of 16, but I repeat that in our experience the two 16's seem to match perfectly in the great majority of persons.

Stern: Is it not possible that you have different degrees of contraction or coiling, which have nothing to do with translocations, which you mentioned several times, in cases where there are differences in sizes? In other words, would it not be quite possible to find different sizes without an abnormal distribution of the genetic material?

Patau: That might be. I would like to stress that length as such really doesn't mean anything. In particular, when it comes to things such as the arms of 16 and, most certainly, the short arms of the acrocentrics, one simply has to compare masses. I would never say that two 16's are different merely because they are of different length. What you normally find is that one chromosome of a homologous pair is a bit shorter and that it then also looks a bit thicker.

Stern: You know, in the 1930's, with the old technique, some Russians—I have forgotten whether it was Andres—measured certain chromosomes in relation to the longest, which, I suppose, was No. 1. They had five different individuals, I believe, three Russians and two Japanese, and, by taking the longest chromosome as a unit, they found that there were differences between the Japanese and the Russians. Now, I realize that this work was done by techniques which are now outdated, but since they restricted themselves to the largest chromosomes, it might be worth while to do this kind of thing again.

Patau: We have found considerable differences in chromosome length between samples from different persons that were taken at the same time and treated alike, but I do not know whether the observed differences would consistently recur in samples taken at other times. When there are big differences in contraction, it seems that the length ratio between large and small chromosomes of the same nucleus decreases with increasing contraction. In the extreme, you reach a point where the short arms simply become spherical. They cannot shorten any more, while the long arms can go on shortening; so there is differential contraction, and one can certainly not expect the length ratio between say, chromosome 1 and chromosome 16 to be the same in metaphases with different degrees of chromosome contraction.

Lejeune: About the contraction, I would add a few words, that the pictures we used were normally occurring metacentrics, without any colchicine, which makes a very big difference in the recognition of the medium-sized group, because, the more contraction you get, the less is the difference between chromosomes with a quasi-median centromere or, rather, distal centromere.

Another fact is that if we compare our own data with the data of Dr. Chu or Dr. Tjio, where they were using colchicine, it turns out that they do find the big chromosome is relatively bigger than we find it. I don't know why, but that would be a kind of indication that the contraction is greatest when the chromosome is short, because in our data, we find that the one is relatively less long than if you measure it in colchicine-treated material. If so, there is a big danger here, because if the degree of contraction is related to or correlated with the length of the element, when you are dealing with a chromosome with a centromere which is not in the middle, there would be a differential contraction between the short and the long arms. So the same chromosome measured without colchicine and with colchicine would show an apparent shift of the position of the centromere.

This is the main reason why we study pictures of chromosomes untreated by colchicine (the only pictures we had). What is not known is whether the particular treatment used to spread the chromosome has the same effect on contraction; that is, possibly, it acts more on long arms than on short arms. That, we just do not know. But it is still another possibility to explain the apparent shifting of the position of the centromere in a truly identical chromosome. All these statistical studies, therefore, have to be made on some consistent sample which is treated by the same technique, and I would not be surprised, if the same plot were made with colchicine, that we would find a similar pattern, but with some shifting in the points.

Ephrussi: Yes, but I would like to raise the following question: As you pointed out before, your statistics were obtained on preparations accumulated over a long period of time. Hasn't your technique changed during this period at all?

Lejeune: No. All the preparations were made with exactly the same technique, the same technique of spreading and the same technique of nourishing the cell. It is a consistent sample. It is one year's work.

Patau: I would like to support you in that. You have published pictures, and they have shown a remarkable consistency, from the first to the last, in the appearance of the chromosomes, so there are certainly no major shifts.

I am glad you said one thing which seems important to me. If you use chromosomes of different contraction, I quite agree that you will find shifts, and therefore any such statistical evidence should be limited to a narrow range of chromosome contraction. But as you also said, you would expect to find essentially the same pattern. It would be distorted, but chromosomes of similar length would be affected in the same way.

Lejeune: Exactly.

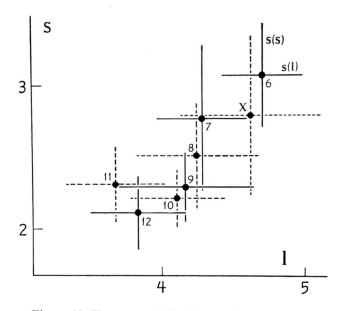

Figure 12. Karyogram of the C group, based on measurements and identifications by Muldal and Ockey (30). $1 + s(1)$: length (and its standard deviation) of long arm in percent of total chromosome length of male C group; $s + s(s)$: same for short arm.

Patau: I think that you could do your analysis also with colchicine-treated material, but you would have to take the precaution to make the analysis separately for different classes of contraction. If you could do that, I am sure you would get patterns that are not too different from yours.

Neel: Perhaps, with this note of agreement, we could move on to that slide of Dr. Patau's.

Patau: Figure 12 illustrates how problematic the pairing-off by length in the C group is. Mulday and Ockey (30), who believe they can identify the individual C chromosomes, measured them in 14 mitoses of one male and presented their data for each of the 8 chromosomes as a graphical frequency distribution. From values obtained by measuring their histograms, I computed the mean length and the standard deviation of each chromosome arm, both expressed as percent of the total length of the C chromosomes. The result is shown in this figure as a karyogram. As you can see, there is no chromosome to which there does not exist at least one other, so that the length difference of the two long arms is smaller than the standard deviation of either arm length. The same holds true for the short arms. I think this shows conclusively that you cannot reliably pair off the C chromosomes on the basis of such length measurements alone. At least for part of the C group this would still be true, even if the standard deviations could be considerably reduced.

I would agree that you are probably quite often correct when you identify No. 6 by length, but you can't always be correct, because this karyogram shows that it frequently overlaps with the next chromosome.

Motulsky: What are the coordinates there?

Patau: The abscissa is the relative length, in terms of the total length of the C group, of the long arm; the ordinate is that of the short arm. Dr. Lejeune used as coordinates the centromere index and the length of the whole chromosome. That does not matter. Any chromosome is characterized by two parameters, unless, of course, you have a secondary constriction as a marker: length of the two arms or the centromere index and the total chromosome length. You can easily convert one pair of quantities into the other. This figure rests on data collected by authors who believe they can pair off homologues, and I think that it demonstrates conclusively that pairing-off by length alone does not mean much.

Herzenberg: Maybe they used the wrong method of pairing off, because if you rearrange the data on the basis of your points, then, you could say that the standard deviations did not overlap.

Patau: I doubt it. These authors paired the most similar appearing chromosomes; any other method should lead to still larger standard deviations.

Chu: The success of making karyograms, however, depends on one important prerequisite, that is, the quality of the cytological preparation. If you have a poor preparation, naturally you will have a bigger scatter. Furthermore, it is not justifiable to plot on the same karyogram the chromosome measurements by one author and those by another, because the first person might have used colchicine and the other might have not. Finally, in order to make it statistically meaningful, one has to collect large samples of reliable and uniform materials.

Patau: Of course, I cannot testify to the quality of Muldal and Ockey's preparation, but it is worth noting—

Chu: I am speaking in general terms.

Patau: —that two sets of data of undoubtedly high quality both yield a coefficient of variation of 5.8 percent of the chromosome length. One set consists of Levan and Hsu's (25) measurements on ten pairs of chromosome 1 in what they termed exceptionally good material. The other set also consists of ten pairs of measurements, by Rothfels and Siminovitch (34), on the largest chromosome of the rhesus monkey, again a chromosome that can be identified beyond question. If you have seen the published pictures, you will agree that these authors had very beautiful slides with long chromosomes, where errors of measurement ought to be negligible. Thus, in two independent investigations on very favorable material a coefficient of variation between homologues of about 6 percent has been found. This is quite a bit when compared with the differences in length between similar nonhomologous chromosomes that you have in the C group.

Lejeune: When you say 5 percent, you mean 5 percent of the length of this particular chromosome?

Patau: Yes.

Lejeune: That is something we studied, in our material, on 48 male cells and 50 female cells. For chromosome No. 1 we found that the difference between the two homologues was 5 percent. For chromosome No. 2 of those same cells, the value was 5.7 percent; this value represents a difference between the lengths of the two elements, related to the mean length of those two elements; so it does agree extremely well with the later data that we found, roughly, a 6 percent difference in length between two homologues that we are sure we can recognize statistically.

Patau: Then, you would agree that it is the optimal?

Lejeune: Exactly. We got 5.8, plus or minus, 4.4, so it is very good agreement.

Patau: Yes. The C chromosomes are somewhat smaller, so the error of measurement comes in a bit more. But I think one can also say that in good material, the error of measurement is small compared with the genuine variation that you have in the slide.

Lejeuene: Entirely.

Patau: There has been quite a debate on how to measure chromosomes, but I don't think it really matters, if it is carefully done, whether you use photographs or, what I personally prefer, camera lucida drawings of individual chromosomes put in the middle of the field. Under any and all circumstances, you are up against the limited resolving power of the light microscope. Around your chromosome image you have a diffraction fringe, and there is a degree of arbitrariness in the choice of the points at which you begin measuring. The main thing is to be consistent. If you are, and if the chromosomes are not too small, your relative error of measurement should be quite small.

Of course, if you take a photograph with high contrast, as everybody does, you can get chromosomes that really have a sharp outline, but this is a bit of photographic fakery. There actually is a diffraction fringe. By modifying the photographic technique, you can get thinner or thicker chromosomes without being able to tell which version is most nearly correct.

Photography raises still another problem—I think, Dr. Chu, you mentioned it in Rome, or am I wrong? At any rate, somebody mentioned that he found in photographs the image size of a given object to depend somewhat on the location of the object in the field—in its center or in the marginal zone.

Chu: I did not mention it, but I certainly can confirm what you just said. When we measure chromosomes, we always move them into the center of the microscopic field.

Another thing is the error that can be introduced by photography. For example, some chromosomes may be slightly out of focus and the images obtained do not represent their true morphology. In the process of printing, if the time of developing varies a little bit, the same chromosome on the same negative may appear to be larger or smaller. We have to use our common sense and depend on both microscopic observation and photographic record, and not to base our judgment on a single photograph alone.

Patau: Yes. Of course, in many cases such errors may not be large enough to matter when compared with the length variation of the chromosomes themselves—and I am quite certain that this variation exists to a large extent already in the living cell. However, I take for granted that fixation and preparation of the slides will bring in some additional variation.

Incidentally, if the mirror of my camera lucida is adjusted according to the marks provided by the factory, the mirror will not be at the

45° angle it ought to have. Here you have another source of small errors.

Chu: Yes, that is exactly what I mean.

Patau: However, if you watch the obvious error sources, then, I believe, the errors of measurement in the case of large chromosomes will be negligible compared with the variation that is present in the slides. I am satisfied that Dr. Lejeune's measurements are technically accurate enough so that the error of measurement is negligible.

Neel: It impresses me, as an outsider, that we are closer to a consensus here than cytogeneticists seem to have been in recent years. Would it be fair to summarize by saying that in a statistical sense, one can probably distinguish between most and possibly all chromosomes, but that in the usual preparation, where you have, let's say, only four or five really good plates to count, you cannot distinguish between individual chromosomes of certain groups?

Patau: Yes, with that I would agree, at least in principle. I am not yet certain, really, how far in practice the statistical evaluation of measurements will lead. I would need more evidence, obtained for instance by breaking up his sample of 50, before I could judge whether Dr. Lejeune's method gives us the true identity of any, of some, or of all C chromosomes.

There is one point at which different methods have led to quite different results. As you all probably know, German (8) and independently, Morishima, Grumbach, and Taylor (29) found that in most cells of the female there is one C chromosome that is late-labeling with tritiated thymidine as shown by autoradiography. In XXX cells there are two such chromosomes, and in the male there is none. I don't think there can be any serious doubt that this late-labeling chromosome is one of the X chromosomes.

We have investigated this, too, and there is no question that this presumed X chromosome is not one of the longest C chromosomes.* This does not necessarily prove that Dr. Lejeune's identification is wholly at fault, because it is conceivable that the one X chromosome in the female that is not late-labeling, which is presumably also the one that does not form a sex chromatin body, is longer at metaphase than the one that is late-labeling and forms, presumably, the sex chromatin body. At any rate, in the female at least one of the X chromosomes belongs in the middle range of the C group rather than in the upper range, where Dr. Lejeune puts it. I will show you the picture.

* This work was done in cooperation with Dr. S. L. Inhorn and was supported by grant MH 04871–02 from the U.S. Public Health Service.

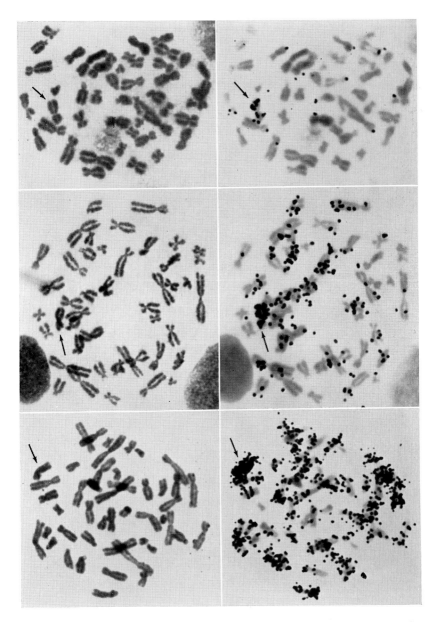

Figure 13. Three female cells, before (left) and after (right) autoradiography. Arrows: late-labeling C chromosome, presumably an X.

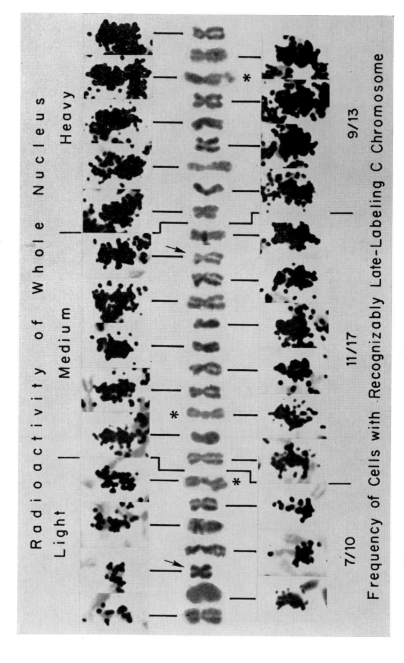

Figure 14. 27 late-labeling C chromosomes with their autoradiographs. Arrows: chromosomes with a too large or too small arm ratio. Asterisks: chromatid or chromosome breaks.

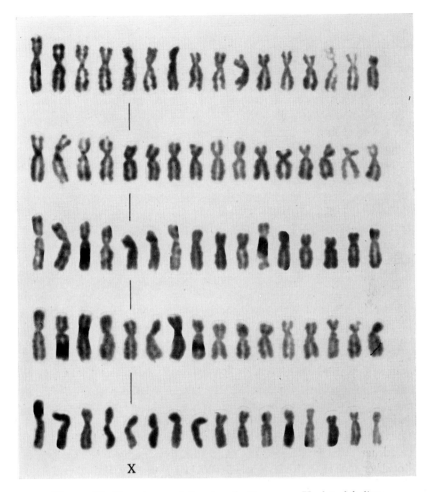

X

Figure 15. Karyotypes of five female C groups. X: late-labeling.

Bearn: I think that Dr. German even goes so far as to say the late X is probably close to the 8, in terms of size.

Neel: You mean the late-labeling?

Bearn: Yes, the late-labeling. If you make the assumption that the late replicator is an X chromosome, not an autosome, then it will frequently come in the size category of the 8.

Chu: When the slide is shown, may I make one comment? It is fairly convincing that one chromosome of this group in the female is late-labeling. Since the identification of the X is made in the male and labeling is done in the female, there remains a possibility of variation in length of the two X chromosomes in the female.

Patau: This is the point I just tried to make: that we have no assurance that the late-labeling and the other X have the same length at metaphase.

Neel: I have the feeling that you are so accustomed to disagreeing that when you agree, you have trouble recognizing it, sometimes. [Laughter]

Patau: Figure 13 is merely to show the method. First, we expose the cells for four hours to tritiated thymidine and then fix immediately. This means that all chromosome segments that are labeled must have synthesized DNA after the time when the thymidine was added, and those that are unlabeled must have synthesized before.

Second, once you have the autoradiograph, a radioactive chromosome is covered by silver grains, and you cannot study its morphology; so what we do is to analyze, as far as possible, as many plates as possible and photograph every one of them. Then we dismount the slide again, put the film on, and so forth, and rephotograph every mitosis that proves radioactive. We have here (Fig. 13, left) three mitoses photographed before applying the film, and here (Fig. 13, right) the corresponding autoradiograph. We found that with this method somewhere between one-third and one-half of the metaphases are labeled, ranging from slightly to heavily labeled. Regardless of the degree of overall-labeling, a majority of cells in the female show one C chromosome, marked by arrows in the figure, that is noticeably more heavily labeled than the other C chromosomes, although there are outside the C group sometimes autosomal segments that label just as heavily; so it is not altogether true that the late-labeling C is always later labeling than all other chromosomes.

You also find some cells in which no C chromosome stands out, but in the majority there is one that does. In the male, you do not find it except for a very few borderline cases. We can therefore fully confirm the results of the authors mentioned before.

The first question was: are these late-labeling C chromosomes compatible with each other? The answer is that the majority are fully compatible (Fig. 14). However, there are a few whose arm ratio differs significantly from that seen in the majority. Such exceptional late-labeling C chromosomes are marked in the figure with an arrow.

There are two possible and not mutually exclusive explanations for these exceptions. One relates to the observation I mentioned before:

that you do find some cells in which none of the C chromosomes stands out by a significantly heavier label, which means that the delay of DNA synthesis in the presumed X is subject to statistical variation, as is no doubt the onset of DNA synthesis in all chromosomes. I think we may then expect to encounter occasionally, at one tail of the distribution as it were, a C chromosome that is not an X, but nevertheless happens to be a little more radioactive than the other members of its group. The other possible explanation rests upon the fact that there are quite a few chromatid and also chromosome breaks as a result of the tritium incorporation. In Figure 14 you see three C chromosomes that show this effect; they are marked by asterisks. From left to right, we have a chromosome with a chromatid break, a dicentric chromosome, and one that has one chromatid break and, apparently, one half-chromatid break. Now, if we have a late-labeling C that differs significantly from the great majority of late-labeling C chromosomes, there is obviously the possibility that the difference had come about by a chromosomal rearrangement resulting from breaks that had been induced by the tritium.

The majority of the late-labeling C chromosomes agree morphologically very well with each other, and since there are plausible explanations for the occasional occurrence of exceptions, I take it for granted that at least the majority of the late-labeling C chromosomes do represent the same chromosome, namely an X.

In Figure 15 we have five karyotypes of the C group. In each, the chromosome marked with an X is the late-labeling one, and it certainly is not one of the longest. In these slides, there was obvious differential contraction for which one must try to make allowance when attempting to put chromosomes into a plausible order. Unfortunately, there was also some of the nonuniformity of staining that is so common in dried-on mitoses and can cause the impression that homologous chromosomes lying in different areas of the spread have different masses. In order to avoid this error source, we prefer for critical work Feulgen-stained squash preparations, but for autoradiographic work, the drying-on technique is by far the most convenient. At any rate, the placing, among the other C chromosomes, of the presumed X according to its size or, rather, mass is debatable, but it seems clear that its true place cannot be to the left of the fifth and may well be further down.

Lejeune: I have a question about the late-labeling. I am not myself familiar with the technique. I would just ask the question, whether it does occur in some cells, that the late-labeling one is, let's say, a big acrocentric chromosome? Does it sometimes occur or does it never occur that the late-labeling chromosome is an acrocentric?

Patau: Yes. I mentioned that when I speak of a late-labeling C chromosome, I mean relative to the other C chromosomes.

Lejeune: No, I don't mean the C group. What is the frequency that the late-labeling chromosome is not in the C group, but is a big acrocentric—one that we can recognize specifically? Does that occur at all?

Patau: Possibly. I believe, at present, we cannot yet identify the medium-sized individual acrocentrics, the D chromosomes.

Koprowski: Excuse me, but I would like a clarification. Dr. Lejeune calls them "big sized" or "medium sized." What do we call them?

Lejeune: There are two kinds of acrocentrics, those which are very small, 21 or 22, and those which are medium sized but which are big for acrocentrics. [Laughter] Let's say there are two kinds of acrocentrics. Three pairs are medium sized and two pairs are very small. We can call them medium-sized acrocentrics or big.

Koprowski: The ones I refer to, the medium and big, are the same?

Lejeune: Yes, the same.

Patau: We agree that they are the big ones among the acrocentrics, but they are smaller than C chromosomes, so they belong in the medium range, when you consider all chromosomes. But I am willing to go along and call them the big acrocentrics. Some are relatively early-labeling, but there is at least one pair which is strikingly late-labeling.

Lejeune: But this is a very important point, because it would prove that sometimes the X chromosome is an acrocentric. [Laughter]

Patau: Well, we know that the X chromosome is a C chromosome.

Lejeune: No, what I am trying to find out is, what is the constancy of recognition we have of the X chromosome using late-labeling as the criterion? If the late-labeling one can be an acrocentric, then, we cannot say that the X chromosome is an acrocentric, since we have an uncertainty, with the resolving power of that technique, about the X chromosomes themselves.

Patau: No, we don't pick it out as the most late-labeling chromosome. We pick it out as the most most late-labeling among the C chromosomes. We know already that the X belongs to the C chromosomes.

Lejeune: In that case, I am not so confident as I was previously, because, in any group, you do not label at exactly the same time. You have to find one first and one last.

Bearn: I think, in some of Dr. German's recent experiments, he has found that No. 18 and the 16 may also replicate late. In many instances the 21 or 22 and the Y may also label relatively late. But one constant and unequivocal late replicator is the X; in other words it is the one in the C group.

Patau: In the first place, you do not find, with very rare exceptions and these are always borderline cases, a clearly late-labeling C in the male. In the XX female you find one and only one. That is a unique situation. Take a pair of chromosomes that, in my opinion, can very often be distinguished without any question, namely 17 and 18. I should specify that we go mostly by the length or, rather, the mass of the short arm. Now, I have gone over our photographs, looking not at the autoradiographs but at the pictures taken before, using also earlier identifications made directly in the microscope, and have numbered the two 17's and the two 18's. Only then did I look at the autoradiographs, and there is no quesion that, with roughly the same constancy with which the presumed X is marked, both 18's label later than the 17's. But it is, again, a statistical effect. Sometimes you may find three chromosomes with about the same degree of labeling, and one that is more heavily labeled, but this is virtually always No. 18. The time difference in labeling between 17 and 18 is clearly highly significant and will, I believe, provide an independent method to check whether the extra chromosome in what we are convinced is 18 trisomy is really 18 and not 17. The autoradiographic method is good enough for that purpose.

Neel: Some of us are a little bit confused about the sequence of labeling. If the one X was always the last chromosome to label, this would have—

Patau: Of the C group.

Bearn: In females.

Neel: Yes, in females; this would have a bearing on the much-discussed Lyon hypothesis. Now, are you suggesting that the X is not always the latest-labeling chromosome in the complement, that sometimes other chromosomes label even later?

Bearn: In females?

Neel: Yes, always in females.

Patau: It is simply so that the average period of DNA synthesis may be thought of as specific for each chromosome and each chromosome segment. In female cells, the one late-labeling C has an average period that begins later and ends later than that of any other chromosome, even though it partly overlaps with the average period of many chromosomes. All these periods are, in onset and duration, subject to considerable variation as a result of which a D chromosome, for instance, may occasionally be just as heavily labeled as the presumed X. Because of the statistical nature of the evidence, you cannot take too seriously what you see in any single cell, but if you have a sufficient number of cells, you can certainly establish that one chromosome pair is, on the average, much later-labeled than a certain other pair. The difference between 18 and 17, for instance, is quite striking.

Steinberg: When you have a triple X female, Klaus, how often are the two chromosomes in the C group late-labeling? What percentage of cells would show that?

Patau: Since we have started working with autoradiographs, no triple X has been available to us. It has been stated by Morishima, Grumbach, and Taylor (29) that in triple X cells there were either one or two late-labeling C chromosomes. I don't think they gave frequencies of manifestation. If we should run across a triple X case, or the like, we certainly would investigate it with this method.

Chu: Has Jim German done any?

Bearn: No. It is noteworthy, though, that in several laboratories there is a surprising degree of agreement, for instance between Dr. Patau and Dr. German.

Patau: Yes. He was, and so was I, very pleased when we discovered that we had found exactly the same thing. He told me after my talk in Corvallis that he could confirm every observation that I had made.

Bearn: The short arm of No. 3 seems to replicate asynchronously. Have you noticed this?

Patau: Yes. I think so. But I am going to analyze it more fully.

DeMars: I think that Dr. Lejeune is reasonably disturbed by an element of circularity in the reasoning that relates late-labeling to X-ness. We are working on a very difficult sort of experiment that, I think, is very relevant to this. The experiment is based on the ability to observe the sex chromatin mass in living cells.

We have described the sex chromatin in cells cultured from the skin of human females (6). They were grown in perfusion chambers and observed with phase contrast. One can observe in living cells that have more than one X chromosome, an object that has the attributes of sex chromatin. I am going to ask Dr. Lejeune to grant a point, that is, that the sex chromatin mass is formed by a single X chromosome.

Lejeune: Well, I would not grant that, because I have no reason to do it. [Laughter]

DeMars: In that case, take off the slide!

Lejeune: I would accept that it is a current hypothesis. [Laughter]

DeMars: The notion here is this: one can compare nuclear masses in the living cell with nuclear masses in the same cell after acid hydrolysis and Feulgen staining. One can observe in the living cells objects that correspond in size and position to the typical sex chromatin masses after staining.

Herzenberg: Are some of those tetraploid [the ones with two sex chromatin masses]?

DeMars: That is an assumption based on the large size of the nucleus and the presence of two sex chromatin masses instead of one. (Studies made with the microspectrophotometer after the conference showed that the large nuclei that contain two sex chromatin masses, instead of the single mass characteristic of diploid, diplo-X cells contain amounts of DNA that indicate tetraploidy.) The reason for this exercise is just to show that the object observed in the living cells corresponds to the Feulgen-positive object called sex chromatin, and it is not important for the argument whether or not a nucleus is tetraploid.

The pertinence of this is that objects like this can only be seen regularly in living cells in the last few hours of interphase; that is, I have sat in a warm room with them and watched them.

You can see an object of this kind in a cell only in the last few hours in interphase under conditions where the average generation time is about 20 to 24 hours. Earlier than this, in a small minority of cells, you can see something that has the optical attributes of the sex chromatin mass, but is distinctly smaller.

Because I could not observe a large one regularly in young nuclei, I set out to make a study of this. Working with the chambers, I watched cells divide and then watched the daughter cells. These observations continued for about 19 hours, so that when I fixed the cover slip I could later pinpoint cells of known age relative to the mitosis in which they originated. I then made a Feulgen stain and related the presence or absence of a sex chromatin mass to the age of the nucleus.

The experiments involved 159 cells of ages between a half hour and 19 hours after the mitosis in which they arose. The ages are, therefore, related not only to the time scale but also to the biological scale of the intermitotic interval.

You can see (Fig. 16) that as the ages of the nuclei increase, the nuclei get larger; the cells were indeed growing. We can draw a cutoff point here, where cells are 16 hours or more old relative to the division in which they arose. These are obviously selected from the 159 nuclei that I referred to. Every cell 16 hours or older in this experiment has a large sex chromatin mass. I put one nucleus in because it is at the

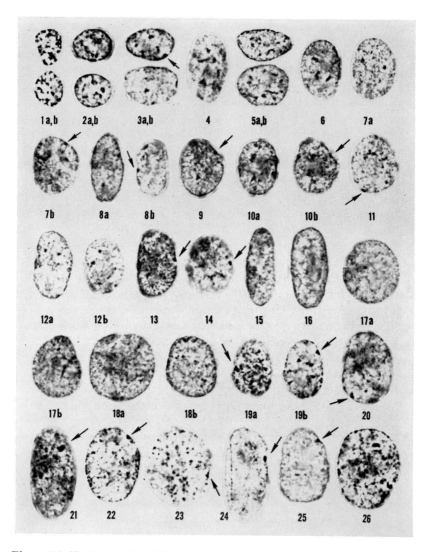

Figure 16. Nuclei of cells cultivated from a human female and stained with the Feulgen reaction. Increasing number designations indicate increasing ages of the nuclei during interphase. These ages range between one-half hour and about 20 hours here. Only nuclei 16 hours old or older show a typical sex chromatin body (nuclei 19 through 26).

From Robert DeMars, "Sex Chromatin During the Mitotic Cycle of Cultivated Human Cells," *Journal of Cell Biology* (1963).

beginning of prophase, and at that point you sometimes have several big blobs and you can't really say which one is the sex chromatin mass. With the exception noted, cells 16 hours or more old had it.

If one looks at these six nuclei (Fig. 16: cells 15 through 18b) about 14 to 16 hours old, one can see nothing comparable to a sex chromatin mass. In a high proportion of younger nuclei one can see a Feulgen-positive blob on the periphery, but you can see that it is always smaller than what is usually referred to as sex chromatin. You can also see that in a high proportion of these nuclei, there are other Feulgen-positive blobs not on the periphery. One does not know which of these, if any, is sex chromatin.

Ephrussi: Is this a stained preparation?

DeMars: Feulgen-stained, after hydrochloric acid hydrolysis. It is photographed with phase contrast, not because it is especially good for bringing out these details—in fact, it makes them look sloppier to the eye than if observed with bright field—but because phase contrast eased the difficulties of relocating the cells after the chambers had been disassembled and the coverslips stained and remounted.

The question at this point is: Is there sex chromatin in the early part of the interphase at all? And so one of the experiments that has to be done is to identify these smaller objects, with sex chromatin, if possible. This, obviously, is relevant to the Lyon hypothesis, which is a very detailed version of a hypothesis concerning dosage compensation in female cells. Question 1: Is there sex chromatin in early interphase?

Now, these observations show that if one of these smaller objects in a given cell is a sex chromatin mass—and I think that is likely—then it probably represents an X chromosome before it has replicated. Their genesis is reasonably in the forward motion, and they are about half the size of these objects found later. One way I like to think about these observations is that you do have a condensed X chromosome in the beginning of interphase. It replicates and, when replicating, disappears and is undetectable as a Feulgen-positive condensation. It condenses again after replication and reappears toward the end of interphase as a typical sex chromatin mass.

I can add to this some comments for which I do not have pictorial support. You can observe objects with the optical attributes of sex chromatin in young nuclei of this age, but they are harder to see; they are smaller. I believe they are sex chromatin. By watching the complete intermitotic cycles of numerous cells, I have been able to watch the object disappear and then reappear in a few cells. It was then present continuously for several hours, right into the beginning of prophase.

Atwood: Do they appear at the same point?

DeMars: In those cases, yes. I can come back to this point, if you wish. We will come back now to Dr. Lejeune's worry. If the notion that this is a single X chromosome is correct, and if this is the late-replicating X (and this we are trying to confirm now), then, it should be possible to watch a cell having a small sex chromatin mass and, at the moment it disappears, administer tritrated thymidine. If it is true that disappearance means replication then the chromosome forming the sex chromatin mass should become labeled.

One of the consequences of this is that if that cell is fixed after the sex chromatin reappears, that object should be heavily labeled, against a lightly labeled background.

Second, if the tritiated thymidine is removed and the division allowed to proceed, then the distribution of the label in the interphase nuclei of the daughter cells can be determined. One of the small Feulgen-positive blobs in a daughter of a cell labeled according to the program described may be heavily labeled, allowing its identification with the late-replicating X and, therefore, with sex chromatin. It is a very important point. Alternatively, the daughter cells can be allowed to grow until typical sex chromatin masses appear. These should also be heavily labeled.

Lastly, if it is true that every time, or almost every time, a cell labeled in this way gives rise to heavily-labeled sex chromatin masses in the next interphase, then, this is a confirmation of the Lyon hypothesis. It is a direct way of tracing the substance of the chromosome that forms this into the next cell generation.

The alternatives are the following: If the two X chromosomes can alternate in this kind of behavior, then, a cell labeled at this moment may give rise to daughters that lack a heavily labeled sex chromatin mass. This would indicate that the Lyon hypothesis is incorrect, in this material. If the cell labeled according to the specific program invariably gives rise to heavily-labeled sex chromatin in the next generation, then, this is a very direct confirmation of the notion of the persistent differentiation of the two X chromosomes.

Now, we can make the predictions very detailed. It is known that the DNA in these organisms replicates in a semiconservative way, which means that the two strands of the DNA of the duplex will be distributed equally in two daughter DNA molecules. But if you look at Dr. Patau's radioautographs and other radioautographs, you see that both chromatids of the metaphase chromatin are labeled. Wouldn't you say that is correct?

Patau: Yes. If I may interrupt, I wish to stress that all these things are statistical. In a very few cases, we have seen weakly labeled autosomes that had some silver grains above one chromatid but none above the other. However, in the vast majority of cases it is certainly true that where one chromatid is labeled, the other one is also.

DeMars: So we can say that a cell labeled at this moment can give rise to two daughter cells, and both sex chromatin masses will be labeled almost all the time.

This, I think, will relieve some of the uncertainty relating late-labeling to X-ness, because this experiment is not founded so much on late-labeling as it is on labeling at a specific moment, characteristic of a particular stage in the life cycle of an X chromosome, I think, at the moment at which it replicates, regardless of what the other chromosomes are doing.

This is one of those bright promises that Dr. Ephrussi was talking about to me last night, saying that in this field, or related fields, we have many bright promises, and at the moment that is all this is. We do not have any of these radioautographic experiments finished.

I might add just one comment about this object. Dr. Miles at Stanford has reported frequent associations between a sex chromatin mass and a nucleolus. He did not distinguish between sex chromatin in early versus late interphase. One can see, in young living cells, what I believe is sex chromatin in direct connection with nucleoli. It is more than a fortuitous juxtaposition because the sex chromatin mass is distorted. It projects into the nucleoplasm, apparently touching a nucleolus.

Eagle: The converse would also be true; that the tritiated thymidine added earlier than the sixteenth hour would label other chromosomes and not the X chromosomes.

DeMars: Right; and this would make the observations more difficult, because you will have to distinguish, then, between a heavily labeled sex chromatin mass and a more heavily labeled nuclear background.

Neel: It is apparent from some dubious looks that not everyone is sure of the nature of the Lyon hypothesis. I will ask Dr. Lejeune to state it for us.

Lejeune: I am in a good position to discuss the Lyon hypothesis, especially for people who are not acquainted with it, because I myself am not. The only thing I can say is that the hypothesis is, roughly, the following: In a female there are two X's, and, as a rule, the male, who has only one X, is not grossly abnormal compared to the female, so there may be some mechanism to compensate for the dosage effect which should occur. It is known that in the female mouse, there is a mosaic pattern for those genetically controlled colors of the coat which are sex-linked. In other words, if a female carries two alleles, one in each of the sex chromosomes and each for a different color, she does not show a mixture of the two colors but rather a mosaic pattern, that is, parts of the fur have one color and other parts of it have the other color. It is the so-called tortoise-shell color. This does not occur in the male, which has only one allele, and which has uniform fur, correlated with the allele he carries.

Lyon proposed that, early in development, one of the X's becomes latent, so that in each cell one ends up affecting coat color, and the other is used to make the Barr body, the chromatin corpuscle which is seen in the resting nuclei.

Patau: Excuse me, some may not know that "Barr body" is a synonym for sex chromatin body.

Lejeune: Yes, it is a synonym for sex chromatin body. Lyon said that this inactivation of one X has to be hereditary in the progeny of the cell in which it arose, because of this mosaic pattern I referred to earlier; so if one X—the one producing, say, yellow color—is inactivated, then, all the cells coming out from that cell would fail to show the yellow, but would show instead the allelic color. There are several indications that if an autosomal color gene is translocated to the X in the mouse, it behaves in the same way; that is, it gives the mosaic pattern in the female and a uniform pattern in the male. The Lyon hypothesis, there-fore, is, broadly, the following: Some time early in embryological development one of the X's becomes inactivated, and at random in different cells, but once it has been inactivated in one cell, it remains inactivated in the progeny of that cell. In that way a mosaic pattern develops.

One of the proofs that the mosaic pattern is not due indirectly to the female phenotype is that in XXY mice, the same phenomenon occurs; that is, it is not influenced by the presence of a Y. In man, we do not know anything about sex-linked genes which affect the color of the skin. The only one which Lyon cited is the albinism of the eye—a sex-linked gene which affects eye color. The female carrier shows, in the retina, some areas which are pigmented and some which are without pigment, but those islands of pigment are very small. In my opinion it is questionable whether, when there is a low pigmentation rate, it is not just a statistical effect rather than mosaicism. This is not yet proved in the case of ocular albinism.

Ephrussi: What is the evidence that this is due to inactivation of one of the X's, rather than to somatic crossing over?

Lejeune: There is no evidence as to somatic crossing over.

Ephrussi: Somatic crossing over would give you a mosaic, too.

DeMars: It would have to be restricted to the X, because when you translocate an autosomal coat color marker to the X, it begins to mottle. But if it is in the autosomal location, it does not.

Lejeune: No, because those two genes are alleles.

Ephrussi: Yes, so that is all right. As shown by Dr. Stern many, many years ago, this is what results in twin spots in Drosophila.

Herzenberg: It is very unusual.

Billingham: Could we have a diagram?

Lejeune: I don't understand this.

DeMars: In Drosophila, as Dr. Stern showed long ago, a fly heterozygous for an integumental color marker may have spots that correspond to homozygosity rather than heterozygosity. Similarly, female mice heterozygous for sex-linked coat color markers do not have a uniform coat color corresponding to the heterozygous genotype. Instead, the coat is mottled with areas having color corresponding to "homozygosity" for one allele or the other.

If Dr. Ephrussi is right about mitotic crossing over, then, it probably would have to be restricted to the X.

Ephrussi: I don't have to be wrong or right; I mean, there is such a phenomenon. I am just raising the question. I am not giving preference to this. I am just asking whether there is any critical evidence that these observations are not accountable for in terms of crossing over in the X, that is, somatic crossing over in the X. It seems to me that this would be demonstrated if you had a dominant marker of some sort, say, a specific protein, which would show the heterozygous state. It seems to me that, perhaps, critical evidence could be provided by tracing of a pair of good codominant antigens.

Herzenberg: You could do it simply with two color genes, exhibiting phenotypic dominance in the case of the color genes, especially. With two on the X chromosome, you might expect that both or neither would be inactivated. Somatic crossing over would lead occasionally to one changing without the other, but never the reverse. There should be a polarity to this effect, unless there is double crossing over relative to the centromere.

Lejeune: For a marker in man, we have one which is XgA, a blood group gene, roughly dominant. A heterozygous female, who is A+ and A−, shows the A+ phenotype in her red cells. The difficulty is that this point should be crucial for the Lyon hypothesis but is not, unfortunately. The antisera are not too strong, and if you study an

A+ man, who, of course, has only one locus, the anti-A+ do not agglutinate all his red cells; most of them are agglutinated, but some are still free.

In a heterozygous female, if the Lyon hypothesis is correct and is reflected in this particular system, we should find that half of the cells are agglutinated by the antisera and half remain free. But, for the moment, as far as I know, much more than half are agglutinated. Since less than 100 percent are agglutinated in the male, then, if there was a mosaic red cell population, much less than half should be agglutinated, if half of the cells had an XgA nonfunctioning chromosome.

Herzenberg: That is only true if the antigen is a cell limited one, but we don't know where the antigen is made or whether it migrates from one cell to the other.

Neel: There seems to be a consensus, if this is not a good antiserum, it is not going to provide a critical test. But there is another trait which may be of some value. This is the sex-linked G-6-PD deficiency.

Gartler: I think some evidence can be furnished on this one point. However, I doubt if we can accurately differentiate between somatic crossing over and inactivation. What we had hoped to do, was to begin with tissue from heterozygous individuals and to clone out individual cells. You should then, if the hypothesis is true, have clones which are low in enzyme level and clones which have normal G-6-PD levels. Of course, you would expect the same phenomenon on the basis of somatic recombination.

Neel: But can you answer a question of fact, whether you get two kinds of cell or two kinds of clone?

Gartler: In the work we have done so far, we have not been able to clone our normal lines effectively. We have some indirect data that I will present tomorrow, which unfortunately can be interpreted in more than one way.

Motulsky: But Beutler has shown that in heterozygous females there were two kinds of cell, about one-half of which were mutant and one-half of which were normal.

Neel: That work is under strong attack by the Chicago group at this time.

Motulsky: There is one other kind of evidence which we presented at the recent meeting of the American Society of Human Genetics at Corvallis. Ectodermal dysplasia in the male manifests with hypohidrosis, hypodontia, and hypotrichosis. We studied female heterozygotes with ectodermal dysplasia and found occasionally that there was patchy absence of sweating. More interestingly, two of these women were hemilateral sweaters, suggesting that genetic inactivation of the X chromosome carrying the mutant gene occurred very early and all the descendants of the originally inactivated cell did not sweat. Consequently, these women did not sweat over the ventral half of their body, they did not have hair on that side, and the phenotype was hemilaterally that of the disease. We ruled out *chromosomal* mosaicism of the nonsweating and nonhairy side by showing that the involved skin was XX and not XO, which also might have explained the phenotype.

Patau: But your observation doesn't rule out somatic crossing over.

Steinberg: Mary Lyon referred to some mice which were heterozygous for two sex-linked mutants in repulsion. If there was somatic crossing over you would expect some wild-type spots to be adjacent to spots showing both mutants. This was not found. Apparently, large spots, one of which shows one mutant and the other of which shows the other mutant, are obtained, and no wild-type spots showing both mutants occur. That would eliminate somatic crossing over.

McKusick: And no doubly mutant spots?

Steinberg: No, no doubly mutant; all the spots show one mutant or the other.

Szybalski: The frequencies of somatic crossing over, as known in other systems, are definitely too low to explain the above-described phenomenon.

Ephrussi: I just don't think we can take this as a definition, that the somatic crossing over can be excluded on the basis that it is usually a rare phenomenon. In these particular animals or particular individuals, it may precisely be a rather regular mechanism occurring with high frequency, and, in fact, coordinated somehow with certain developmental stages. I don't think we can exclude this.

Szybalski: At any rate, it could not be the type of crossing over observed in fungi or because of the too high frequency of crossing over.

Neel: May we ask Dr. Stern a question of fact? As I recall it, you worked with yellow in Drosophila, a sex-linked trait. What about somatic crossing over in the autosomes of Drosophila?

Stern: I will answer that question in a minute, but with respect to what Dr. Steinberg said, that you would also expect from crossing over wild types, this is true. With regard to your question, Dr. Neel, there is crossing over also in the autosomes. It is rare, but by no means very rare. In Drosophila you can greatly increase it by x-irradiation in larval stages, and if you can use x-irradiation to increase it, it is conceivable that in mammals the thing just occurs anyway. I don't believe that this is the interpretation, but it is possible.

Neel: But, then, would we agree that if we do not observe the same kind of mosaicism for autosomal traits as we do for sex-linked traits, this would be indirect evidence against somatic crossing over as the explanation?

Stern: No, this would be just a question of what the relative frequency is.

Let me say one more thing regarding the evidence on these very interesting sweating pictures which were shown at Corvallis. If this were the mechanism, I would expect, in women who are heterozygous for color blindness, quite frequently to find one eye color blind and the other not. Such cases are known, but they are exceedingly rare, I understand.

Motulsky: Most of these cases are males. I looked into that, so this would rule it out.

Stern: Of course, one could say that the retina comes from a different part than the body surface, to some degree, and one cannot predict one thing from the other. But it was very striking that the two types of skin in your cases were represented by such large patches. You would expect this relatively frequently for the color-blind eyes, too.

McKusick: The observations in heterozygous ocular albinism suggest, however, that the differentiation occurs rather late, because there are many blocks of pigment (9).

Ephrussi: I would come back just for one second to a statement of Dr. Szybalski's. I think one should really not take anything for granted; for example, the frequency or the rarity of somatic crossing over, say, in Drosophila or any other organism. One used to make the same reasoning, say, about the frequency of spontaneous mutation.

Now, it is known that in Drosophila or in plants—and Demerec has done some work on this—there are frequently mutating genes and these genes have a high frequency of mutation in some somatic tissues, sufficient to give almost a constant pattern, while their mutation in the the germ line is much lower; so I think that one just cannot extrapolate.

Stern: I might mention, for instance, the color patterns in, let's say, Friesian cattle—the black and white irregular spots. There is some kind of determination at some early stage as to whether a certain area will be pigmented or nonpigmented. These are not sex-linked phenomena. What the determination is, we do not know. I don't think it is somatic crossing over, although there is no proof against it, either. But it seems to me that this mechanism of making spots may be of many different types, and even the X chromosomal spottings may be of the same type as in the Fresian cattle. You get the same thing in fox terriers, for instance.

Lejeune: There is another point which is difficult to accept entirely in the Lyon hypothesis. It is the fact that we have data on abnormal sexual content of sex chromosomes, and they do not fit entirely the hypothesis. If we suppose that one of the X's is inactivated in the female, then, an XO female should be exactly like an XX female, with one X not working.

The other difficulty is that when we consider a triple-X individual, there is a very big difference in the phenotype if a Y is present. Specifically, the triple-X woman, generally, is of normal intelligence, but the XXX-Y person is really feebleminded; so in that constellation, it does prove that having three X's does not mean the same thing, if a Y is added or not. Nevertheless, in normal people, the fact of having one X and one Y does not decrease the intelligence as compared to having two X's, one inactive (on the Lyon hypothesis).

There is one way to escape this contradiction, and it is one that Lyon used, which is to say that the chromatin body appears in human embryos around the twelfth day after the beginning of the division of the first blastomere. All the X's present are working during the early embryonic period, and then, after a time, one is blocked in a two-X person, two are blocked in a three-X person, and three are blocked in a four-X person. I agree that with that restriction to the hypothesis, you can get a picture more consistent with what we know.

Nevertheless, there are still little things which do occur, particularly things which develop later in the life of a normal person. The synostosis between the ulna and the radius, which occurs specifically in the XXY people is not present at birth. We have cases which do not show it at birth, but it is almost the rule after they are twelve years old; so it does prove that even in the late development of the total individual, the number of X's still plays a role. Hence, there is evidence that X-chromosome dosage is not only effective in very early embryonic development, but continues to have a role in the makeup of the individual during his growth. If that is the case, I suppose that having three X's and a Y is not the same as having one X and a Y, even for late growth.

Renwick: I am sure that Dr. Lejeune would agree with me that one can get out of the radio-ulnar synostosis problem by saying there is some early lesion which does not show as synostosis but leads to synostosis, some basic difference at an early stage of development, due to the functioning of both X's in the presence of Y.

Lejeune: Well, we are dealing here with a morphological trait, and it does appear long after birth. I mean that if, very early, there was something happening, let's say, in the morula or the gastrula, it would surely continue to have an effect on the growth of the radius. That is very possible, but I do not see any grounds for proving it.

Renwick: No, I was using this as a means of escape, for the Lyon hypothesis.

Lejeune: Oh, I agree, there are always escapes. [Laughter] But the more escapes you have to use to retain the hypothesis the less proof for the hypothesis.

Patau: I would say, if the Lyon hypothesis were correct, it would still leave the possibility that for certain genes the inactivation is not complete. There is one synthetic activity of the DNA molecule that must go on anyway—DNA reduplication itself.

As Dr. DeMars pointed out, it is apparently at this time that the sex chromatin body disappears. Indeed, one of the things that makes the Lyon hypothesis plausible is that, as far as we know, DNA synthesis generally takes place only when the chromosomes are widely dispersed. If there is a period during which the sex chromatin body is completely dispersed, a period in which DNA is synthesized, why should not some other gene activities also take place in that period?

Atwood: If you consider the primary gene action to be a transcription from DNA into RNA message, the message formation and DNA replications are most likely mutually exclusive in time. The dispersion of one chromosome for a short time compared to the other could mean that it replicates, but does not make message.

Patau: But who says it is dispersed just long enough to make only DNA?

Atwood: Oh, well, sure.

Patau: Furthermore, we know that the frequency of cells with a sex chromatin body is quite different in different tissues. It is, for instance, rather low in the buccal mucosa, so there may well be tissues in which the X rather frequently is dispersed beyond the period necessary for DNA synthesis.

DeMars: I don't think that Lyon stated baldly anywhere that all of the genetic and phenotypic functions of the X chromosome are inactivated. I think this is not necessary. If she did, then, I think, a very convenient escape is just to say that some are not. That is enough.

The other thing is that I am very interested, and I think we should take seriously, this connection to the nucleolus; that is, I believe that one can see an indubitable sex chromatin mass which has a real connection with a nucleolus, and to me that means that some of that X is functioning, is creating phenotype. This is speculation, but the connection to the nucleolus, I think, is unmistakable.

Herzenberg: I don't get your reasoning there. What has the nucleolus got to do with the functioning?

DeMars: A nucleolus is a factory.

Herzenberg: It makes ribosomes. That is what they think now, anyway.

DeMars: Well, I don't want to pursue this too far. We don't know what the nucleolus is. But I think that it is very suggestive.

Ephrussi: I was just going to point out that if you start compromising a little bit on this inactivation by assuming that not all genes may be inactivated, but some may cofunction, this really brings this case much closer to the Drosophila situation, where we have the phenomenon, first described by Stern and Muller, of the dosage compensation.

In Drosophila, it is very well known that some alleles at a given locus, for example, the white locus, are subject to dosage compensation, and others are not.

Stern: And, perhaps, one should add that in Drosophila there is no dosage compensation by means of suppression of activity of one of the X chromosomes, but there is a different kind of mechanism in which both X chromosomes are active.

Ephrussi: How do we know that?

Stern: I think we know it, for instance, from the point of view that if you have two X chromosomes and you have a recessive in both of them, you get one phenotype, but if you have a small deficiency opposite the recessive, you get another phenotype. In other words, you have two kinds of females, one of which has two doses and the other of which has only one dose, and you get a striking phenotypic difference. Thus, it is not that one X chromosome is knocked out, as a rule, because it has an effect.

Ephrussi: This, I think, is precisely what cannot be generalized to all the alleles at one locus. Isn't that the case with eosin and apricot, which act differently when opposed to a deficiency?

Stern: Oh, yes, I know now what you mean. If you have a female with two apricots, you have a different eye color than if you have a male with one apricot. Therefore, what would you conclude?

Ephrussi: That the other allele was doing something.

Stern: Yes, it was doing something.

Ephrussi: Contributing to the effect.

Stern: Now, take the third case, where you have a female in whom you have one apricot in one chromosome, and the actual physical deficiency in the other one. Then, you do not get the male effect, and you do not get the effect which you would have in a female with two of them, but you get something else. In other words, you can show that the whole X chromosome does something in contrast to the whole X chromosome minus the deficiency, doing something else. I'm not sure if I made that clear.

Renwick: This could not be due to a type of mosaicism, could it, in which you could not pick out the different patches because of diffusion?

Stern: No. Mosaicism does not exist in Drosophila, except in special position-effect cases, where it is very frequent. But, in the normal X chromosome or autosomal genes, you have no mosaicism, I believe. If it occurred you would be able to observe it, because when you have these special position effects, then, you do get mosaicism for eye colors.

Atwood: Isn't the Notch deficiency an example of how the Drosophila X chromosome is balanced within itself? If you bring in the deficiency on a small fragment of the tip of X, the phenotype does not appear. This shows that some part of the X other than the locus of the deficiency is also involved in producing the phenotype.

Patau: Definite proof for the Lyon hypothesis does not exist. As an alternative, somatic crossing over is a possibility, but I don't think a very likely one. I can't forget that we have in Drosophila somatic chromosome pairing of a very intimate kind, which certainly does not occur in mammals. But there is something else. The rule that the maximum number of sex chromatin bodies is invariably one less than the number of X chromosomes obviously reflects the existence of a very special mechanism. Its nature is unknown, but I find it difficult to believe that such a mechanism should have developed and been retained unless there was some advantage to it.

Even if the Lyon hypothesis is not carried to the untenable extreme of saying that a complete inactivation of one X chromosome has done away with the need for dosage compensation, it still allows us to view the evolution of the sex chromatin mechanism as advantageous in that it lessened the need for dosage compensation. The Lyon hypothesis, as far as I can see, is so far the only idea that makes any sense out of the very strange mechanism that causes the maximum number of sex chromatin bodies to equal the number of X's minus one. It is for this reason that the Lyon hypothesis seems to me inherently plausible.

Atwood: Before going on, I want to be sure I understand the disagreement between the late-labeling results and the outfocusing results. Could we have the slide that shows the drawing made from the outfocused picture, the one with the eight blobs (Fig. 4)?

Patau: According to Dr. Lejeune, the X chromosome is one of the largest C chromosomes.

Atwood: Well, then, I am sure that the objection that, possibly, these blobs are random noise can be explored formally, without further experiments, and I have a feeling that it will turn out that they are not random noise.

If these spots (Fig. 4) are real, what you have to assume to reconcile it with your late-labeling is this: first, the male X has the same length as the late-labeled X in the female. The early-labeled X in the female is the longest of the group. Second, the late-labeled X in the female must be the same size as some other member of the group, so it falls into one of these other spots and does not form a ninth spot. Is that all reasonable?

Patau: That is possible, yes. However, I don't know whether it would in the female give a clearcut spot where the X is marked, because only one of the X's would be accumulated there.

Atwood: I didn't understand that.

Patau: If it were so that the late-labeling is shorter than the early-labeling X, you would have in the female only half the accumulation at the spot marked "X", because the late-labeling would be much more in the middle, about where No. 9 is.

Atwood: I don't think you could tell from the outfocusing picture just what the density was.

Patau: No.

Herzenberg: Well, 6 and 8 happen to be closest, and that is how he got the result.

Lejeune: I would like to stress a point. The scatter diagram gives you the point, but it does not give you the name of the point, so what I did was to compare statistically the sum of the cells, to detect what the point could be for the X. Outfocusing cannot tell you where the X is.

Neel: What is this attachment to the X on your slide [Fig. 5]?

Lejeune: It means the greatest density, and the fact that there are a lot of things around that density. We could come back to this later.

Neel: And a greater degree of blurring than you observe with other spots?

Lejeune: Yes.

Renwick: Nevertheless, you did use the fact that there were eight spots as slight evidence in favor of your interpretation, whereas, now, in the Lyon hypothesis, one expects nine.

Lejeune: Why should there be nine?

Renwick: Because there are two different kinds of X's.

Lejeune: If you suppose that they are not of the same length, one of them may fall into another group and, if it does, you will not see it.

Herzenberg: Since 6 and X seem to be the ones that are being disputed, and they are so close together in this representation, I can see the possibility of confusion in this thing.

Lejeune: Exactly, but that is what occurs in the cells. It is very difficult to say if it is a 6 or an X.

Patau: I might say that I am convinced that Dr. Lejeune's method, in principle, must work.* The only question is whether your number of nuclei, even though it amounts to a terrific piece of work, is sufficiently large. There is a practical limit to the number of mitoses that we can measure, and whether any practical number would suffice is the question. I think it might well be so that some of your points are significant and the others are not.

Lejeune: I would say that the best proof that the number is not sufficient is that I was obliged to use the diffraction picture, because if I had gotten a hundred thousand points, the concentration would have shown itself, without any optical trick, exactly as in a picture in a newspaper.

Patau: I don't think we should leave the identification problem without mentioning the possibility of developing specific treatments to bring out secondary constrictions, which might permit us to identify more chromosomes than we can at present.

Some secondary constrictions have already been described. I know that Dr. Lejeune has for years been aware of such a constriction in chromosome 1; it can be seen in Figure 17 close to the centromere in

---

* Afterthought: This should be qualified. There is no assurance that the true density distribution, as approached by increasing the number of measured mitoses, would show eight peaks (or nine, if in the female the two X's should differ in length), for this would presuppose that there are no two C chromosomes whose mean locations have a distance that is smaller than the standard deviation of a single-chromosome distribution. If the two locations were that close, there could not be two separate peaks. I wonder whether some of Dr. Lejeune's points of accumulation are not in fact too close to each other to be real. However, even if the true distribution had, as I suspect it would have, fewer peaks than there are C chromosomes, it might still be possible to compute the mean location of every chromosome, but this would be an exceedingly tedious analysis, probably requiring the use of an electronic computer.

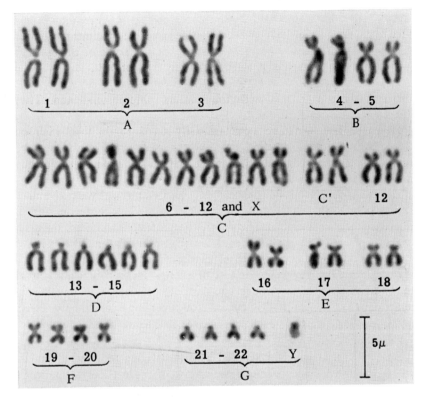

Figure 17. Male karyotype. Note secondary constriction in one chromosome 1 and in both numbers of pair C'.

the upper arm of the first No. 1. We, and others independently, found a secondary constriction in one of the smaller C pairs, which we called C' (33). The karyotype shows how the identification of one pair, C' in this case, can aid that of other pairs: the chromosomes 12 are clearly homologous since the smallness of their short arms distinguishes them from all other C' chromosomes once C' has been set aside. Unfortunately, the usefulness of secondary constrictions has so far been very limited because of their low frequency of manifestation in ordinary preparations. Sasaki and Makino (38) have a paper in press in which they show very beautiful secondary constrictions which they obtained fairly regularly by means of a calcium-free culture medium. These constrictions include the known and some new ones.

Bayreuther: I would like to add here that we occasionally have observed secondary constrictions in chromosomes of the mouse, rat, hamster, and human karyotype. They occurred in cultures which had been subjected to cold treatment or starvation of some of the essential amino acids in an attempt to synchronize the cultures.

Lejeune: This works very well in *Vicia faba*.

Bayreuther: It works with mammalian chromosomes too. These are incidental observations.

Lejeune: But we have systematically tried to do that with our cultures, and I must say that the results were not very convincing. We could not always tell whether something was happening repeatedly in the same chromosome.

Bayreuther: Yes, I quite agree, in cultures not fully synchronized one gets a confusing pattern of induced secondary constrictions. In fully synchronized cultures, however, the pattern is uniform, probably because of the fact that the cold treatment acts at a population of cells at about the same stage of chromosome reduplication.

Patau: You always have a test of such a method in that you already know several secondary constrictions. If they are brought out, it means that the method is capable of revealing secondary constrictions, and we can have more confidence in its usefulness.

Lejeune: Yes.

Bayreuther: It should be added here that Gläss reported secondary constrictions to occur in the chromosomes of the rat karyotype in the process of regeneration after hepatectomy (2).

Viruses could perhaps be used as tools for the identification of chromosomes. In studies about the interaction of cytocidal viruses with the chromosomes of animal cells, mouse and chicken embryo cultures have been infected with cytocidal viruses of four different types: (1) DNA viruses with intranuclear phase of reproduction (polyoma, herpes), (2) DNA viruses with cytoplasmatic phase of reproduction (vaccinia), (3) helical RNA viruses (influenza), and (4) isometric RNA viruses (EMC, Sindbis). Infected cells entering mitosis show at metaphase heavily fragmented chromosomes. The breaks are of the nature of chromosome breaks and are located randomly. Addition of puromycin to the medium at 10 gamma/ml at the time of infection reduces the frequency of chromosomes fragmented, probably via inhibition of early proteins. It has been observed for the chicken karyotype that specific chromosomes are fragmented at specific sites under these conditions. These again are preliminary data. They are brought up only to show that techniques and tools for the identification of morphologically undifferentiated chromosomes are by no means exhausted (38).

Lejeune: Well, the problem of the recognition of the chromosomes is quite difficult in the normal karyotype, but, of course, it is still more difficult in abnormal karyotypes. The way I propose that we go into the discussion is by emphasizing that the great problem of translocations in human beings is the problem of identification, because the chromosomes so produced are not normally present in the human karyotype. We have, first, to pick them out as abnormal chromosomes, and, secondly, to label them considering the chromosomes from which they are derived.

I would like to show a few pictures of various types of translocations in humans, illustrating the difficulty of this problem (Figs. 18 and 19). Figure 18 is not a perfect cell because it was the first translocation we had, and our technique was not entirely perfect, but this translocation is interesting because it has been found again. The patient had a curious disease, with many abnormalities of the vertebrae. The karyotype of this individual showed the 45 chromosome, and we can see (Fig. 19) that there was one of the smallest acrocentrics in the bottom row lacking.

We have another medium-sized chromosome which is an extra chromosome in this particular group. Of course, the chromatin body was negative, as in the normal male, and there was no sexual abnormality, so we thought that we had to consider the lack of the small chromosome here and the presence of the medium-sized chromosome. Its long arms could be matched rather well with one of the big acrocentrics, and the extra part could be matched very well with the size of the missing small acrocentric.

This is the general principle with which we are working in human translocations; that is, we first pick out the abnormal chromosomes, and now we see what is lacking in the rest of the karyotype, and we try to figure out the simplest way to explain what has occurred to produce this abnormal chromosome. In this case, two chromosomes are lacking, one a big acrocentric, and one a small acrocentric. The medium-sized chromosome present is supposed to be the result of their fusion.

In this case, we tentatively said, just on the basis of what we supposed to be the 21 and the 22, that this was a translocation between 22 and 13, on purely cytological grounds. It does appear, that the same translocation or a comparable one has been found, by Moorhead, Mellman and Wenar (28) and it was carried by a woman who had the same karyotype but who was XX. In that case we can probably

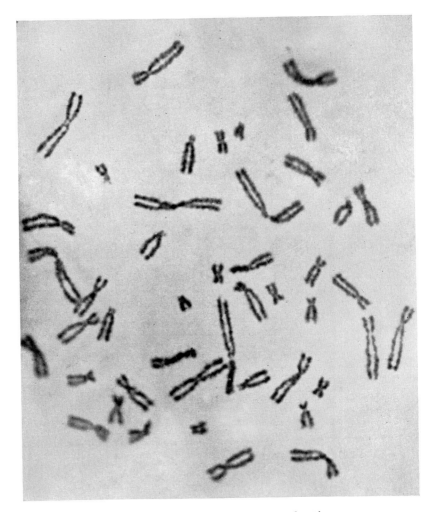

Figure 18. A case of 22 to 13 translocation.

say that it was really a 22 that was translocated. This woman had many children, some of whom were carrying the translocation, and one of them was not. She (the child without the translocation) had two normal 22's, but she had three 21's; she was a mongoloid. Now, if the translocation in the mother had been from 21 on to the big acrocentric, then, the mother would have had only two doses of chromosome 21, and only one free, so she would really not have been able to

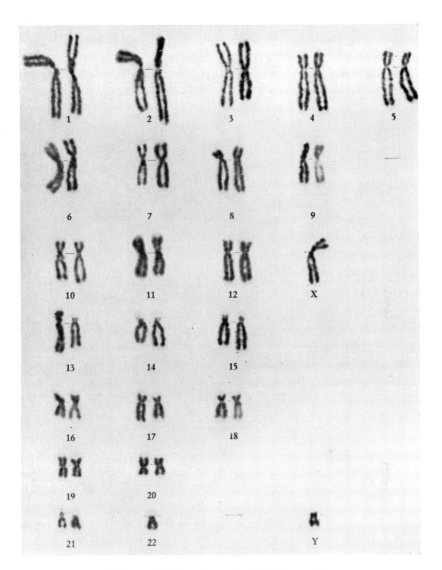

Figure 19. Karyotype of cell in Figure 18.

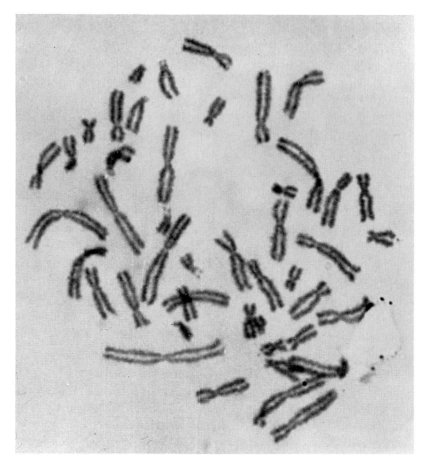

Figure 20. Klinefelter XXY with a 14 to 15 translocation.

transmit two of them to the child without also transmitting the translocated chromosome. This is a direct inference from the family that, probably, the translocation involved the 22. I am assuming that the mother was heterozygous for a 21 translocation. We supposed the abnormal chromosome included the 13 chromosome, so she had that. Now, to produce a mongol, as we know from the cases of mothers with translocations of 21, the two chromosomes, the translocated one and the free 21 go to the same pole, and, after fertilization by a normal sperm, you do get the equivalent of a trisomy 21. But the mongol produced by this mother did not have a translocation. She had six big acrocentrics,

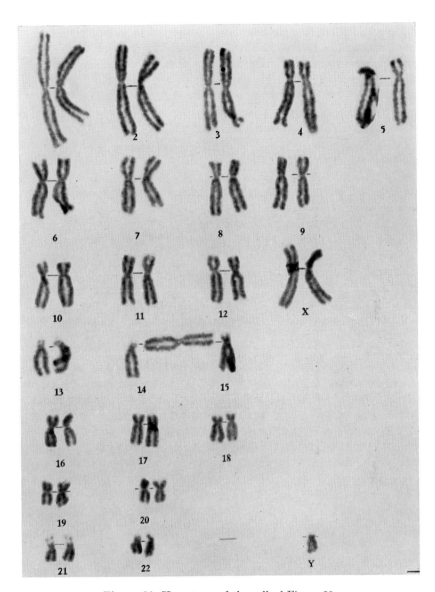

Figure 21. Karyotype of the cell of Figure 20.

and she had three free chromosome 21's, so the process was related to the fact that the mother had an unbalanced karyotype. Thus, I suppose there was not a 21 in the translocation, but a 22. This is a point of inference which can help us to try to see what the translocated part was.

Renwick: You are excluding the possibility of the nondisjunction or disegregation, as you call it, in the male?

Lejeune: In this case, it would be unlikely, that, having a translocated karyotype in the mother, the abnormality of the child would not be somewhat related to the mother's anomaly. I agree that it is possible in this family, but, with the accumulation of data, I hope to be able to prove that it is unlikely.

Figures 20 and 21 show the chromosomes of an exceptional case of Klinefelter's syndrome; the patient had 46 chromosomes, and the karyotype illustrates another type of translocation.

There was one chromatin body in the cell. On the karyotype, he has two X's and one Y. But two of the big acrocentrics are lacking. He has only four instead of six. He has a big chromosome, with a medium centromere, which could resemble a chromosome 3, but the centromere is perfectly median. That is extremely consistent in all the cells; here we had 50 cells as good as that one.

In this case we could suppose that the chromosome is not the 13, which we are confident we can recognize rather well in most of the cells, with its short arms and the big satellites. But we were confident that it was a 14-15 chromosome and not an isochromosome.

The reasoning is as follows: Unfortunately, we could not get the parents of this individual, but the implication was that the abnormality was existing in one of the parents. If so, it could not be an isochromosome, because if it were, let us say, 14 and 14, the child would have been trisomic for 14 and hemizygous for 15. However, he showed classical Klinefelter's syndrome, without any other abnormality. This particular translocation between big acrocentrics has now been found in different patterns, and some families show a partial segregation for this unknown chromosome. In those families it is obvious that it is a hybrid chromosome, because of the production trisomy-13 syndrome.

One case recently found showed the transmission of this type of chromosome and the production of the trisomy for this type, the trisomy described by Dr. Patau.

Patau: Could we discuss this for a moment? Your reasoning that this is not an isochromosome depends entirely on your assurance that you can identify 14 and 15?

Lejeune: No. In the family which was described by the British workers (Harris and his associates), they got three generations, in which they could follow the transmission of these big chromosomes, with only four big acrocentrics in the karyotype. They found nine carriers and they found nine normals.

Now, if that particular chromosome had been 14 and 14, every time it was transmitted, the egg would have been diploid for 14. Any new sperm coming would have produced a trisomy for 14.

Ephrussi: Yes, but you also base your reasoning on the fact—I don't know whether it is a fact or a hypothesis—that the trisomic for either 14 or 15 would result in a very severe condition. Is that a fact?

Lejeune: Yes. The fact is that we don't know of any normal persons who are trisomic. Everyone carrying a trisomic for one of the big acrocentrics dies at around six months of age.

Ephrussi: But do you have direct evidence that trisomy for 14 or 15 creates a severe trauma?

Patau: No, it is indirect, but the facts seem fairly conclusive. To begin with, the frequency of mongolism is fairly high. If the other small acrocentric chromosome permitted viable trisomy, it should have been found by now. The number of karyotypes that have been reasonably well analyzed is large enough. It is unbelievable that such cases should not have been found repeatedly. Equally, a trisomic for 19 or 20 should have been found. It has never been found. Thus, it seems likely that trisomy for all but one of the three smallest chromosomes is lethal. Moreover, mongolism is a severely abnormal condition—

Ephrussi: That is triple what?

Lejeune: It is triple 21 mongolism.

Patau: Well, this is another point, but one of the—

Ephrussi: But my question is really this: Suppose that a trisomic for 14 or 15 is perfectly normal. Is it sure you would have detected it?

Lejeune: More than a thousand entirely normal people have been investigated, and no one was trisomic for one of the big acrocentrics. Well, I suppose we would have detected it surely.

Ephrussi: Well, that is my point.

Patau: The syndrome caused by trisomy for the big acrocentric chromosome that we call D_1, the condition that Dr. Lejeune referred to, is quite rare. Therefore, we must grant that trisomics for the other two big acrocentrics might not yet have been found if they were normal. But, surely, one should have found trisomics for the small acrocentric that is not related to mongolism. It has not been found as yet. No case has been found of trisomy for 19 or 20. This suggests strongly that these are lethal conditions. Futhermore, the only two types known of trisomics for chromosomes larger than the mongolism chromosome are still more abnormal than mongoloids. These two chromosomes, 18 and D_1, are of comparable size, and the two trisomy syndromes are clinically of similar severity. They are practically lethal conditions. I think all this taken together makes it extremely unlikely than any big acrocentric could be present in triplicate without greatly affecting the phenotype. I think it likely that we have already run out of chromosomes for which viable trisomy is possible.

Chu: May I recall one case of a study by Jacobs and coworkers (21), in connection with sex chromosomes? One of the individuals studied was a 46/47 mosaic. The extra chromosome in cells with 47 chromosomes was similar in size to those of pairs 10 and 11. No cell with two sex chromatin bodies was observed in buccal smear preparations.

Lejeune: But the explanation is that it proved this chromosome was, in fact, an abnormal X. It was probably XX and Y. That is the explanation they gave.

Chu: I just wanted to know if you recalled the same case.

Lejeune: Oh, yes. But, as far as we know, there is no possible variation for the true number in normal people. There can be variations in the total number, just because some are joined together to form a new chromosome, but a true triplication of a number of genes has not been found in normal human beings thus far.

Patau: We should recall the situation in plants. By now there are quite a number of species in which trisomics for every chromosome have been produced and studied. The general rule is, at least in diploid species, that every type of trisomic is clearly distinguishable from the normal and from every other type of trisomic. Therefore, if trisomics for one D chromosome were fairly normal although trisomy for D_1, 18, or even the much smaller mongolism chromosome causes multiple and highly severe anomalies, this would stand in an extraordinary contradiction to all we know about plant trisomics. The evidence from plants clearly indicates that numerous genes on every chromosome are involved in trisomy effects. This is also suggested by the multiplicity of seemingly unrelated anomalies that make up all known autosomal trisomy syndromes in man.

Lejeune: Figures 22 and 23 show another type of chromosomal translocation, that is, a typical Turner's syndrome, which has only one X. Let's say it is chromatin-negative.

The karyotype is quite interesting. It is evident that there is only one chromosome 2 here, so one chromosome 2 is lacking in every cell. Instead of it, we find that there are, in fact, a number of medium-sized chromosomes, enough to try to make up two X chromosomes.

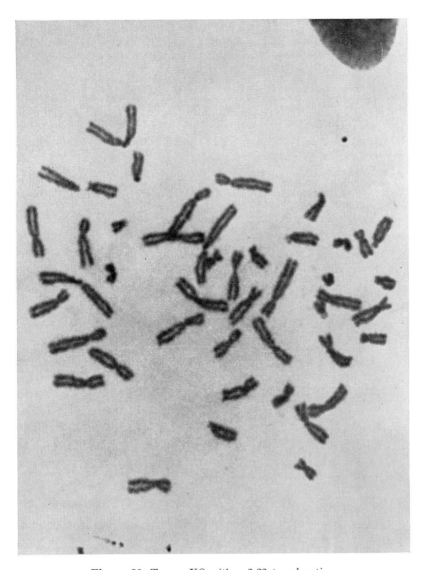

Figure 22. Turner XO with a 2-22 translocation.

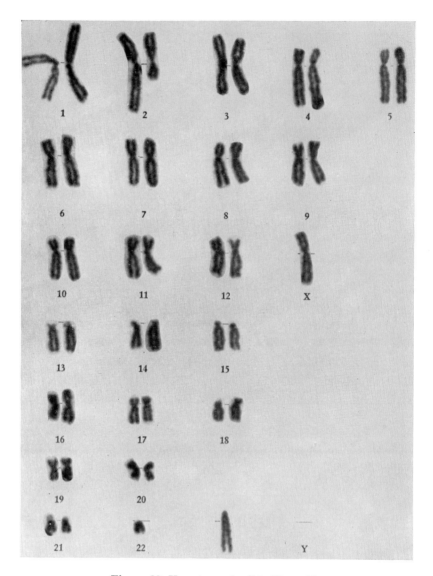

Figure 23. Karyotype of cell in Figure 22.

This girl consistently had a negative Barr body in three different examinations, and clinically she is a typical case of Turner's syndrome. We deduce that she has one X and, besides this, she has only one 2 chromosome. In addition, she has only one 22 chromosome, and she has a new chromosome, a big acrocentric, which is really much bigger than the biggest acrocentric.

To fit this together, we first had to look at the mother. The mother had the same constitution, but she had two X's.

Szybalski: The mother is normal?

Lejeune: The mother is phenotypically normal. I will speak about the family later. We figured out that chromosome 2 is present, surely, and part of the other one could be the extra medium-sized chromosome. When we come to the small chromosomes, there is only one 22 and a big acrocentric, which does not belong to any group in the human karyotype. We suppose that part of the long arm of chromosome 2 was translocated onto chromosome 22, so that it formed this big acrocentric.

Now, measurements could be made to determine whether the sum of one 22 plus the lacking segment (of chromosome 2) would add up to the size of this particular acrocentric. Unfortunately, these measurements are not accurate, because we have to know what this particular chromosome (the abnormal medium-sized one) is, and the length of the deleted 2. It belongs to the medium-sized chromosomes, and, with the difficulty of matching, we are not entirely sure that we can recognize it properly. However, our calculations showed that, depending on how we matched this medium-sized chromosome, there was enough material in the abnormal acrocentric to account for both the deleted segment of the 2 and the other 22, or there was not enough material. In that particular case, we cannot determine definitively, whether there was a loss of genetic material or just a translocation without any loss.

We are presently inquiring into the genetics of this family. We know that the mother is phenotypically normal. She had these 2-22 translocations, with 46 chromosomes and 2 X's. She had four boys, who now have children, whom we have not yet examined, and a girl, plus one other child who died earlier and about whom we have no information. The girl has a translocation and is XO. But the study of her chromosomes was not finished when we left.* In addition, there were

* Afterthought added by Dr. Lejeune: Three of the four boys carry this same translocation and one of them has transmitted it to two children. The translocation is now known in three generations.

three spontaneous abortions which could be related, possibly, to an unbalanced mechanism produced by the translocation in the mother.

The point which arises from these observations is that we now have in our laboratory relatively few chromosomal abnormalities for sexual development. We have, roughly, 45 of them, and I say "roughly" because I don't remember exactly, but it is between 40 and 50. What is curious is that three of them have a translocation beside the XO and XXY condition. We have two families among the Klinefelter's patients in which there is an autosomal translocation running in the family and one among the XO patients, in which the mother has the extraordinary 2-22 translocation.

It seems rather unlikely that this is a random process, and one of the indications or inferences that we could draw from the data is that once you have an autosomal imbalance from a translocation, the probability of having another abnormality in the progeny is increased. This would mean that if there is a translocation in the autosomes, it does diminish the efficiency of the pairing of the other chromosomes at meiosis and perhaps influences segregation during mitosis. We do know, of course, that the translocation can be involved itself; I mean, in the progeny of a 21-13 carrier mother, half of the children receiving the translocation are normals, while half of the others are mongols. In this case the free 21 has segregated to the same pole as the translocated chromosome. If there was not impairment of the meiotic process, only normal children would be produced, half with the translocation and half without it. It gives us, therefore, a first clue to the production of chromosomal aberration. At least for those that do occur at meiosis, translocations in the autosomes do increase the mis-segregation not only of the chromosome involved in the translocation, but also mis-segregation of chromosomes which are different, such as the sex chromosomes.

If somebody has other data about sex chromosome abnormalities related to autosomal translocations I should like to hear about them.

Stern: In Drosophila, this is very well established. Several investigators have shown that if you have translocations between the second and third autosomes, you increase primary nondisjunction of the X chromosome by a very large factor, and, also, if you have inversions in an autosome, in heterozygous conditions, you increase primary nondisjunction of the X chromosomes; so this fits very well.

This is true, but not in the male, apparently. There is no such interchromosomal effect in the male.

Lejeune: In our cases, there is a suspicion that it does occur also in the male, because in the case of the Klinefelter, it was the father who had the translocation.

Stern: In that respect, it must be remembered that the meiotic process in Drosophila males is so abnormal in regard to absence of crossing over that the Drosophila analogy should not be carried too far. In man, I think, I would expect it in both sexes.

Renwick: I think an interesting point comes in here from the Drosophila data. Without those, one would not be able to distinguish between two hypotheses: one, that the translocation causes a predisposition to nondisjunction, and, two, that the same predisposing factor causes both the translocation and the nondisjunction, whereas, now, in these Drosophila data, the translocations and inversions were presumably actually induced.

Stern: Yes.

Renwick: Therefore, the nondisjunction, if one ignores the effect of X rays, is shown to be related to a direct effect, or the presence, of the translocation and not related to a previously present predisposition.

Lejeune: Yes, but predisposition is pretty difficult to understand when the family carries a translocation for successive generations. If you do get, in some generations, abnormal segregation for other chromosomes, it seems to be related to the chromosomal rearrangement.

Renwick: Suppose there were a single gene effect?

Lejeune: Unfortunately, it is known in Drosophila that some genes can produce nondisjunction, and we cannot be sure that it does not occur in man.

Gartler: What about the sticky gene in maize that Beadle described?

Lejeune: We just don't know in man for the moment. But I would not say at all that it cannot exist. Possibly, such genes occur in our species.

Steinberg: We have one family that indicates it does exist in man. As far as we can tell, the chromosomes in both parents are completely normal. They have had one mongol, which is a translocation mongol, and another mongol, which is the usual triple-21 mongol.

Lejeune: Yes, but the question I would raise is whether this mechanism of chromosomal change has not a general meaning. In those particular families the parents who seem to be normal can have, nevertheless, a very big rearrangement among the medium-sized chromosomes that we cannot detect, and which could be the cause of the nondisjunction, or other rearrangement, in their progeny.

Steinberg: I agree.

Lejeune: It is, just for the moment, a hypothesis, but, having those data at hand, it seems sensible to suppose that in some families, in which there is a constellation of chromosomal catastrophes, that the parents may have something hidden, which is a structural change.

Motulsky: We have a child with translocation mongolism of the 15/21 variety. The father and mother are chromosomally normal. The sister of the father has typical mongolism with trisomy 21. The father had fairly severe X-ray exposure over a six-months' period immediately before conception. Possibly, there is a genetic mechanism in this family which causes trisomy and translocation. Possibly, X rays potentiated the effect of this predisposition and caused translocation in the child of the irradiated father.

Patau: We had one family with D_1 trisomy, and, thirteen years earlier, birth of an XO.

Lejeune: The sister was XO.

Patau: Yes.

Stern: In Drosophila, we know something about the mechanism. When we have translocations or inversions in autosomes, then, the two partners have pairing difficulties and that makes them available to nonhomologous pairing with the X chromosomes, and, on that basis, we do then get abnormal segregation for the X chromosomes.

Chu: This nonhomologous pairing is one of several patterns of distributive pairing in a model proposed by Rhoda Grell (12). According to her, the sequence of meiotic events in the female Drosophila are: exchange pairing, exchange, distributive pairing, and disjunction. Under normal conditions a large proportion of chromosome tetrads pair and cross over, and for these the pattern of distributive pairing is set by exchange. Distributive pairing is also operative when rearrangements or aneuploids are present. Under these abnormal conditions, pairing between nonhomologues, or between extra homologous loci present may lead to abnormal segregation.

Lejeune: What I wanted to bring into the discussion was not precisely this topic. It was just that it is one phase of what we know in man, and it is corroborated by the data in other animals and especially in Drosophila, that autosomal rearrangements can produce sexual disorders by abnormal segregation of the sex chromosomes. That is one point that we have to keep in mind. In those cases, we have some indication at least that the abnormality arises at the meiotic process. I am not guessing whether it was at the first reduction phase or at the equational meiosis.

On the other hand, from the human data, we have contrary evidence, and I would like to comment on that briefly.

Neel: Could we wait until after lunch to begin this new topic?

Lejeune: Fine! I propose to postpone it, then.

Chu: In addition to the fact that autosomal rearrangements can bring about abnormal segregation of sex chromosomes, an autosomal translocation may also cause nondisjunction of the autosomes homologous to the translocated chromosome. The case in point is the nondisjunction of a chromosome 21 with a 15/21 translocation.

Lejeune: I suppose we could really discuss that with the main problem of the time at which it does occur. Other data point in the same direction.

Renwick: There is an interesting relevance here to population genetics. If the translocation does lead to excessive nonhomologous pairing with an X, this automatically produces some sex abnormality in the offspring, and the translocation is selected against in this way.

Stern: May I just mention that one should not think only about translocations. Inversions are not measurable with your present techniques, and they may be quite frequent and may have the same effects.

Lejeune: I'm sorry, Professor Stern. I should have said "chromosomal rearrangements," in the very broad sense. Of course, inversions are exactly as important, in my opinion.

Stern: And they may be very much more frequent.

Lejeune: Yes.

Patau: Dr. Uchida and I have investigated a family in which there are two brothers (unpublished). One has a mongoloid child of whom we never got the chromosomes; the other's marriage to a woman with normal chromosomes produced ten known pregnancies. Three led to the birth of mongoloids, of whom one died; the two others proved to be typical trisomics. There were three abortions; the rest were normal children. The birth of four mongoloids to two brothers can hardly be a coincidence, so there must be something carried by the brothers. We obtained material only of the father of the three mongoloids, and his chromosomes look normal.

There are two possible explanations: first, we may have some gene in the two brothers that somehow makes meiosis less orderly. In that case, of course, chance might also have produced 18 or D_1 trisomics, but since mongolism is much more frequent, their absence would not be surprising. The other possibility is a chromosomal rearrangement of a kind that cannot be recognized in the microscope, and there you can make a number of models which fit quite well. The simplest is that the two brothers carry an inversion in one mongolism chromosome and that this inversion causes nondisjunction.

Lejeune: I would like to continue this afternoon at the point where I broke off. We acquired, or at least we tried to acquire, the impression that chromosome accidents occur, surely, during the meiotic process. Now, I would like to stress that we have other indications, in which we are pretty sure that they may also occur *after* the meiotic process. The first evidence, of course, is mosaic individuals, which are a mixture of various karyotypes. This is particularly well established in the case of the X chromosomes.

In this instance, we have individuals who probably were born from an egg that was normal or abnormal, but the change in the chromosome content arose during the first few splittings of the zygote. The origin of this abnormality is not meiotic, is not included in the parent, but can be determined by observation of certain exceptional cases. I would like to refer briefly to two observations, which some of you probably may know and some of you may not, made in our laboratory.

These were made on twins who were monozygotic, but who, nevertheless, did not have the same karyotype. Since I do not have any relevant slides, I had better show it on the blackboard. There is a set of twins. One was a normal male with XY, and the other was a Turner XO. The two children were pretty much alike as to color of hair, and form of the ears and so on. All the blood groups were identical, and in this family fraternal twins would have gotten the same similarity with a probability lower than 5/10,000.

Reciprocal skin grafts took exactly like autografts, and after 80 days it was possible to take out a piece of the XY skin which was transplanted in the XO sister, and this biospy grew out, yielding a double population of XO and XY cells. I could not tell whether the biopsy was obtained solely from these skin grafts or possibly included some tissue of the carrier, because of the size of the biopsy. We could not be entirely sure that the mixture was in the graft and was not in the environment of the graft.

Koprowski: What was actually started, a biopsy or a tissue culture specimen?

Lejeune: A tissue culture of the biopsy.

Koprowski: You grew out the biopsy and cultured the cells of the tissue?

Lejeune: Yes. It turned out that there were two populations, XO and XY. In addition, from this girl, we had tissue culture from the skin, with two different biopsies of the skin, and a biopsy of the peritoneum, and there was no evidence of any XY cell, in that girl.

Billingham: Your grafting test has given the sort of result one might expect if a feeble chronic homograft reaction had occurred, accompanied by a slow surreptitious invasive replacement of graft epithelial cells by epithelial cells of host origin. Wouldn't this situation be consistent with the results of your blood group studies?

Lejeune: In a moment, I will come to that. After one year, we took a biopsy of the skin of the girl that had been transplanted on the boy, and it turned out that there were very few XO cells; in fact, there were two in something more than 55, so it seemed that there were still some XO cells surviving, but they were outnumbered progressively by the carrier cell. Nevertheless, there had not been any visible reaction on the skin. The graft was still very soft, looking really different from the skin of the boy. It still looked like a girl's skin.

This is the only evidence we have that those twins were probably monozygotes—the reciprocal graft took, and the probability that they should have been so much alike for blood group studies was of the order of 5 in 10,000.

Now, the other observation we have is of another set of twins, in which there was one normal boy and one boy with trisomy 21, a typical mongol. In those two boys, it was assumed that they were monochorionic. The mongolism was not recognized at birth, and they were recorded as identical twins or monochorionic twins. After recognition of one as a mongol, then, probably there was some doubt in the mind of the obstetrician. Those boys are now four-and-a-half years old, and they were studied for blood groups. They are entirely identical. The probability that brothers would be alike [concordant] is less than 2 in 10,000; so we suppose that these twins are also heterokaryonic monozygote twins.

If we look at the palm and fingerprints, this set of twins is interesting, because, looking at the triradius proximal to the digits, they are exactly alike in both, but the mongol has a typical mediopalmar triradius and the normal has not. But if you look at one pattern which is not very frequent, on the thenar portion of the hand, there is a particular image in both twins, and, also, the pattern is a mirror image in both twins; so there are at least anatomical reasons to believe that they are really monozygous.

Another thing is that on the first metacarpus, they have one small incision which is just a radiological finding, but which is, perhaps, significant, for both have exactly the same abnormality in both hands.

Unfortunately, with these twins, we were not allowed to make reciprocal skin grafts, because the parents refused. But, some day, I hope, we will persuade them to agree.

The only phenotypical difference that they have, if you exclude the mongoloid features in one, is that one has the hair a little bit curled, while the mongol has straight hair. It is known that, most of the time, mongols do not have curly hair, compared to the general population. It is not impossible that in chromosome 21, there are some genes which have a dosage effect on that particular property of the hair.

However, the interest of these monozygous twins is that we have an indication that being so alike for all blood groups, they have to have come from the same egg. Hence, we know that the abnormality of the karyotype occurred after fertilization of the egg.

Now, the problem is to know at what moment this can occur, and this is very interesting. If I could venture a guess, I would like to consider that fertilization poses a special problem. With karyogamy, you put into the same cell chromosomes which were living in different organisms for years.

It could very well be that this is a very sensitive stage, and it is at this very stage that abnormal segregation of chromosomes can occur, at the first division or the second division. I suppose that there are at least experimental data which support the view that the karyogamy is the most sensitive to radiation damage. I know that Dr. Chu could tell us something about what occurs in the mouse after radiation at this point.

Chu: This work of experimental induction by radiation of chromosome loss or nondisjunction in the mouse was done by L. B. Russell and her associates in our laboratory (35). There are a few sex-linked dominant genes in the mouse, such as tabby coat color, which exhibit different phenotypes at the heterozygous and hemizygous states (Ta/Y δ = Ta/O $\male$ = Ta/Ta $\female$ distinguishable from Ta/+ $\female$ = Ta/+/Y δ distinguishable from +/+ $\female$ = +/O $\female$ = +/Y δ). The XO females and XXY males can be detected genetically if proper markers are used. Cytological studies have confirmed the exceptional sex chromosome types (45, 36).

The spontaneous incidence of XO mice in certain stocks is about 1 percent. The frequency of XO's can be significantly increased by X irradiation on the day of fertilization. In the mouse, almost a full day elapses between fertilization and the first cleavage. It was possible to test the effect of irradiation at various times during that day. The time of mating cannot be certain. The best evidence of mating is the presence of a vaginal plug. Groups of mated females were irradiated at different times of the day, and it was found that the most sensitive period for the induction of XO animals was at 11:00 o'clock in the morning. Histologically, it is the time before the fusion of the male and female pronuclei.

Mrs. Russell also used markers on several autosomal linkage groups to find if there were any autosomal monosomics. So far the result is negative. Either the data are as yet insufficient or autosomal monosomics are lethal in the mouse.

Another interesting finding is the relatively higher frequency of X^mO than X^pO animals.

Induction of sex chromosome losses or nondisjunction has been studied by irradiating the different stages of meiosis in both sexes. The frequency of induced XO's obtained by irradiation of spermatozoa (37) is lower than that by irradiating the pronucleus stage.

Stern: Dr. Chu, you said you could discover a case of an XO mouse by phenotype. Was that in terms of the mutant gene that is carried, or in terms of something like Turner?

Chu: No, the XO mice are fertile and the XO women are only occasionally fertile.

Stern: And it is not phenotypically distinguishable from an XX in the female?

Chu: It is phenotypically distinguishable.

Stern: But only if you have a gene marker?

Chu: Yes, that's right.

Stern: That's what I wanted to get at.

Neel: At the moment, XO types seem to be relatively much more frequent in the mouse than XXY, whereas, in man, it is just the reverse: the XXY type is much more frequent than the XO.

Chu: Yes, that's right.

Neel: Do you think that this apparent difference is due to our method of detecting these types in the mouse, or do you think this is a valid difference, and, if so, why?

Chu: Well, a priori, we have no reason to say that there should be a species difference or no difference; only, we cannot do any experiment or get any experimental data in the human. The incidence, however, suggests that the problem is a real one. I am afraid we have no answer for it.

Neel: You are convinced that it is a real difference between the two species?

Chu: At least from the data up to date, it looks that way. But I don't know. Dr. McKusick may know.

McKusick: Don't you think it is possible that in man XO cases are more often lost before birth than are XXY cases? We know that fairly major congenital malformations occur with the XO state in man but not with the XXY state. In the mouse there is, perhaps, no such association of congenital malformations with the XO Turner syndrome.

Chu: Although the frequency of their occurrence is low, the XXY mice can survive perfectly well, except that they are sterile. The viability of XO mice is not really comparable to the normal.

Dr. Welshons and I did one experiment to find out about the survival of XO mice. When an XO female is crossed with a normal male, one would expect XX, XY, XO, and YO in the progeny. Presumably, a YO animal is nonviable. In the actual breeding data, the ratio of normal (both sexes) to XO was not 2:1 but was about 4:1.

The same experimental cross was made; 10-day-old embryos from each cross were dissected out and set up individually in tissue culture. The ratio between normal and XO was about the same as that found at birth. Counting the dead embryos, we found that the litter size (6.4) was not smaller than the normal for that stock. We assume that the elimination of XO embryos must have occurred after fertilization and before 10 days of gestation.

Another thing was that among 120 or so embryos from 25 such crosses we did not find any YO individuals; presumably the YO constitution is not compatible with life.

Stern: I wonder if, when one thinks of the proportion of XO's to XXY's, there are not two processes, which have been discussed by you, Dr. Chu. First, there is nondisjunction in meiosis, producing XY and O sperm, if it is in the male, and XX and O eggs if it is in the female. Second, there is nondisjunction in an early cleavage or division. Nondisjunction in fertilized XX eggs would lead to XO.

If the Y chromosome is not susceptible to cleavage elimination, then, it would not contribute at all to the abnormal types arising from abnormal mitoses. In other words, cleavage elimination occurring in XX eggs only would lead to XO mice. Meiotic processes of nondisjunction would lead to both XO and XXY. Now, if in man and the mouse these two kinds of processes occur in relatively different frequencies, then you could account in the mouse for getting mostly XO's, and in man for getting a larger number of XXY's.

Neel: And in the mouse, with proper chromosomal labeling, one could get some idea of what the off types were.

Herzenberg: But, as you said, it was nearly always an X^mO.

Chu: They are more frequent spontaneously. There have been a few cases of proven X^pO's induced by radiation.

Herzenberg: It looks, does it not, as though it is not nonmeiotic nondisjunction here, but the elimination of the sex chromosome of the male pronucleus?

Chu: It seems that in Mrs. Russell's experiment (35) the paternal X or Y appeared to be more susceptible to external environmental influence. In other words, at 11:00 o'clock, when X ray was given, more X^mO's than X^pO's were produced.

Herzenberg: 11:00 o'clock after fertilization or 11:00 o'clock after—

Chu: At 11:00 o'clock in the morning. At this time, the ovule was found to be fertilized, but male and female pronuclei had not yet fused.

Stern: On the other hand, the male parents of XXY sons had been marked so that one knows those sperm which brought in both an X and a Y.

Chu: Yes, in the XXY mouse we studied we know the Y and one single X were from the father and another X from the mother.

Motulsky: Something is known in man concerning the maternal (X^m) or paternal (X^p) origin of the X chromosome in the XO syndrome. There are some difficulties, because you are much more likely to ascertain X^mO cases than X^pO cases. To find X^pO cases you need a mating of a homozygous woman (i.e. color-blindness, or glucose-6-phosphate dehydrogenase deficiency or Xga positive) with a normal (or Xga negative) male and then demonstrate that the XO offspring is also normal (or Xga negative). Since there are few homozygous women, the bias would be toward finding X^mO cases—as result from the more frequent matings. I know of six cases where the Turner syndrome was of the X^mO type. I think Dr. McKusick had another three or so.

McKusick: Yes. I think the number must be up to a dozen or so by now. We have an X^pO, proven by the Xg^a blood group (27). The mother in this case is Xg (a−). The Turner case, who seems to be a nonmoasic XO case, is Xg(a+). The father is dead. Lindsten has a similar X^pO case (26).

Motulsky: By the way, Dr. Lejeune's famous twin case must be of the X^mO type, since she started out as X^mY.

Lejeune: The twins are likely to be, in fact, an X^m, but with the Xg^a, we could not prove that, because everybody was—

Motulsky: No, but you can prove it because the other twin is XY.

Lejeune: Yes, the other twin being XY, it was very simple. It was the loss of the Y which produced the XO Turner.

Billingham: What do "m" and "p" mean?

Lejeune: The general use is that X^m means that the X chromosome came from the mother, and X^p that the X chromosome came from the father.

McKusick: It seems to me that in man the relatively greater frequency of the XXY state as compared with the XO state could be explained, at least in part, if a lot were arising at first cleavage. The male zygote would give rise to a YO cell line, which would be lethal, and to an XXY, nonmosaic Klinefelter cell line. The high primary sex ratio would also favor this XXY preponderance. The female zygote would, by the same mechanism, give rise to a mosaic of triple X cells and XO cells. I think, in this line, it is of interest that XXY cases arising at first cleavage in a male zygote would be $X^m X^m Y$, and in man, all the Klinefelter's that have been testable have, as far as I know, been $X^m X^m Y$.

Lejeune: I am not sure that they have been proved, all of them, to be maternal. I think that Polani has one in which a nondisjunction was likely to have occurred in the father.

McKusick: Really? Perhaps, I should have said it the other way round, that I didn't know that any $X^m X^p Y$ had been demonstrated in man.

Neel: It is on the basis of color vision, isn't it?

Lejeune: Yes, on the basis of color vision. In the two cases of Klinefelter's with an autosomal translocation which we have, the translocation was carried by the father, and, of course, we could not say whether this was a true gametic abnormality, but if it was, the two X's should come from the father. Of course, it could as well be that the translocation has done something to the first cleavage, but it seems less likely than that it affected the meiotic process.

McKusick: I think that you can demonstrate with a pencil and paper that the Xg^a system is the only one that gives critical evidence on the $X^m X^p Y$ situation. Color-blindness does not. If the father is color-blind, the mother may be heterozygous, you see.

Lejeune: Exactly.

McKusick: But the Xg^a system does give positive evidence. It seems to me that I did hear some third-hand information that there might be such a case proven with the Xg^a. I don't remember it.

Motulsky: I wonder, whether a study of the relative proportion of mosaic cases in clinical Klinefelter's syndrome as compared with clinical Turner's would give us some answers to this problem. In other words, if one finds quite a few more mosaics in Turner's syndrome, this would suggest that mitotic errors during cleavage more commonly cause Turner's syndrome. This is my impression. I read a recent series of 24 Turner's cases by La Chapelle (23), and I think that 12 of his were XO and the rest were more complex, such as mosaics and isochromosomes.

Lejeune: Yes, it seems to be the case, really, that most of the Klinefelter's seem to have a uniform karyotype, and a good part of the Turner's, let's say, are XO/XX mosaics. In some instances, they are known to be an XO/XX/XXX mosaic, which is not typical Turner's, but looks like Turner's. A lot of others are known to have one X, a big one which could be an isochromosome for the long arm of the other X; so at least in the case of the Turner's type of abnormality the frequency of the mosaic seems to be rather high. It would not be safe for the moment to say that all of them are mosaics, but maybe a few of them which have been reported as being true XO, if examined on more biopsies and more tissues, would reveal a hidden mosaicism, which was not detected.

Crow: I think this would argue for the embryonic selection hypothesis; perhaps pure XO's frequently do not survive the normal gestation period.

Lejeune: Yes, that is not impossible, but it is difficult to say, because that poses a technical problem about the detection of the mosaics. It is very likely that some people from whom you culture a piece of skin have a uniform karyotype in that particular piece of skin, but it is not good proof that they are uniform over the whole body. It is a very difficult practical problem, because you cannot study many biopsies, on the one hand, and, on the other hand, even if you do many biopsies, you don't study the whole body. So I suppose that the best way for the moment is to study the blood, which is the most generalized tissue of the body; in fact, in the Turner's syndrome, almost all the mosaics have been found in the blood.

Fraccaro recently reported a case in which there was no mosaicism in the skin. It was a true XO in the skin, and it was a mosaic in the blood; so if skin would have been the only source of chromosomes, the mosaic would not have been found.

Stern: It has been assumed in this discussion that these mosaics originate from XX eggs which then lose an X, but it is also conceivable that they start as XO's, and they have a disjunction which leads to an

XX cell which has some selective advantages, and therefore they can, secondarily, go back to the normal maternal XX conditions: $X^m X^m$.

DeMars: Is mosaicism now discovered by multiple biopsies of the skin at all? All of the mosaics that I know of, where only skin has been used, have been pepper-and-salt, each bit of skin showing both cell types. The results with Turner's would seem to be strikingly different from this, in the sense that there has been a powerful segregation of the two cell types. Are there other types of mosaicism for other chromosomes that have been manifested in skin biopsies, in the sense of one biopsy showing only one cell type and a different biopsy showing the other cell type?

Lejeune: No. You mean, a kind of geographical mosaicism?

DeMars: Yes.

Lejeune: It is not really true, but in one case reported, there was a mosaic for the 21. The very curious child was phenotypically between the normal and the mongoloid type. Some of the skin biopsies showed one or two mongoloid cells, say, three triple-21 cells out of 50. Some of the skin biopsies showed more than half, which were of the mongolian type.

Krooth: When you say "some of the biopsies," do you mean some of the cells?

Lejeune: Different skin biopsies from different parts of the body.

Steinberg: Jim, didn't Margery Shaw have a bilateral mosaic?

Neel: Yes, Margery Shaw and Ann Craig have a Turner's, in which, from one cheek, one gets the male chromatin pattern, and, from the other cheek, one gets the female pattern, but it is a "low" female count, suggesting an XO/XX mosaic.

DeMars: It is my impression, then, that the mosaicism is being manifested by the X chromosome in Turner's quite differently from the other autosomes that have been shown to be mosaic, or is this just too small a sampling?

Neel: By that you mean, in the case of mongolism, which is the only other one where there have been any data, mosaics have been much rarer?

DeMars: No, it is not so much that they are rarer, but every time you take a piece of skin for a mosaic for 21, it is mosaic in any biopsy you take, even though, in two biopsies, it may be only two cells out of 50 that show the trisomic, whereas, in another biopsy, it may be 50 percent. But the point is that every bit of skin has both cell types represented.

Neel: Is this a fact?

Lejeune: Yes.

DeMars: There are other cases I know of where autosomes are involved, but you have said that in a set of 23 or 24 Turner's, 12 of them were mosaic, but could be found to be mosaic only by looking at the blood, and that no skin biopsies showed the mosaic?

Lejeune: No, that is not perfectly true, because of the number of cells which are scored in different biopsies. Before you can say that in one biopsy there is surely no mosaic, the number of cells you require is enormous. Let us suppose you want to detect a 50-50 mosaic, if you have 16 cells, all of them with the same karyotype, then, you suppose that the cells of the biopsy are uniform. But you have no reason to believe, really, that if there is a mixture in the body at the beginning, every piece of skin should show the same percentage, everywhere. If there are local variations, it does not prove that they are geographical mosaics, really, but just that the population has not mixed perfectly well.

Another point that we could make is that in tissue culture, when you have the two types of cells, they are not growing exactly at the same rate. For example, for the XY skin, we took back from the Turner, the first 12 cells we had were all XO. With the second subculture, it was only then that the XY cells came out. The reason is not very clear, but it could be that, being on an XO carrier, the XY's were inhibited by an unknown mechanism, and they needed to be free for a long enough time in the tube to grow again.

Eagle: To what extent does the relative frequency of these two types of cells in culture provide a clue to their relative frequency in the parent skin explant?

Lejeune: It is a very difficult point to answer. I would suppose that if you have a culture which is running, let's say, more than three subcultures, you should detect the mosaic, if it does occur at all, because the cell may become free.

Eagle: There may be a difference not only in the relative growth rate, but also in the rate at which these cells wander out of the explant and in the proportion of cells which will subculture. The relative frequency in culture may, therefore, give no indication whatever of their relative frequency in the originating skin.

Lejeune: Yes, I agree entirely with that. What we can say is that there is a mixed population. To extrapolate it and to say, in a particular explant, that there were 35 percent of this karyotype is a precision which has no physiologic meaning.

Koprowski: Can you make a valid comparison between blood cells and cultures of skin; conditions seem to be entirely different?

Lejeune: Yes. When we say that the mosaic seems to be low in the skin and high in the blood, it could just be related to the growth of the two clones in the two different media. That is no proof that there is a difference inside the body for those percentages.

Crow: Many years ago, in the *Journal of Heredity* (47), there was a picture of a woman who had some sort of skin disease on one-half of the body and normal skin on the other half, with a very sharp line of demarcation along the center line. If this is a genetic change, it must imply that the cells of the two genotypes were sharply segregated to right and left sides presumably in the very beginning cleavage stages.

Herzenberg: I think that Dr. DeMars brought up this point. I believe, if I am correct, your reason for bringing this point up is that all this about the inactivation of one X earlier this morning seems to have some possible connection here. I haven't quite understood from this discussion whether or not you agree with DeMars' contention that in the mongolism situation, the mosaicism is of this pepper-and-salt variety, whereas in the Turner's situation it seems to be, or may be, of a geographical type, despite the technical problems involved. (I am referring now only to skin—not blood.) You might expect the same sort of technical difficulties in both cases, a priori. Is there an observational difference in the kind of mosaicism you get or isn't there?

Krooth: I don't think so.

Lejeune: I think the most obvious thing is that the mosaicism seems to be much less frequent in mongolism than in sexual disorders.

Patau: And also much less frequent in the other types of autosomal trisomy, although it does occur.

Motulsky: Also, less in Klinefelter's than in Turner's.

Patau: My coworkers and I (43) have studied a patient who is essentially a mosaic for D_1 trisomy. There are two cell types, both with 46 chromosomes and both short of one normal D. Instead, there is in the one type, which I will call "essentially normal," a telocentric D, in the other an isochromosome. On cytological grounds, one can here really be fairly certain that it is an isochromosome, obviously derived from the long arm of D_1. The cells with the isochromosome are essentially trisomic. We found both cell types in the blood, in a bone marrow culture, and in a tissue culture from the skin. Dr. DeMars made these cultures. Of a later skin culture, we analyzed at first only seven mitoses, five of which were essentially normal and two essentially trisomic. About three months later, 58 cells from the same skin culture all proved to be of the essentially normal type. Now, this is a statistically significant change from the ratio 5 to 2, P being equal to 1 percent. Here seems to be a case of selection in culture, the essentially normal cell type being favored.

It appears that Dr. Uchida has observed a similar selection in the body of a clinically atypical D_1 trisomic (unpublished). At first only cells with seven D chromosomes were found. Because of the incompleteness of the syndrome, I made the guess that this patient might turn out to be a mosaic. Later, Dr. Uchida confirmed mosaicism in the blood. In still later blood samples, she found no more trisomic cells; all cells were normal. This suggests selection in the child. If this occurs, we shall have to face the possibility of still another methodological complication. It might happen that mosaicism of the embryo, let's say, with a preponderance of cells with an abnormal chromosome complement, had caused a severely abnormal development, and yet, all we find in the child are normal cells.

Krooth: There are two technical points about the problem of mosaicism that I have often wondered about. If one gets cells from a skin biopsy, one usually can karyotype at about six weeks or possibly a bit earlier. If one gets cells from a blood culture, one can karyotype at about 24 to 72 hours, depending upon variations in technique. Assume, for simplicity, that it is 24 hours. This means that the cells within the blood culture have had time to undergo one or, at most, two divisions, so if you see 50 mitotic figures, this gives you quantitative information about 50 or 25 cells in the intact host.

However, if you see 50 mitotic figures in a cell line that is grown in culture for weeks, it is unclear from how many cells in the intact host those 50 mitoses came. Possibly, they were all descended from just one cell, whereas, in the peripheral blood culture, you are probably counting many more cells which correspond to cells in the intact host. In most biopsy dishes, there is rather a mess, with fibroblasts going in all directions, and it is not clear how many of the cells have come out of the explant, and then given rise to other cells and how many have died or failed to grow.

The other technical point that I wanted to ask about concerns the phrase, "skin culture." We all know, of course, that they cannot be demonstrated to be skin, in the sense of deriving from the germinal epithelium of the skin itself. It is rather unclear which cells in the intact host they correspond to. But if you try to infer their behavior in the intact host from their properties in culture, one quickly observes that *in vitro* they are migratory. They wander all over the dish. Perhaps, they wander also *in vivo*. Hence, many of the cells at one site may recently have come from some other location. One cannot compare it to, say, epithelial mosaicism in plants where one is dealing with an epithelial cell that appears to be rooted permanently in the region where it is found.

Lejeune: Well, I could answer the question about the origin of the cells in tissue culture. The way we do it ourselves is by removing the explant, so any mitoses which occur at any subculture are coming directly from the explant and cannot have come from the same cell that had previously undergone mitosis.

Krooth: I don't understand. You remove—

Lejeune: We put the explant on a slide; then, we remove the explant, and we put it in another vessel. Those cells which are now on the glass, we let grow, and we look at their chromosomes.

Krooth: But how can you be sure that all of those cells which were present at the time you removed the explant came directly from the explant? Perhaps, they came from but one cell which walked out of the explant and then divided several times, and, while this was going on, you took the explant away.

Lejeune: Because, particularly, we can look at the first growth of an explant, and we see a lot of cells going around all the explants. An explant is pretty big compared to the size of one cell. We can really figure out that there are migratory cells of different origin.

Krooth: What you say satisfies me intuitively, but it is an intuitive argument, and, probably, one would want time-lapse motion pictures or some other objective evidence.

DeMars: I think that time would take care of that. You have so many cells that one cell just couldn't account for what you see in several days. I think we've got Lejeune's method. In several days, you can see more cells than could be accounted for by not only one, but probably many.

Lejeune: Yes. We can get a good outgrowth in eight days and have the chromosomes made, enough chromosomes, on one preparation of eight days' growth. It is quite unlikely that in eight days, we could have enough offspring of one cell, which can divide only once every 24 hours.

Eagle: But his point still has validity. If there is a complete corona of cells around an explant, it is unlikely that this derives from one or two cells which have wandered out of the explant.

Lejeune: It is what we do have.

Eagle: But you have no information as to how many generations have transpired within the explant before there is outgrowth, and it may be that you have 10, 20, or 50 cells which are pushing out of the explant, which, within the explant, derived from one cell.

Lejeune: Well, it seems not likely, in eight days, because of the number of cells. We know that they cannot divide more than once in every day.

Krooth: Are you sure about that? Cell generation time *in vivo*, measured with tritiated thymidine, has been recorded as low as 12 hours.

Herzenberg: May I ask what the relevance of all this is? I don't think Dr. Lejeune would insist for a moment that he has a representative sample of all the cells in his explant. I don't see the relevance.

Neel: I think the relevance is that if we contrast the results of a blood culture versus a skin culture, there may be a greater possibility in skin for a disproportionate representation of the descendants of relatively fewer cells than in blood.

Herzenberg: In one case, you have relatively few cells with relation to what you are putting in there. That's all you can say. You have different cells coming out of one place. That may very well be the case.

Krooth: It is possible that in your peripheral blood culture you sample a different proportion of the cells from the intact host than you do when you culture cells from a solid tissue biopsy. Therefore, the frequency with which you find mosaicism in these two different sources of cells may not necessarily be of biological significance.

Ephrussi: Maybe I am a little confused by this, but I share Dr. Herzenberg's feeling that this is not very relevant, for the following reason: suppose you use an old-fashioned method, let's say, make sections of a fresh explant and examine them. You get a certain number of mitoses which are the only means for the classification of the cells. Whatever proportion you find there, *in situ*, would not mean any more than what you are doing now, because if the division rate of the two cell types is not the same, your deductions concerning the proportion of the two cell types *in situ* would be completely wrong.

Stern: May I mention a case, which I do not remember in detail, reported by Klinger in Rome last year. This was an embryo that was a mosaic for male-femaleness in a variety of tissues. I don't know whether the female parts were Turner's or normal female. In all tissues one could see cells with sex chromatin and others without it. He also made explants of different parts and got, for different parts, actual chromosome counts. Otherwise, he used the old-fashioned method of sectioning, and he found that the amniotic tissues of these embryos were all mosaics in about the same proportion; so this was *in situ*.

Patau: May I ask Dr. Lejeune. Do you think that your cultures do contain epidermis outgrowth?

Lejeune: Morphologically, no. The outgrowth is fibroblast-like.

Patau: So all that we sample, quite possibly, is mesoderm?

Lejeune: Yes.

Patau: We don't have the endoderm and, very likely, we don't have the ectoderm, except, of course, for Barr bodies.

Atwood: You did not mention, I think, the karyotypes of that last set of twins, Dr. Lejeune.

Lejeune: The one was entirely normal, and the other was trisomy-21 (free), without any translocation.

Atwood: There must have been at least one complementary cell which was monosomic.

Lejeune: Yes. The problem of the origin of those twins is amusing, because there are two hypotheses possible. If the egg had been trisomic for 21, and then it split and one of the 21's was lagging in the anaphase, we would have got a child who was cured of mongolism and a child who remained mongol. That is one of the possibilities. The other is that the twins began from a zygote containing two 21 chromosomes and, at the two-cell stages, there was no abnormality. At the second division one of the daughter zygotes continued normally, and the other one yielded a triple-21 cell and a haploid-21 cell.

The haploid 21 is not known in man and maybe it is lethal and could therefore have disappeared, resulting in the birth only of the mongol. I think that the interesting thing about those mosaics and the carrier twins is that they show us that, surely, in man, we can pretty well assume that there are at least two mechanisms: one which is the meiotic one, and one which is a blastomeric one. Another proof of the meiotic one is, perhaps, to be found with the translocation case of mongolism, namely, that when the mother is carrying a translocation for a 21 on a 13, her progeny are, roughly, one-third translocated normals, one-third chromosomal normals, and one-third mongols.

Using the same hypothesis that haploid 21's are not viable, it would mean that in every two cells of the translocation-carrying mother, in every two meioses, one nondisjunction occurred—which is a fantastic frequency.

Let us consider that in the progeny of translocation fathers, this phenomenon did not occur. There are now 45 children known to be born from a translocation father and only one is a mongol. The frequency of nondisjunction in that case—I suppose we are entitled to speak about nondisjunction—is really extremely high in the mother, and it is pretty low in the father. It could be that it is related to the different processes of meiosis in both sexes. In the ovary the chromosome remains a long, long time in a kind of primordial stage, and it is not clear whether the chiasmata are terminated or not at this time. At least it is quite sure that the ovarian chromosomes are joined soon after birth and remain more or less joined during the whole life of the individual.

Herzenberg: Is there a possibility of just different viability or meiotic drive or something of that sort? The incidence of nondisjunction might be the same, but the effectiveness of the sperm in fertilization might be extremely low in this case.

Lejeune: I suppose that an unbalanced sperm would not be as powerful as a balanced one. This cannot be tested for the moment.

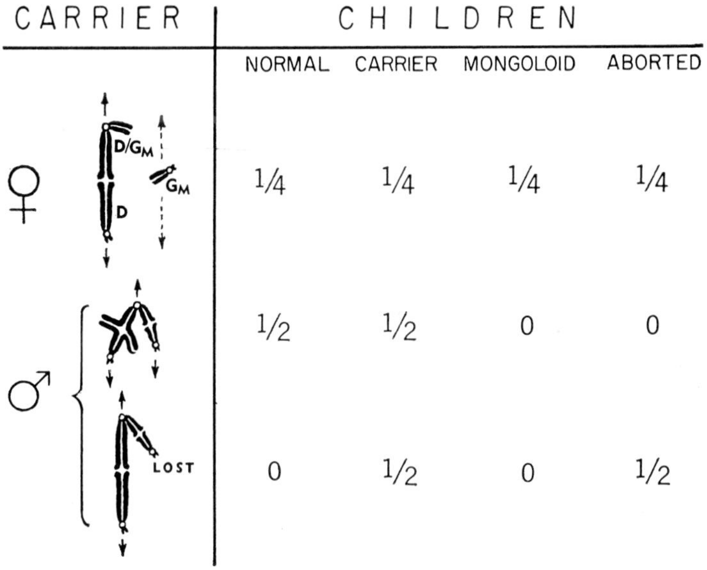

CARRIER	CHILDREN			
	NORMAL	CARRIER	MONGOLOID	ABORTED
♀	1/4	1/4	1/4	1/4
♂	1/2	1/2	0	0
	0	1/2	0	1/2

Figure 24. Diagram to illustrate how different configurations of the involved chromosomes at the first meiotic metaphase may bring about different segregation ratios in the offspring of translocation carriers of the D/G$_M$ type (G$_M$: mongolism chromosome). The three possibilities shown are not the only ones, but these fit fairly well the three types of data cited by Hamerton and Steinberg (16): female carriers, three families with male carriers, another family with male carriers.

Patau: However, it is entirely possible that this difference between the sexes is merely a matter of pairing, chiasma formation, and so forth, in meiosis. A diagram will illustrate this (Fig. 24). If in the female only bivalents are formed, combining the D (a large acrocentric) and the translocation chromosome, and if the mongolism chromosome, present as a univalent, is distributed at random, you may get the three viable types of offspring in equal proportions. However, there may be complications that would distort these ratios. The univalent may sometimes be lost. It is also possible that the bivalent shows preferential orientation, so that the translocation chromosome goes more often into the egg and the D more often into the polar body, or vice versa. In the male, trivalent formation has been observed by Hamerton and coworkers (15). This might be the rule, and to the extent that the trivalent is disjunctionally arranged, the offspring might contain only carriers and normals in equal proportions. But this is not a necessary consequence of disjunctional trivalents: the small mongolism chromosome might fail to reach the pole to which the normal D goes, in which case the only viable offspring would be carriers. It appears possible that different D chromosomes differ sufficiently in their chiasma distributions to bring about different segregation ratios.

All I can say is that on cytological grounds we cannot give any expectations for the segregation ratios in the progeny of carriers of translocation mongolism. All observed ratios can, hypothetically but plausibly, be explained by well-known meiotic mechanisms. For purposes of genetic counseling, we simply have to rely on empirical data.

Stern: And what we know about the viability of sperm in Drosophila, which is deficient for large chromosomes, is that it seems to be not affected. Muller, many years ago, wrote a paper called, "The Nonfunctioning of the Genes in the Spermatozoa," and this was on the kind of evidence that segregating sperm, which had big deficiencies or even whole chromosome arms lacking, was apparently quite viable and fertilizable.

Herzenberg: If I recall correctly, in Drosophila, there isn't very much of a maternal age effect on those characters. Isn't this also true for nondisjunction, that there isn't a very large maternal effect? Yet, in mongolism in man, you have an extremely strong maternal effect. One can't help but think, when you have this differential transmission of translocation mongolism, female to male, and compare that with the age effect, on ordinary trisomy, perhaps, there is no very large selective factor involved in the male against transmission of trisomy or, rather, disomy, in that case.

Gartler: One might resort to the old idea that a sperm carrying an extra piece of DNA cannot move as fast as one carrying less, which would account for these results.

Ephrussi: I don't know if my recollection is correct, but isn't that generalized statement about the inactivity of the genes in the spermatozoa contradicted by the effect of the very first Y-located gene in Drosophila, namely that which affects the motility of the spermatozoa?

Stern: That is one very special case. It is a Y chromosome.

Ephrussi: Why is it special?

Stern: Well, this is a fact.

Ephrussi: It is special with respect to location?

Crow: It is not the gene content of the Y chromosome of a particular sperm that determines this motility. It is the gene content of the fly that produced the sperm.

Ephrussi: Is that so? I didn't know that.

Stern: Yes. In the XO male, half of the sperm is X sperm, and it is just as immobile as—

Ephrussi: Yes, I see.

Crow: May I ask a question of the mouse geneticists here? Has anyone tried at any time to use double-marked X chromosomes in mice, to see if there is any association between aneuploid progeny and noncrossover gametes? Is this feasible in mice at the present time?

Herzenberg: It should be. I don't see, offhand, why not. But I don't know.

Crow: One wonders if it might not be true in mice, as well as in Drosophila.

Renwick: One needs not to go as far away as Drosophila, I believe, for evidence that the genes, or the chromosomes, are not autonomous in the sperm. I believe Snell (40) has shown in mice carrying translocations that the various possible sperm are equally viable.

Herzenberg: Well, there is a very good example in mice of preferential fertilization (4). In the case of the T-locus, one allele is transmitted much more frequently than the other one.

I don't know of any real explanation for this, but I was going to ask before, since the spermatozoa are differentiated, one would expect that some genes would function there as well as one would expect some genes to function in all differentiated tissues. Which genes, we don't know. It might just be that the genes on the 21 chromosome or some genes there function in the sperm.

Patau: Not in the sperm, but in the spermatids.

Herzenberg: Somewhere in the process of spermatogenesis.

Pateau: Yes. It seems rather unlikely that in the extremely dense spermatozoa any gene would function, but in young spermatids you have an interphase nucleus with well-dispersed chromosomes. There is certainly no a priori reason why at that time some genes should not have effects that will later play a role in the formation of the sperm.

McKusick: There is a possibly related matter; namely, the fact that all the offspring of triple X females, which, according to the last information I had, totaled nine, have been normal males or females. Does anyone have any information over and above this? Have any exceptions to this rule turned up?

Lejeune: For the moment, I am not aware of any triple X child born from a triple X mother. But now, when you are dealing with triple X mothers, you have no real proof that the ovaries were triple X. If these mothers are mosaics, they can have normal ovaries. There is a reason, maybe, why they function at all. If they have normal ovaries, it doesn't matter for the children. This is a very difficult problem.

McKusick: I should think it would be quite possible that some of them are mosaics.

Lejeune: At least, some eggs are known to be XO/XXX, that is, due to an early error in the cleavage. If a small XX stem line can remain in the gonocytes, they are still able to build a normal ovary inside an abnormal body.

Herzenberg: Dr. Lejeune, are you going to speak about the mother-age effect?

Lejeune: I would like to say a few words about it. I would just say that, for the mosaic, we have no really good data on the effect of the maternal age. We do have rather good data, however, for the trisomic.

Curiously enough, the mother's aging does increase the frequency of mongolism and also of the two other kinds of trisomy known, namely, the 13-15 and the 17-18. That is curious, because, for mongolism, it was previously supposed that it had something to do with the shape of the 21 chromosome.

Let me come back to the fact that almost everybody agreed that trisomy in mongolism is determined by trisomy for a small acrocentric, which has satellites. Now, it is fairly sure that those satellites have something to do with the constitution of the nucleolus, or at least we know, just by mitotic figures in the blood, that there is a tendency to association between chromosomes bearing satellites.

The hypothesis was rather nice, that if those chromosomes have something to do with the nucleolar material, and if they are related to the nucleolus by the satellites, the 21 chromosomes are for a long, long time very close together in the female nucleolus. Maybe, they get a little sticky or something of that kind, so that they have a greater tendency to nondisjunction as the mother ages. This reasoning could hold true, possibly, for the 13-15 trisomy, which also involves an acrocentric, but for the 17-18, in which no body is detectable as a satellite in either of those chromosomes, the maternal age effect cannot be related to this idea.

We have also to consider that, possibly, most of those trisomies do occur by a mis-segregation during the first cleavage of the fertilized egg, and, if that were true, the maternal age effect could occur in any chromosome and be a very general thing; at least, in Drosophila— and I will let Professor Stern explain this, which he can do much better than I—there are indications that the aging of the egg does increase the mis-segregation of the chromosomes. Hence the aging of the mother in mongolism need not be related to the disjunction of the chromosome, but could be related instead to a very general phenomenon concerning the effect of aging of the egg on the stability of the chromosome you put in. I wonder if Professor Stern would comment on the data in Drosophila?

Stern: I think what you are referring to is a very special case. In Drosophila the X chromosome is normally a rod, but there are X chromosomes which are rings. If you bring the ring chromosome by a sperm into an egg which itself has the rod chromosome, then it is found that the ring gets lost very often, thus resulting in mosaicism. What Dr. Lejeune refers to is that if you age the eggs, that is, not aging the females but keep the females from laying their eggs, so that you age the egg itself for a few days, or ten days, which is a long period, then you get a greatly increased elimination, not of the mother's X chromosome but of the father's ring chromosome. Here, then, is a cleavage mechanism in which the age of the cytoplasm of the egg, whatever this may mean, plays an important role.

Herzenberg: When does fusion occur in Drosophila?

Stern: Twenty minutes after fertilization.

Herzenberg: And aging is occurring, then, after fertilization?

Stern: No, this aging occurs by keeping a virgin female for a long time on very poor food, so that, while she has eggs, she does not lay them. Then, you mate her, and she lays these old eggs, which have just been fertilized.

Herzenberg: Then that is almost analogous to the XO situation in the mouse, where, again, what is lost is a male chromosome. In that case it is an irradiated fertilized egg, and in this case, an aged fertilized egg; these might very well be the same kind of damage.

Stern: That's right.

Herzenberg: But this, in man, does not seem to be a loss of the male chromosome, but, on the contrary, it is an extra female which has got in there.

Lejeune: Yes, but this process could be exactly the contrary of a loss, if I may specify that, because if there is a mis-segregation of two 21's, you can get three of them in one cell.

Stern: In the Drosophila case the ring chromosomes get into the fertilization nucleus. This follows from the fact that in most cases, or in a large number of cases, part of the animal which develops has the two X chromosomes and part has lost the ring.

Herzenberg: Where does the ring go, then?

Stern: It goes into the cytoplasm, presumably, and then degenerates, but nobody knows.

Herzenberg: Somewhere, it lags behind in the anaphase in the cytoplasm.

Stern: Yes, but it gets, first, in the fertilization nucleus.

Herzenberg: I haven't heard any people who work on mongolism ever consider the possibility that it had nothing to do with the genetic nondisjunction, the maternal age effect, but that it does have very much to do with the selection or nongenetic phenomena in the decision to have an individual arise from the egg.

Lejeune: You mean that the young mother should expel the abnormal egg, whereas an old mother would keep it?

Herzenberg: Expel it or select against it.

Lejeune: If this phenomenon is very early, we just cannot detect it. The only thing we can say is that if this phenomenon does occur, which is not impossible, it has to be very early; otherwise, it would increase the frequency of the abortions, and there are no indications that there are more abortions with young mothers than with old mothers. It is the contrary—at least the frequency of spontaneous abortions goes up with the age of the mother.

Herzenberg: But isn't there a lot of folklore in medicine, if it is not true—perhaps, Dr. Krooth can recall the data—that there is supposedly a mongoloid occurring not too infrequently, or, to put it the other way round, that, perhaps, you have a mongoloid birth after one or two abortions in an individual, particularly with older mothers?

Maybe this doesn't stand up statistically, but it is stated by some of the so-called mongolism experts.

Lejeune: It has been repeatedly claimed, but it has never been really proved.

Krooth: If the maternal age effect were due to some sort of uterine selection factor, which changed with the mother's age, then, wouldn't you expect the maternal age effect in translocation mongols also? If the maternal organism is sort of surveying the fetus and saying, "This won't do; out you go," then one might expect that the maternal age effect would occur among translocation patients. The fact that it occurs only strikingly in the nontranslocation mongols, i.e., the trisomics, is perhaps evidence that is causative.

Stern: I have one similar argument. There must be by now about ten or more children from mongol mothers, and there is a perfect 1:1 ratio, that speaks against selection.

Atwood: If the nondisjunction of other autosomals is a cause of abortion and a general mechanism such as you suggested, Dr. Lejeune, for age effect is working on all of these autosomes, then, the abortion rate should parallel the mongol rate. Is this true?

Lejeune: It would parallel the mongol rate, multiplied by the number of other autosomes. Let's say it would be something like 40 out of 500 or 600.

Atwood: It would be a much higher rate, but the age effect should have a similar curve.

Lejeune: Aging has a striking effect on the frequency of abortions.

Crow: But not nearly so steep as with mongolism.

Lejeune: Oh, I would not say so. I don't know exactly how the shapes of the curves compare, but I think they are going on quite the same way.

Krooth: I think there are differences in shape. There has been work on a whole series of congenital catastrophes, published by Yerushalmy (46) on stillbirths, neonatal mortality, and so on. What Yerushalmy found was that for each birth rank, if one tabulated the risk of the particular congenital catastrophe, whether it be a stillbirth or something else, against maternal age, one got a U-shaped curve; in other words, there was an optimum maternal age. Similar data have been reported by Neel and Schull (32) on abortions. In the case of the incidence of mongolism, the curve fits best the algebraic expression, incidence $= e^{(ax+b)^2}$, where x is the maternal age and a and b are constants. Hence, the incidence of mongolism increases exponentially with maternal age, and in fact, even more than that, since the index is squared.

Motulsky: But isn't it true that trisomic mongolism is a separate entity, apart from abortions and all kinds of things besides that, so it is a little unfair to compare it?

Lejeune: Yes, it is unfair, because if we take mongolism as the basis of the frequency of this mis-segregation of chromosomes, let's say, it is 1 in 600; now, multiply that by, let's say, 50, for the number of chromosomes, roughly, and you will get something less than 1 percent.

Neel: But that 1 to 600 is for the population average. If you restrict attention to women over 40, what is the frequency of the mongol child?

Motulsky: One in forty.

Neel: So it is 1 in 40 or 50. Then, if you multiply that by the number of chromosomes, you're in trouble.

Patau: You can't.

Lejeune: No, you're not in trouble, because women no longer get children after this age. They become sterile, effectively.

Patau: You can't multiply by the number of chromosomes because there is no reason to assume that different chromosomes have the same nondisjunction rate. In general, smaller chromosomes are more frequently given to nondisjunction than bigger ones. The range of chromosome sizes in man is very considerable, and the mongolism chromosome is one of the two smallest chromosomes. There is every reason to assume, for any organism, the existence of an optimal crossing-over rate. It might well be that man has more than the genetically desirable number of cross-overs, because the chiasma frequency had to be adjusted so that nondisjunction even of the smallest chromosome is rare, though probably not as rare as in the case of bigger autosomes which have, at least in the male, an average of much more than one chiasma. It agrees with this expectation that the 18 and D_1 trisomics are much rarer than mongoloids. It is true that this might also be the result of a high prenatal mortality of 18 and D_1 trisomics. If so, it would be remarkable that their survival rates until birth should be so similar. The fact that trisomy for D_1 is somewhat rarer than that for 18, which is a little smaller than D_1, further suggests that the frequencies at birth of the three trisomy syndromes reflect nondisjunction rates rather than survival rates.

Neel: Yes, but aren't we going around in a circle? We were simply speculating that if nondisjunction did occur at the same rate with respect to the other chromosomes, it should be reflected in a much steeper climb in the abortion rate. You have now given us a mechanism why you don't think it occurs at the same rate.

Patau: This is probably true in general. When you have very different chromosome sizes, an exceptional univalent is usually a small chromosome.

McKusick: Let's hear why chiasmata protect against nondisjunction.

Patau: If you don't get them, the chromosomes will fall apart and be distributed randomly.

Atwood: Hughes-Schrader (18) has compiled some examples of orderly meiosis without chiasmata.

Patau: Quite, but in mammals, I think, we have every reason to believe that it holds true for both sexes.*

Herzenberg: Maybe, Dr. Patau would like to repeat his statement. If I understood him correctly, perhaps, this isn't true in Drosophila, either. Am I not correct in understanding it that way, that chiasma formation is not necessarily and, in fact, in this case, is definitely not, related to the frequency of nondisjunction?

Stern: In the female?

Herzenberg: Yes, in the female.

Chu: I think so, yes. I think what you said was generally correct.

Herzenberg: Rhoda Grell (12) has reported that there appear to be two times when chromosomes come together, or two processes involved of chromosomes coming together in Drosophila, one for crossing over and one for distribution.

Stern: Cooper showed that in a certain percentage of the X chromosomes in the female they do not undergo crossing over, there cannot be any chiasmata, and, yet, there is a normal frequency of nondisjunction. This is true. Of course, in the Drosophila male, where there are no real chiasmata, there is another mechanism operating.

Herzenberg: Is the fourth chromosome in Drosophila a subject of nondisjunction more frequently than the other chromosomes? It is very small.

Stern: It is very frequently subject to nondisjunction, but its relative frequencies, I do not know. You see, Drosophila has only four pairs of chromosomes. Nondisjunction of the large ones, the second and third, usually give inviable combinations, unless you make crosses in which you bring two compensating abnormal gametes together; so all you can compare is nondisjunction of the small chromosome 4 and the X chromosomes. I think the fourth chromosome is probably more liable to nondisjunction than the X chromosomes. I think it is true, but I don't know that critical experiments have been done, and by "critical experiments" I mean we now know that you have

* Afterthought: This was not meant to include the XY bivalent.

to control inversions and other chromosome rearrangements in other chromosomes. In the older work, this was not known and was not done.

Renwick: It would be interesting to get recombination frequencies at different ages in human data, but a near compromise would be to analyze the mouse data, which, surely, should be adequate to give us the answer to this. What is the effect of age on the recombination frequency in the mouse?

Herzenberg: It varies with different markers. Bodmer (3) has recently published on this in the work that he did over a period of years in Fisher's laboratory in Cambridge. It just depends on the particular situation you set up. He was basing his experiments on the same presupposition, that the more crossing over, the less nondisjunction, and vice versa. But this did not seem to turn out.

Neel: When you say it varies according to the marker, do you imply that different chromosomes behave differently?

Stern: Yes, I think that is right.

Crow: Going back to the earlier topic, I think Rhoda Grell's hypothesis is a very interesting one; but whatever the hypothesis, it is necessary to take into consideration the strong association between genetic crossing over and normal disjunction. There is an abundance of data both for X chromosomes and for translocation heterozygotes in Drosophila.

Patau: I think that most cytologists would still accept that in the great majority of organisms chiasmata are necessary for regular disjunction. But, incidentally, if the age effect of mongolism should reflect, as I think it does, increased nondisjunction due to a failure of chiasma formation, this would not necessarily mean that in a larger chromosome the crossing-over frequency between two genes would also show the age affect. You have, first, to ask for the probability of getting at least one chiasma, and that is all you may get in the case of the small acrocentrics of man. That probability is normally extremely close to one, but it does, if our interpretation is correct, drop a little below one in older women.

The postulated effect of age on the probability of getting at least one chiasma is clearly not large enough to show up in any set of crossing-over data we are likely to get on man. What you might detect could be an age effect, either on the average location of the first chiasma or on the frequency of one or more additional chiasmata, a frequency that depends on interference. None of these effects would have any direct bearing on nondisjunction. I don't think that any data you might collect on an age effect on crossing-over, let's say, in the human X chromosome, would be relevant to the causation of mongolism.

Lejeune: I would just say a word about all we have said, that at least we have indications that in man chromosomal aberrations can occur at meiosis and at the first segmentary division. I would like to stress the point that a very nice observation that Dr. Gartler could speak about shows that there is still another mechanism, but I would not discuss this, because it is not mine.

Gartler: This is the case of an XX/XY true hermaphrodite (7) who resulted from double fertilization. The patient was first seen at two-and-one-half years because of an enlarged clitoris and what was thought at the time to be coincidentally associated heterochromia simplex. Chromosome studies of leucocyte cultures showed an approximately 1:1 XX/XY composition, all cells having 46 chromosomes. Further studies on biopsies obtained at laparotomy demonstrated that the patient was also XX/XY mosaic in other tissues than blood, and that the mosaicism was markedly asymmetrical. The pertinent data are given in Table 1. At this time we postulated that this individual resulted from double fertilization and began to look for evidence of

TABLE 1

Results of Chromosomal Studies on Various Tissues

Tissue	XX cells	XY cells
Skin (right abdomen)	3	10
Skin (left abdomen)	8	1
Ovary	10	0
Ovotestis (ovarian part)	9	2
Ovotestis (testicular part)	.2	12
Clitoris	4	7

mosaicism in autosomal markers. The heterochromia simplex could be considered along this line though the genetics of eye color leaves much to be desired. At any rate the patient had one hazel eye and one brown eye, her mother had hazel eyes, her father brown, and she had both brown and hazel-eyed siblings. Thus, her father was apparently heterozygous for eye color and may have contributed two alleles for eye color to the patient. Blood group studies by Dr. E. Giblett demonstrated that the patient had two populations of red blood cells in approximately equal proportions, as characterized by two differences: one population was MS^u/MS and R^1/R^2, while the other was MS^u/Ns and R^1/r. Blood-group studies of the parents showed that the father contributed two different alleles for both the MNSs and Rh systems while the mother's contributions were identical. It is clear that the father not only contributed an X- and a Y-bearing sperm, but also two different MNSs alleles, two different Rh alleles, and possibly two different eye color alleles. The mother's contributions are identical as far as we can tell. She was heterozygous at four loci at which we could have detected two different maternal contributions.

Thus these data support the idea of the origin of this patient through double fertilization.

Neel: Stan, since the mother's contribution is the same in both halves, what does this tell you about the two functional egg nuclei?

Gartler: The two-egg nuclei could have been derived from one egg nucleus by mitotic division prior to fertilization, they could represent an egg nucleus and a polar body, or two independent egg nuclei. Unfortunately, the present data do not permit us to distinguish between these possibilities.

Neel: She is heterozygous at every one of the loci, all five, isn't she?

Gartler: No, only at four. The probability is 1 in 16 that this distribution could occur in two independent eggs.

Neel: How about the polar body?

Gartler: Well, that would depend on how far the loci are from their centromere.

Crow: It depends on the relation of the genes to their centromeres.

Gartler: But we don't know anything about this.

Crow: Historically, perhaps, it is interesting that R. A. Fisher postulated at one time that there were three kinds of twins: the usual two kinds we know of, plus one derived from a single egg and two kinds of sperm. He did it because of some metrical data which were trimodal. The data weren't too good, and the hypothesis was given up, accordingly.

Herzenberg: You could detect this kind of situation, then, by grafting from the father. You should expect that a graft from the father would be accepted by the child, and no other case would show acceptance of the graft.

Steinberg: Not necessarily, because you don't know all the loci involved in the graft. You measured just a few of them.

Billingham: You might expect the father's graft to live longer than the mother's graft.

Herzenberg: Yes, you're right. I'm sorry.

Renwick: But it is worth while, surely, to know the Gc system. The heterozygote is a common type.

Gartler: Dr. Giblett did the blood grouping, and she has all the material frozen from this little girl. Recently, I know, they checked the new blood group, and, unfortunately, both parents were the same type, so—

Renwick: What happened to the Duffy groups, for instance?

Gartler: Dr. Giblett has done much more work on this aspect of the problem recently. I only reviewed those data pertinent to proving double fertilization.

Renwick: But she mentioned Gc and Inv.

Steinberg: You stand a good chance of finding heterozygosity at the Gm locus in the white population, but the chance at the Inv locus is not too good.

Renwick: You have a good chance in the Gc. It is the commonest type.

Gartler: If we found one marker which demonstrated a two-allele contribution by the mother, this would eliminate the possibility of the two maternal nuclei having resulted from a mitotic division of one egg nucleus prior to fertilization. However, it wouldn't differentiate between two independent eggs, and an egg nucleus and a polar body. I don't believe we can ever hope to decide between these latter possibilities.

Another way of looking at this question is to consider the marked asymmetry in distribution of the two cell types in this patient. Such asymmetry seems more compatible with the fusion of two separate embryos than with double fertilization of a binucleate egg. On the other hand if this patient actually originated from double fertilization of a binucleate egg, then the asymmetry found in this patient indicates that cells on different sides of the body are delineated at an extremely early stage in development.

Lejeune: Going a little further, we were starting with meiosis, then with the zygote and errors at the first cleavage, and we could possibly study what we call acquired errors, that is, those which occur much later in the life of the individual. I will not try to discuss the general problem of the chromosomes in cancer, which of course, is a very fascinating problem, but a few days would be required for us just to look at all the data and discuss them. I would like to try to emphasize one very minor point, however, which is related to leukemia.

Everybody knows that in leukemia, at least in chronic granulocytic leukemia, an abnormality has been repeatedly found which looks as

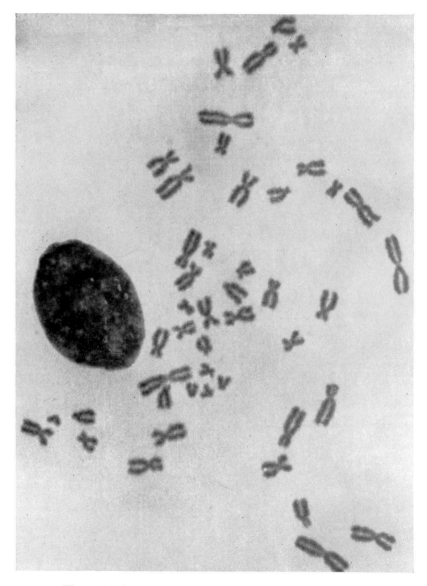

Figure 25. Bone marrow cell, showing the Ph¹ chromosome.

though it were a deletion of part of a small acrocentric chromosome. I would like to skip the first two slides and go to the third and fourth, just to show you what a so-called Philadelphia chromosome looks like, and to discuss the various difficulties which arise with this particular chromosome.

Figure 25 shows a bone marrow cell, and you see in the picture that the acrocentrics are not all of the same size. There are four of them, and one is really smaller than the others. The karyotype is the next.

The karyotype (Fig. 26) shows a great difference in size between the chromosomes which are normal sized, namely the Y and probably 21-22, and one small chromosome which looks as though it had lost part of the big arms. The interesting part of this is that it is consistently found in most of the chronic granulocytic leukemias.

Ephrussi: Dr. Lejeune, could we see that slide again? I don't understand, in this case, why they are paired this way. I would say, from a picture of this magnification and at this distance, that the one on the left, numbered 22, really pairs with what you call the Y. The little one [the smaller 22], if anything, goes with the right-handed 21.

Lejeune: With this one [indicating]?

Ephrussi: Yes. I don't understand the basis for this pairing, in particular, the left 22 with the Y.

Lejeune: The first thing I would say is that I cannot pair them correctly, because that is a bone marrow prepared with colchicine, and pairing after colchicine is not too good.

Ephrussi: But wouldn't you agree that the 22 on the left looks much more like the Y than like the 22 on the right?

Lejeune: Yes, that would be true as well. It demonstrates the difficulty with the smaller acrocentrics.

Ephrussi: I thought you had some independent evidence for grouping them that way rather than another way.

Lejeune: We have good evidence that, repeatedly, the Y is entirely normal, as compared to this particular one. The Y, when it shows beautifully, has two chromatids close together, which we probably see in the other slides: so it shows that the Y is not involved. This small chromosome cannot be the Y. As to the matching here, I would accept your correction, that we could pair the left-hand 22 with what I have called the Y. But this one is not a good Y.

Szybalski: Independent evidence would be provided by looking at what happens in the female.

Lejeune: Yes, in the female there are four chromosomes, one being much smaller than the others. Of that, I am entirely sure. Two chromosomes—

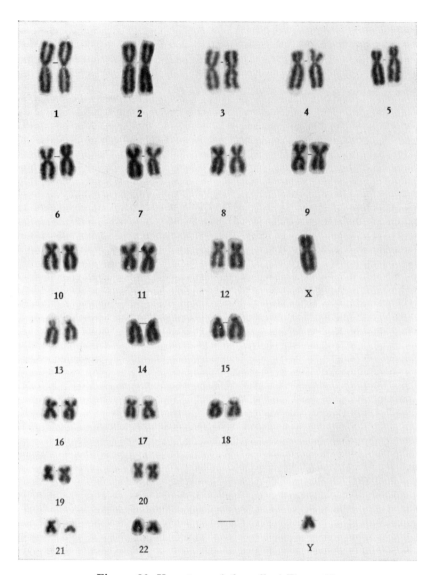

Figure 26. Karyotype of the cell of Figure 25.

Patau: If I may comment on this, in many cases the Y can be identified without any question. I would say that the third chromosome cannot possibly be a Y.

Lejeune: We can simply say that it has been studied, not only in females but also in males, and it is entirely certain that the Y chromosome has nothing to do with the story. What is to be seen in this patient is that there is one small acrocentric which is really too small. There is a problem to know whether this small acrocentric is a 21 or a 22.

Patau: May I ask how you define 21? There are two possible definitions. Some have said: we can't distinguish the small acrocentrics, so let's call 21 that which causes mongolism when present in triplicate. On the other hand, at least in some cases we see clearly two pairs of which one is larger. The general principle, also used at Denver, is that the larger of two similar chromosomes gets the lower number. Do you mean by 21 the chromosome that causes mongolism, or do you mean the largest of the small acrocentrics?

Lejeune: By the 21, I do mean the one which produces mongolism when in triplicate in the cell.

Patau: So it is not a cytologic definition, but, rather—

Lejeune: No, it is just a matter of definition and just saying that the small chromosome which produces mongolism, we call 21, no matter if it is really bigger or smaller than the 22.

Ephrussi: But it does correlate with the cytologic definition, doesn't it?

Lejeune: But the difficulty is that the 21, which does produce mongolism, is, in fact, smaller than the 22. But if you count the satellites, it is bigger than the 22. [Laughter] That is probably one of the sources of the confusion about the distinction between the two chromosomes. To make clear what I mean, I could show a slide.

Chu: I think I might add that our observations agree with what Dr. Lejeune just said about satellite size.

Patau: But satellites are certainly not constant. Sometimes, they are larger, so we can hardly use them for a definition of the chromosome.

Lejeune: To avoid the difficulty of the Y, which is an additional one, I would just comment that in the mongol female, we see, not in every cell but in most of the cells, the centromere of 21 is very close to the end, and there are three chromosomes of this type. In the 22, there is a centromere which is not at the end, and there are two arms. Now, the difficulty is that sometimes there is something beyond the real arm, which is a remnant of a small satellite. Sometimes in a mongol, there are four chromosomes with satellites, three with well-developed satellites, another one which has no satellite, and another one which has very small satellites in the 22.

The discussion as to whether 21 can be identified separately from the 22 is difficult. I would say that we can recognize the 21 in a typical case of mongolism, but I would not say that it is the same in every cell. The problem with the Philadelphia chromosome is that it looks as if a big acrocentric has lost a part of its long arms [indicating on blackboard]. It is very difficult to be sure, because it is so small, it is hard to compare it with the normal 21.

I must say that we have only one case of a Philadelphia chromosome in the laboratory, and I cannot say anything cytologically, because we have not enough data, ourselves. But the Edinburgh group seems to be fairly sure that they can identify the Philadelphia chromosome as looking very much like part of the normal 21 chromosome.

Now, the facts about the possibility that it is a deleted 21 are the following: In mongolism, we have three 21's, let's say, and we have two kinds of phenotype to be seen. The first is on the polymorphonuclear leucocytes which show an abnormality of segmentation in every mongol; that is, instead of having many nuclear lobules they have a tendency to have fewer lobules than normal people. There are one or two less lobes in the mongol. In the general phenotype, there are two characteristics: they are mongols, and they have a tendency to acute leukemia. The leukemic risk is multiplied by around 20 in these children. That has been demonstrated by many different workers; that is, let's say, an inborn chromosomal error.

When we come to acquired chromosomal errors, we have two types: the one is a Philadelphia chromosome, and, in that case, we do find it in chronic granulocytic leukemias, and, in addition to that, there is a decrease of the alkaline phosphatase in most of the polymorphs in the peripheral blood.

We have a second acquired abnormality—which is a haploid 21 clone, let's say—the lack of a small acrocentric. The chromosome is lacking, and so we cannot say for sure what was the shape of the chromosome which is lacking. That has been found in three cases in our laboratory, in acute myeloblastic leukemia, and in this case we have no indication about alkaline phosphatase. But, recently, in three laboratories, considering the fact that, with the deletion of the long arm of the so-called or supposed-to-be 21 chromosome, there was a decrease of alkaline phosphatase in the polymorphonuclear cells, this enzyme has been studied in the polymorphonuclear cells of mongols. They did find an increase and that, compared to normal, the activity inside the polymorphs was in the ratio of 3:2. That has been found in three different samples.

Koprowski: Could you explain once more the activity of the alkaline phosphatase in mongolism?

Lejeune: You measure the alkaline phosphatase histochemically by looking at the coloration of polymorphs. You can also do it by chemical reaction. In mongols it has been found that if you compare a mongol of the same age with some controls, the activity is greater in mongols than in controls; let's say the mean activity of the mongols is greater than in the controls.

Now, if you make a ratio of the mean activity of the mongols to that of the controls, it is 3:2. So the activity in mongols is one and a half times greater than the activity of normal people. Unfortunately, in those cases with leukemia we have observed, there were no data on alkaline phosphatase. All three are dead now, because it was a very acute leukemia that we saw at a very late stage; so I cannot say whether or not it was decreased. It is just that we have no data on it.

However, taken together, these facts seem to lead to the conclusion that it is the same chromosome which is involved in these three aberrations. In mongolism there is a constitutional abnormality of chromosome 21 with increased risk of leukemia, and an abnormality of the alkaline phosphatase without any other leukemic trouble. We know there is a deletion in chronic granulocytic leukemia, and we found, in some cases at least, a deletion [loss] of one acrocentric chromosome in the acute process.

I would not say that this proves that most of the leukemias are related to something happening to the 21 chromosome. Nevertheless if it is true that it is the same chromosome which is actually involved in those three observations, the conclusion would be a twofold one: first, that on the long arm of the 21, there are some genes which regulate the manufacture of the white cells and control the rate of such manufacture; and the second could be that the genes which control the synthesis of the alkaline phosphatase are also located on this particular chromosome.

The alkaline phosphatase observation, that is, the decrease in leukemia, has been known before chromosomal abnormalities were recognized, and once it was considered to be very important, but it has not been much studied recently. Nobody knows why. But now that we know that it begins to make some sense with cytologic investigation, it is possible that in the future, the physiologic use of this alkaline phosphatase property will be found, and it is not unbelievable that it has some relation to the behavior of the cells. In that case, we would have a correlation between a cytological abnormality, an enzymatic deficiency, and, possibly, the pathology of a given trouble of the blood.

Bearn: How decreased is the alkaline phosphatase in the Philadelphia chromosome?

Lejeune: In the Philadelphia, it can be very low; in fact, it is one of the pictures which is not good because, if you have mongolism, you get one and a half more than in the normal, but in leukemia, it can be much less than one-half of the normal.

Neel: What happens to the alkaline phosphatase level in persons with myelogenous leukemia who lack the Philadelphia chromosome? There are changes, aren't there?

Motulsky: No, I know of one case where the alkaline phosphatase was normal and the Philadelphia chromosome was not found. This is quite telling, in relation to—

Lejeune: Yes, it seems, really, that all cases with the Philadelphia chromosome were decreased, and the others which have not decreased do not have the Philadelphia chromosome. But, for the moment, it cannot be said that the statistics are firm enough to be sure that there cannot be any dissociation between those two phenomena.

Eagle: What type of leukemia is increased twenty-fold in the mongoloid?

Lejeune: That is very difficult to tell, because it was considered a few years ago to be only stem cell leukemia. Recent reports are saying that some of them can be of the granulocytic type, but a very precocious, young granulocyte, that is, promyeloblasts or something of that kind. It is acute, and it is surely very different from the chronic granulocytic leukemia. The picture is really different with regard to the blood and the clinical evolution as well.

Atwood: In congenital leukemia, the correlation with mongolism is said to be much higher.

Lejeune: Mostly mongols are born with congenital leukemia.

Atwood: This makes sense because you could say that the leukemic cells are descended from the monosomic 21 cells that are complementary to the trisomic ones.

Lejeune: But those were not involved. There were acute leukemias in two children. One was 7 and the other was 9.

Atwood: No, I mean, if you would now look at the congenital cases, it may be that they represent survival of the monosomic from the same mis-division as the trisomic was formed.

Lejeune: Oh, yes, I understand what you mean.

Stern: Dr. Lejeune, I did not understand your use of the word "clone" in this respect. Are these tissue culture clones?

Lejeune: No. I'm sorry. When I said "clone," I should have said there were two populations, one normal and the other lacking one of the small acrocentrics. When I say "clone," I am going a little too far.

DeMars: Is there any information on the alkaline phosphatase in the leukemic trisomics? Is it elevated in mongoloid leukemic children, as it is, apparently, in the normal?

Lejeune: I have no data. I am not aware of any data on the leukemic mongol for alkaline phosphatase. Those data are on the nonleukemic mongol.

DeMars: Cox and Pontecorvo studied it in cultured cells derived from human foreskin and found that it is formed at different rates under different conditions of culture. In particular, one situation that boosts the rate of alkaline phosphatase production is placing the cells in a medium in which other cells have already grown. In our laboratory this treatment results in a cessation of proliferation and a virtual stabilization of the total protein content of the cultures.

Now, I am extrapolating a lot. If a population of cells is multiplying at a rapid rate, it might have a low level of alkaline phosphatase, as in leukemia, in nonmongoloid children. If these low levels were exceeded in leukemic mongoloids it would bolster the notion that the third chromosome, causing mongolism, was actually boosting the production of alkaline phosphatase. For the moment, I think data about alkaline phosphatase should be interpreted in a reserved way.

Motulsky: There is one argument about that; in so-called leukemoid reaction, where the white cell count may be very high, but the cells are not leukemic, and the Philadelphia chromosome is not present, alkaline phosphatase is normal or high.

Atwood: I don't think these difficulties that Pontecorvo had are very relevant to this, because these are probably cells taken immediately from the blood.

Lejeune: Oh, yes; they are not cultivated at all.

Atwood: Whatever the content was, there was a good reason for his difficulty, anyway; that, probably, while the cells are growing there is enough orthophosphate in the medium. This is an inhibitor of alkaline phosphatase production in microorganisms, and it might very well be in [cultured human] cells.

DeMars: They depleted the phosphate content of their medium and found no effect on alkaline phosphatase production. Was it depleted as much as it is at the end of growth?—that, I could not say. But I don't think we should extrapolate too much from microbial problems. There are clearcut cases where repressors do not work at all in these cells. Arginine does not depress ornithine carbamylase formation at all. I think, for the time being, this alkaline phosphatase data should just be put in the bank for a while.

Herzenberg: A recent paper in JBC (39) indicates that, perhaps, it does; that is, arginine represses ornithine. That is off the topic, though.

I wonder what the correlation is between the Philadelphia chromosome and leukemia. Is there a good correlation?

Lejeune: The correlation is extremely high. The evidence is twofold: first, with untreated cases, as far as I am aware, there are now 21 cases published which were studied in the peripheral blood before any treatment, and, of the 21, there was only one which did not show the Philadelphia chromosome. The other 20 were exhibiting it. Now, the group at Edinburgh was able to show something very interesting: with the regression of the number of white cells under treatment, the Philadelphia chromosome was no longer seen in the peripheral blood. At the time of regression, there were not more than 20,000 white cells per milliliter. Still, it was to be found in the bone marrow—something which fits extremely well the notion of the hematologists that you can have a perfect clinical remission in granulocytic leukemia, with the blood going down to normal, and, nevertheless, still find a leukemic focus inside the bone marrow.

This dissociation between bone marrow and blood under the effect of treatment, at the time the treatment is effective, is quite good proof that there is a competition between two kinds of populations: one with the Philadelphia chromosome and the other without it. The treatment selects, for a reason which is not known, more or less against the abnormal clone. Therefore, it does explain that the abnormal chromosome disappears when the blood count is returning to normal.

Herzenberg: How about the reverse association, that is, the absence of leukemia? How frequent is this disease, and would you be likely to have seen the Philadelphia chromosome in normal individuals by now, in all the thousand or so normal individuals who have been looked at, apparently?

Lejeune: Another point is that in some of the cases, not in every case, the skin has been studied and also the fascia lata, and in all the cases in which this has been studied, the somatic cells were normal.

They did not contain the Philadelphia chromosome. It was found only in bone marrow or in the peripheral blood. The individuals were normal. Apart from their leukemia they had normal cells in their body. The abnormality was found only in the blood cells.

Herzenberg: In the blood cultures that have been done, you would not expect to have found it except, perhaps, in the marrow and the cells coming out of the marrow, if it was there. You say it is not an inborn situation; you don't have it in the zygotes. Well, this doesn't completely fit. It might be coming in; that is, it arose during the early divisions. The question is whether you have any possibility of finding it in individuals who do not have the disease.

Lejeune: As far as I know, no Philadelphia chromosome has been described in an individual who did not have leukemia, but the absence of a publication does not mean the phenomenon cannot occur. I cannot answer this question.

Patau: I would be confident that a competent cytologist would find it in any routine check. It is really quite striking.

Motulsky: The established disease has the same order of frequency as mongolism, that is, 1 in 500.

Lejeune: There are 60 cases where the Philadelphia chromosome has been looked for now recorded in the literature, up to three weeks ago, and, of the 60, it has been surely found in 51. In the other nine cases, there were eight of them which were studied after treatment. But at least it was surely found in 51 of 60 cases, which is a very high proportion.

Renwick: I understand that the Edinburgh group (20) find different lengths for the Philadelphia chromosome.

Lejeune: Yes, and they say that it can be greater in some individuals than in others, but there is no variation within one individual; that if one individual has a very short Philadelphia, he has a very short Philadelphia in all the cells which contain it. Some other individuals may have a big Philadelphia chromosome, but it seems to be extremely consistent within each individual. It is to be expected, because it is a kind of random loss, to get the clinical picture, it has to include some specific loci.

Renwick: In fact, if one had a big enough batch of data, one could really map the site accurately (on the hypothesis that a single locus is involved) by finding the longest possible Philadelphia chromosome.

Lejeune: Yes. There is good reason why the sensitive locus is quite below what we see.

Renwick: If one accepts provisionally the alkaline phosphatase story, which I don't actually accept, the same mapping procedure could apply for *its* locus; so it would not be surprising if one did find some long Philadelphia chromosomes associated with normal alkaline phosphatase levels, assuming certain relative positions on the chromosome.

Lejeune: Well, that would be interesting, because it would be telling us whether the alkaline phosphatase locus, if it is really involved (which is still in question), is close to the locus which is sensitive to leukemia or whether it is that very locus.

Atwood: You can't tell whether the deletion in the Philadelphia chromosome is interstitial or terminal. It might always be interstitial.

Lejeune: Yes, it could be interstitial.

Atwood: So, then, the locus might not be near the end.

Lejeune: Yes, I agree with you, but it would be curious that, repeatedly, you have a middle portion lacking. Most likely, it is one break and, if it is one break, it has to be on the distal part.

Atwood: If you believe in telomeres, the interstitial location seems more likely. A terminal deletion would tend to be unstable at first; it may start bridge-breakage cycles, and so on.

Crow: Has anybody observed bridge-breakage-fusion cycles with the Philadelphia chromosome?

Lejeune: No, there is no fusion-breakage cycle.

Neel: What happens to the alkaline phosphatase assay in the case of an infection, with a "shift to the left," as it is called, on the part of the polymorphonuclear leucocytes?

Motulsky: It goes up.

Neel: It goes up? All right. Here, you have a congenital shift to the left.

Renwick: Yes, but the latest letter, to which Dr. Lejeune referred, is by King, Gillis and Baikie (22), in which they did control the reaction rate by measuring the white count, and they argue, I think, with some justification, that this deals with that point.

Neel: That the 3:2 ratio exists after you make—

Renwick: After you make the correction.

Lejeune: No, I was going a little too fast. The 3:2 ratio refers to the activity which is reported for each polymorph.

Neel: I'm not talking about number of polymorphs, but, rather, the fact that you have here, as you describe it, an immature polymorph, with a shift to the left, just as you observe in infection, except that it is congenital; so if the alkaline phosphatase content goes up in infection per polymorph, then, this might be a secondary phenomenon rather than a primary.

Herzenberg: Aren't there many possibilities that this is secondary? I assume that these assays were done on whole tissue of some sort; I mean, on a sample of blood, not on individual cells.

Lejeune: It is also scored just by a coloration technique.

Herzenberg: A histochemical technique, you mean?

Lejeune: Yes, a histochemical technique, which gives a coloration of the polymorphs, and you do count those per cell. There are four or five categories you can recognize quite well; so you see the cellular level.

Renwick: Dr. Neel, surely, the only way in which your hypothesis would fit the whole data would be if the maximum amount of alkaline phosphatase levels were in slightly immature cells, but certainly not in the very immature cells that you are getting in leukemia;[*] in other words, for your hypothesis, you must have a curve starting from a very low level in the very immature cells and rising to a peak at the band cell stage, and then diminishing again to the normal adult polymorph.[†]

Neel: Yes. At the moment, I am not trying to explain the whole phenomenon, but just that one aspect of it.

Renwick: But the data must surely be known about this, whether slightly immature cells have a higher alkaline phosphatase level.

Neel: Alice Stewart (41) has drawn attention to the fact that in children who develop leukemia, the history of repeated childhood infections is often striking, and she has questioned whether this repeated stimulus to the hematopoietic system or the related antibiotic therapy may play a role in leukemogenesis. Everybody knows that mongols go from one infection to the next, and one wonders what role that is playing in their increased risk of leukemia.

Lejeune: But the very reason why they are going from one infection to the next can be just because they have something abnormal in their polymorphs, instead of it being the reverse.

Neel: Yes; we don't know which is cause and which is effect.

[*] Afterthought: This discussion on immature cells in leukemia is largely irrelevant since a further letter by Baikie (1) reminds us that, in his chronic myeloid leukemia series, the scores of phosphatase activity were made on the mature polymorphs, ignoring the immature cells.

[†] Afterthought: Such cells (band cells) apparently have a *lower* level than do mature polymorphs (24).

Lejeune: At least, it seems likely that if they have more infections than normal children, it is just because they are mongoloid.

Krooth: One of the difficulties in this is that with existing methods, you cannot do a histochemical procedure on the cytoplasm of the same cells you have karyotyped; so you cannot show, for example, that those cells in which the Philadelphia chromosome is present have an altered level of alkaline phosphatase compared with those cells from which it is absent. If you could show that, then, you would be relatively unassailable.

Lejeune: Yes, that is right.

Eagle: Except for the point Bob DeMars made, and that is, the rapidly growing cell may have a low alkaline phosphatase activity just because it is rapidly growing.

Krooth: And the Philadelphia chromosome would then be seen as a chromosome which caused accelerated growth and thereby lowered the alkaline phosphatase?

Eagle: Yes.

Bearn: It may be important in conditions such as macroglobulinemia, where you would like to show that the cells with the particularly long chromosome, are actually synthesizing 19S.

Krooth: Right, if there were only some way to look at chromosomes without breaking everything open.

DeMars: There is. Excuse me! [Laughter] I expected dead silence when that was said. Please finish.

Krooth: Well, the only other comment I was going to make, which I think is an anticlimax [laughter], was that there does exist a dominant gene which has been described both in man and in the rabbit by Nachtsheim (31), called the Pelger anomaly. In this disease, there is a hyposegmentation of the nuclei of polymorphonuclear cells. One wonders what the chromosomes and alkaline phosphatase level would be in those cells. It is possible that this, to some extent, might serve as a control, in addition to patients who have got infection with a leukemoid reaction.

Lejeune: I know nothing about alkaline phosphatase in Pelger anomaly, but I know that the chromosomes have been looked for, and they seem to be normal.

Herzenberg: Don't you think, on the assay, we should backtrack quite a bit and realize, first of all, that alkaline phosphatase is a bunch of enzymes, probably; that the assays are very crude ones, in general, from the point of view of the enzymologist, and that those kinds of things should really be straightened out before one goes much further in drawing conclusions, in addition to all these questions about the kind of cells involved and the relationship with such things?

Renwick: I think that one of those points can be dealt with. In fresh leucocytes, the extractable alkaline phosphatase is predominantly of one electrophoretic type on starch-gel; the remaining types represent such small components that they might be ignored, fairly safely, for a crude estimation (Renwick, 1961, unpublished).

Herzenberg: This is in fresh leukocytes?

Renwick: Yes.

DeMars: Do you want to proceed, Leonard? I was going to address myself to the uncertainty principle that is bothering Dr. Krooth and bothers me very much and everybody who works with tissue cultures. This is the question of destroying the cell in characterizing it. I see no reason why we can't apply, in cases like this, the principle of indirect selection, as has been worked out in bacteria.

This would necessarily have to be applied to cells that can be propagated fairly indefinitely. We might take the case of 21 trisomy, in particular. The problem is to isolate *de novo* from a culture of normal cells, a type of cell that has high alkaline phosphatase even though we have no way of directly selecting for such cells. One might proceed by making a histochemical stain of a portion of the culture and then determining, by microscopic examination, the frequency of cells that have high alkaline phosphatase content. On the basis of this frequency, the remainder of the culture is distributed in a series of subcultures in such a way that the probability of a subculture receiving a high phosphatase cell would be low. In this case, there would occasionally be a "jackpot" culture that was relatively enriched for such cells.

By applying this method in stages, one might hope to isolate a pure culture of cells that had high alkaline phosphatase. This is achieved by indirect selection for the siblings of the cells killed by the staining procedure. One could then have a viable culture, isolated on the basis of its high enzyme activity. It would be viable, and one could examine the chromosomes, and I see nothing wrong with this idea in principle at all.

Koprowski: Except the wrong cell to start with.

DeMars: In what sense?

Koprowski: I don't think you would be able to do many subcultures of blood cells.

DeMars: I said it would have to be applied to a cell that could be cultured indefinitely.

Lejeune: Yes, but this alkaline phosphatase is not to be shown in every cell, as far as I know, and I just don't know if it could be recognized in a fibroblast. I don't know if anybody could tell that.

Koprowski: There is no activity in tissue culture of alkaline phosphatase in fibroblasts.

Renwick: That is not correct.

De Mars: That is not true.

Renwick: I have been doing electrophoretograms on alkaline phosphatase from cultured fibroblasts from skin, and I know that Rody Cox found, by his method, that there was none, in some strains. But this was just lack of sensitivity of the method. If you take enough cells, you can show quite enough.

Koprowski: Would you be able to distinguish between the population of macrophages and fibroblasts in tissue culture, basing your observation on the level of alkaline phosphatase in the two-cell systems?

Renwick: I think you would have to use an extremely sensitive histochemical method, certainly, with very long incubation times.

Bearn: How many fibroblasts do you need to demonstrate activity by the starch-gel method?

Renwick: We usually require about 100 milligrams wet weight for our gels, because of the difficulty in solubilising the phosphatase.

DeMars: You can make a perfectly good colorimetric determination of alkaline phosphatase cells with 10^5 cells (about 100 micrograms of total cell protein).

Neel: Dr. Lejeune has a last subject, which forms a natural transition into tomorrow's discussion.

With my friend Dr. Jerome, data were collected suggesting a shift in the tryptophan metabolism of mongoloid children. The facts which were ascertained were the following: In the mongol, the excretion of some byproduct of tryptophan metabolism is less than in normal people. It is less for 5-hydroxyindolacetic acid, it is less for indole acetic acid; and it is less for xanthurinic acid.

Now, our working hypothesis, two years ago, was that, probably, there was somewhere an increase in another of the pathways of tryptophan metabolism, which was inducing a loss of tryptophan load in one direction, so that it was preventing the formation of these byproducts for which we tested. The difficulty is that these data have to be questioned: We have not yet found anything which is increased in the mongols. This is very disagreeable. If they have only a loss of something, it can, of course, be related to a loss or a deficiency of the absorption of tryptophan, or maybe to the fact that they have a special flora which is adapted to the trisomic individuals and which is using more tryptophan than the normal flora of normal individuals. Such an explanation, however, seems rather unlikely. This kind of thing can be very misleading, and it is very difficult to tell just what you are dealing with.

Nevertheless, the very interesting thing about this kind of research, even if it is not perfectly rewarding, I would say, is that there is for the moment no other possibility—to think about the effect of the trisomy—than to suppose that, somewhere, something is accelerated by an enzymatic process, which is multiplied by 3, as compared to 2 in normals. Some of these effects on 5-hydroxyindolacetic acid and xanthurinic acid have been found by other laboratories, one published before our own research and the other after. So it seems that there is something going on in the tryptophan metabolism of the mongols, but we cannot tell for the moment what is the real point of the intermediate pathway which is wrong, and we cannot discard entirely the possibility that there is just a general abnormality in the absorption of this amino acid.

The only reason I wanted to point out this kind of work is that it is, in my opinion, a real pity that so few people are interested in looking at the effect of trisomy in man. So far as I know, an excess of genetic material, giving an excess of enzyme, has been observed in bacteria after some phage infection, but I am not very familiar with those data, and, maybe, somebody else could quote them better than I.

DeMars: More pertinent, I think, in the bacteria, when you have a gene both on the chromosome and in an episome, then, the level of the enzyme varies with the dosage; that is, if you have it only in the chromosome, you might have one unit. If you have it additionally in the episome, then, you have several more units per bacterium.

Lejeune: Yes, that is what I was thinking about.

DeMars: Well, you have raised the general question of gene dosage effects in man, defined in chemical terms, and there is really very little evidence on this, especially in enzymatic terms.

There is a general question, or a general doubt, really, as to whether multiplying the dosage of a gene beyond 2 will indeed raise the level of anything. This has never been demonstrated.

Lejeune: Yes, and I think this is very important, because we have to think about why those children are not normal. They have a factory for every enzyme which is normal, and the extra chromosome is also normal; so if it does disturb metabolism, we have to think about some excess of product from that chromosome that has a direct effect on the way we have to search for things, because, instead of a blockage, we are supposed to find an intermediate metabolite in excess. It is most likely, in this case, that some other intermediate metabolite is in lesser amount than it should be. This kind of thing is extremely difficult to demonstrate, but I do not see any other way of trying to understand what the nature of this dosage effect of genes is.

Herzenberg: I think you want to be careful not to discourage those people who might be looking for something lacking because you don't know that having an extra chromosome 21 would not suppress for example the formation of something by a gene on another chromosome. You want to encourage research in that area as well.

Lejeune: No, what I was thinking about was the question of the butterfly mutation. Possibly, Dr. Ephrussi would like to talk about that—about the fact that the extract of butterflies can even help larvae to build their eyes.

Ephrussi: Oh, I haven't followed that story lately, but I understand it is in a complete mess. I am really not prepared to go beyond emphasizing what Dr. Herzenberg said, namely, one should not consider that the effect of an added chromosome must necessarily result in the increase of something rather than in the suppression of something.

Neel: Do we know, for any higher organism, a dosage effect based on a chromosomal change, either positive or negative?

Atwood: Sure.

Neel: At the enzymatic level?

Atwood: Not at the enzymatic level, but at the phenotype level.

Neel: Yes, that's right, but at the enzymatic level.

Gartler: If you accept yeast as a higher organism—

Neel: No.

Atwood: Some endosperm color phenotypes show graded amounts of anthocyanin, depending on the number of active alleles present from zero to three. We might presume there were corresponding enzyme levels.

Neel: But that is a triploid endosperm.

Atwood: Yes, but you could put in—

Neel: It doesn't result from imbalance with respect to a single chromosome. Endosperm is triploid.

Atwood: But it is a dosage effect, just the same.

Neel: I'm asking for a different kind of dosage effect, resulting from the addition of a single normal chromosome. Are there any data?

Motulsky: There is one set of data which should have been mentioned regarding lack of dosage effect with sex-linked traits. Glucose-6-

phosphate-dehydrogenase activity has been determined in triple-X, triple XY's, and others. In all of these poly-X abnormalities enzyme activity has been normal, suggesting that the extra X chromosomes are inactivated and are not putting out any enzyme (14).

Renwick: This could also be done with antiserum globulin levels, which vary.

Motulsky: Yes. I don't know whether this has been investigated in these extra X's.

Bearn: Is the methodology good enough for that?

Renwick: It's good enough to do it, yes.

Stern: I think of one dosage effect in Drosophila which involves normal genes. In recessive mutant genes, of course, dosage effects are well known. If you have a certain normal gene duplicated, then you get hairy wings and extra hairs on the thorax. Dr. Neel did this in his prehuman period. [Laughter]

Neel: I'm glad you didn't say "inhuman." [Laughter]

Stern: This, I think, is a dosage effect of a normal gene. You add to the phenotype by doubling the dose from 1 to 2.

Atwood: Well, what must happen is that if a locus is not subject to control of its output you would get strict dosage effect, but if it is controlled, then the dosage effect would be obscured by the response to repressors and inducers. A change in the number of a particular chromosome would change some controlled loci and some that are uncontrolled, so you would get dosage effect for some genes and not for others.

Crow: It is interesting to compare the different effects you get with two of the white eye alleles in Drosophila, *eosin* and *apricot*. Here you don't know anything about the chemical control mechanisms, but one allele shows a color that is proportional to gene dosage whereas the other is modified by the residual X chromosome.

Bearn: Which one shows it?

Crow: Eosin is proportional to gene dosage. The apricot eye color is constant provided the ratio of apricot genes to residual X chromosome material is constant.

Herzenberg: What about the xanthine dehydrogenase in flies? I remember hearing this in Corvallis, but I don't know the details. Grell (11) showed that xanthine dehydrogenase is controlled by a sex-linked gene in Drosophila. He measured the levels of enzyme in the male and the female and, on a weight basis, it comes out to be identical in the two, although it is hemizygous in the one case. You have dosage compensation, again, but this is at the enzyme level.

DeMars: A possible instance of the dose effect working in reverse, by diminishing something, might be the gamma glutamyl transferase of cultured human cells. No euploid strain or strain with defined trisomy or monosomy, cultured from human skin, has proven to be sensitive to the glutamine-imposed repression on enzyme formation that has been described in cultures of (human) HeLa cells and (mouse) L cells. Some undefined genetic alteration accompanying the evolution of the hyperdiploid HeLa cell from the diploid cell of origin has altered the control over the rate at which the transferase enzyme is produced. Other hyperdiploid strains of human origin, such as KB and conjunctiva, have this property in common with HeLa; the rate of transferase production is repressed in the presence of low concentrations of glutamine in the medium. These strains have more chromosomal material than euploid strains, and it is just possible that multiplication of the dosage of some normal genes has established this repression scheme.

Lejeune: But, as well, they could have lost those loci, because the HeLa cells are very far from having a normal genotype. In the evolution, they can as well have lost this particular property.

DeMars: They have lost the response to the repression?

Lejeune: Yes.

DeMars: Well, no, the HeLa cells could not have lost the sensitivity to the repression phenomenon, because the HeLa cells are repressible, and they have not lost the capacity to form the enzyme, because, in the proper medium, the capacity is expressed to the maximum extent; so the difference between the euploid cell and the aneuploid HeLa cell is one in sensitivity to a repression scheme.

Renwick: But the HeLa cells could have lost the repressor of the repressor.

DeMars: I wouldn't argue with that.

Herzenberg: You can always make a gain into a loss and a loss into a gain.

DeMars: In a general sense, the trisomy would boost the power of a repression mechanism, which would lead to a decrease in enzymatic activity.

Krooth: I think that Dr. DeMars' point places a rather general problem before us, and one which is peculiar to high forms—as distinct from bacteria. There are certain enzymes, for example, which are present at one concentration, say, in the white blood cell, and which are present, in liver, at a concentration four or five hundredfold greater; yet, according to the clonal theory of development, which is taught in schools in this country [laughter], both these tissues, by successive mitosis, have received the same number of chromosomes, and, supposedly, the same genes. There are, therefore, problems in the enzyme levels of human cells for which we have very little clearly relevant data from microbiology to fall back on. It may be that differences in enzyme levels between lines of cultured cells reflect in part this process of differentiation, whatever it is.

Neel: Is there any more discussion?

Motulsky: There is another point in relation to mongolism. Some data have come to my attention, which may be quite interesting concerning the etiology of nondisjunction in mongolism.

In Victoria, Australia, Collmann and Stoller (5) have tried to ascertain most of the cases of mongolism over the last 16 years. They found 1134 cases and noted a clustering of cases in time and in place. If one looks at the data, they have one peak in 1944 or 1945, and then another peak five to six years later. Then, they divided their data into urban versus rural areas. The peaks were still present in the rural districts, but came a year later than in the urban areas. They also pointed out that there were clusters of cases in certain localities.

They raised the question whether some infectious agent might not be the cause of this phenomenon.

With all the recent work on viruses altering chromosomes, I wonder if these suggestions have some merit.

Lejeune: I would just add a word about the distribution of mongolism. It has also been said in this country that there was a relationship between the frequency of mongolism in a given town and the content of fluorides in the water. [Laughter] I suppose those data were statistically as good as the Australian data, and I wonder very much what this means.

Bayreuther: I also have heard rumors about a possible relationship between certain virus-infections of the mother and mongolism of their children. Are these data not reliable? Have they not actually been published by the same group that described the relationship between infection with German measles virus and the rubella syndrome?

Motulsky: Not the same investigators?

Bayreuther: I cannot contribute to the discussion of this point; I have not read the paper either.

I consider it possible that viruses could affect chromosomes and cause nondisjunction of the type associated with mongolism. I have seen mitotic nondisjunction of chromosomes of the dog karyotype after infection with the virus of infectious canine hepatitis, and adenovirus with intranuclear site of multiplication. It is generally known that one of the first manifestations of virus infection in a cell is a change in morphology and consistency of the heterochromatic regions of the chromosomes. The group 21-22 of the human karyotype, which is involved in meiotic nondisjunction leading to the mongolism-karyotype, has long sections of heterochromatin, which could be affected by a virus resulting in nondisjunction because of stickiness. From our experimental data mentioned before and Vogt's and Dulbecco's data about the chromosomal variation in the process of tumor progression of Polyoma virus induced neoplasia *in vitro* (44), it is evident that virus infection, probably via newly synthesized enzymes or the derepression of cell enzymes, can induce chromosome mutations.

Szybalski: It would be enough, let's say, if 70 or 80 percent of this type of modification was caused by viruses and 20 or 30 percent was spontaneous. That would still shift the data making it statistically significant, and relating it to the viral infections. It doesn't have to be 100 percent black or white—that is, all viral or all spontaneous.

Virus could produce also different types of molecular modifications in the host DNA other than through nuclease activities as suggested by Dr. Bayreuther; e.g., it could cause cross-linking of the complementary DNA strands since we have just observed that DNA isolated from fowlpox virus is partly cross-linked (42). We have found also that the antibiotic Mitomycin is a powerful, naturally occurring, cross-linking agent (19).

Herzenberg: Have any of the other statistical people found correlations with mongolism? I know that I found these same papers, and I was very impressed with the information, being a nonstatistician. I showed them to a few people and they were just as negative, just pooh-poohed them. They said that you can always find local distributions. The same thing is true of the dots on the board this morning. But I think that we have to be a little bit serious about it, since we know nothing about the etiology of mongolism or the etiology of trisomy, perhaps some serious consideration would lead us somewhere.

Eagle: If, for mongolism you substitute leukemia, a concentration of leukemia in time and place has been reported in a small community in western Maryland. But there, also, there have been serious reservations as to the statistical significance of the data (17). Now, I don't know to what extent these data are similarly subject to question.

Ephrussi: Is this entirely a question of statistics? It seems to me you could get a completely wrong picture with statistical values if, for example, more care was used in detecting, say, mongolism in one region than in another, or if the doctors were more competent.

The first thing I would wonder about is how the data were selected which were found to be different in different areas. I would have much less interest in the first step, i.e., in seeing whether or not the differences are statistically valid.

Motulsky: The Australian investigators tried to get as good ascertainment as possible by going over death and birth certificates, by writing to doctors and pediatricians and obstetricians, by contacting defective children's clinics and centers, by contacting schools for the handicapped and inserting requests for cases in the *Medical Journal of Australia* and in every important country newspaper. This process was done twice within nine months. They tried hard by many criteria to get all the cases and probably succeeded fairly well.

Steinberg: What time interval did they cover?

Motulsky: 1942 to 1957.

Neel: Certainly, this is the kind of correlation that has turned up time and again in the history of medicine, and most of them have gone down in smoke and flame because of sampling problems or because of the fact that, just by chance, every once in a while, you will get a concentration. If you look long enough for concentrations, something is bound to turn up.

Atwood: Could I return to the age effect just for a minute? One could make the hypothesis for age effect that is similar to Dr. Herzenberg's, except that it works by selective maturation.

Since you have a fixed number of oocytes, then, if, selectively, the good ones are matured, finally, you get to the residuum, which would have to be the majority that are liable to these errors, and then we see the result, increasing frequency. But what is the time, on the average, between sterility and cessation of ovulation? Is there a long sterile period before ovulation stops entirely, or are there two coincident events? You said, if you wait long enough, you can't see where it is going any more because you have sterility, but is ovulation still going on?

Lejeune: Is is quite difficult to answer that. It is known that some women can have children long after they have ceased menstruation. It is very rare, but it does occur—which does prove that they can, nevertheless, produce some ova. But what the frequency of this phenomenon is, I could hardly say.

Neel: He is suggesting that the good eggs are laid first. That is a good note on which to end.

Patau: I am still interested in the question of 21 and 22. At least sometimes, you can clearly recognize a larger pair and we call this 21. This is a cytological definition. On the other hand, 21 is now defined by others as that which causes mongolism. This is a definition by phenotype. I doubt the existence of any published evidence that would conclusively relate the two definitions, in other words, that would decide whether the mongolism chromosome belongs to the smaller or the larger pair. Satellites are seen at the larger pair about as frequently as at the smaller pair and sometimes simultaneously at both pairs. It is certain that the size of the satellites varies. Obviously, satellites are useless for identification purposes.

I think it is also becoming clear that the short arms themselves, not only the satellites, vary considerably among normal human beings. To get really reliable evidence as to whether the mongolism chromosome is the larger or smaller chromosome, one may have to compare the chromosomes of mongoloids with those of their parents. Particularly rewarding might be cases of mosaicism, where one has in the same preparation cells with and without an extra mongolism chromosome. For any given individual, the picture is consistent in the sense that in very good preparations you may find several cells with the same number of visible satellites and that these are then of the same relative sizes. If a satellite is very small, as most are, or if its stem is very short, it may be rarely visible, but somewhat larger satellites will be seen repeatedly. To give only two examples, both of nonmongoloid females with clearly distinguishable pairs 21 and 22: in the one case, of three very similar satellites, fair sized as these minute bodies go, two were located at the chromosomes 22, one, with an unusually long stem, at a 21. In the other case, an unusually large satellite was attached to one 21, a minute one to one 22. In both cases, this was seen repeatedly, except that the last-mentioned minute satellite stood out clearly in only one cell. The relative sizes of the short arms of the small acrocentrics are also consistent in preparations from any given individual. In some persons, 21 and 22 are easily distinguished, both 21's having a sizable short arm, both 22's a minute one. In addition, the long arms of 21 are somewhat larger than those of 22, but this difference can be ascertained only in particularly favorable cells. Therefore, the difficulty of identifying 21 and 22 is much greater when, to give only one example, all four chromosomes have relatively large short arms. There is no question that the morphology of 21 and 22 varies from person to person, and I am by no means certain that there is not also some variation in the long arm, although this cannot compare with that of the short arm.

Lejeune: May I add a word about that? I would never try to make the statement that we can recognize safely every one of those chromosomes, but I would try to avoid difficulty in the scientific transmission of information, and, for the sake of that, I would stick to the point that mongolism is related to trisomy of a chromosome we call the 21, no matter what shape it has and no matter what figure it shows, and I would say that the 22 is the other pair.

There is really no discussion about the fact that this triplication is related to one of those pairs, and always the same pair. As to the fine description of the 21 chromosome, I would just leave open the question of whether we can safely recognize it. For myself, I suppose we can, in very good cells, and we cannot in less good cells. Even in the very good ones, it is still just at the level of the resolving power of the technique, and so it cannot be firmly defined. But, at least, when we are talking about this, I would simply say that the 21 is the one which is found in triplicate in mongolism.

Patau: I am afraid communication has suffered somewhere, for it is obvious that many authors have not got this straight. In their karyotypes, they put the larger chromosomes first and label them 21. In their texts, they write: "The mongolism chromosome, as everybody knows, is 21." Apparently they have not realized that this sentence is a definition of 21 by phenotype and not a morphological characterization of the mongolism chromosome.

Lejeune: It was agreed in the Denver agreement that if we could relate a given chromosome to something, we would stick to the number, even if subsequently better cytological procedures showed that it was a little larger than its number indicated. I just think, for convenience, we shouldn't worry about whether it is 21 or 22, but just say it is 21.

Patau: Except that the numbers in the Denver system were all linked to morphological characteristics and never to the phenotype. The Denver definition of 21 rested upon the presence of satellites, which are now known to occur at both 21 and 22. The trouble with the definition by phenotype is that one can sometimes distinguish the two pairs by their size. In that case, one will wish to number them, say, in a karyotype, even if one is not yet certain which is the mongolism chromosome. I don't see why one should want to bring in a number merely to use it as a synonym for "mongolism chromosome."

REFERENCES

1. BAIKIE, A. G. Polymorph Alkaline Phosphatase and Genes on the Mongol Chromosome. *Lancet,* **ii:** 937 (1962).
2. BAYREUTHER, K. Interaction of Cytocidal Viruses with Chromosomes of Animal Cells. *Annual Report,* Division of Biology, California Institute of Technology, **140** (1962).
3. BODMER, W. F. Effects of Maternal Age on the Incidence of Congenital Abnormalities in Mouse and Man. *Nature,* **190:** 113 (1961).
4. BRADEN, A. W. H. The Influence of Time of Mating on the Segregation Ratio of Alleles at the T Locus in the House Mouse. *Nature,* **181:** 786-87 (1958).
5. COLLMANN, R. D., and STOLLER, A. A Survey of Mongoloid Births in Victoria, Australia, 1942-1957. *Am. J. Pub. Health,* **52:** 813 (1962).
6. DEMARS, ROBERT. Sex Chromatin Mass in Living, Cultivated Human Cells. *Science,* **138:** 980-81 (1962).
7. GARTLER, S. M., WAXMAN, S. H., and GIBLETT, E. An XX/XX Human Hermaphrodite Resulting from Double Fertilization. *Proc. Nat. Acad. Sci.,* **48:** 332-35 (1962).
8. GERMAN, J. L. DNA Sythesis in Human Chromosomes. *Trans. N. Y. Acad. Sci.,* II, **24:** 395-407 (1962).
9. GILLESPIE, F. D. Ocular Albinism with Report of a Family with Female Carriers. *Arch. Ophthal.,* **66:** 774-76 (1961).
10. GLÄSS, E. Die Identifizierung der Chromosomen im Karyotyp der Rattenleber. *Chromosoma,* **7:** 655-69 (1956).
11. GRELL, E. H. The Dose Effect of ma-1$^+$ and ry$^+$ on Xanthine Dehydrogenase Activity in Drosophila Melanogaster. (Abstract) *Records Gen. Soc. Amer.,* **31:** 87 (1962).
12. GRELL, R. F. A New Hypothesis on the Nature and Sequence of Meiotic Events in the Female of *Drosophila Melanogaster. Proc. Nat. Acad. Sci.,* **48:** 165-72 (1962).
14. GRUMBACH, M. M., MARKS, P. A., and MORISHIMA, A. Erythrocyte G-6-Pd Activity and X-Chromosome Polysomy. *Lancet,* **i:** 1330 (1962).
15. HAMERTON, J. L., COWIE, V. A. GIANNELLI, F., BRIGGS, S. M., and POLANI, P. E. Differential Transmission of Down's Syndrome (Mongolism) Through Male and Female Translocation Carriers. *Lancet,* **ii:** 956-58 (1961).
16. HAMERTON, J. L., and STEINBERG, A. G. Progeny of D/G Translocation Heterozygotes in Familial Down's Syndrome. *Lancet,* **i:** 1408 (1962).

17. HUEBNER, R. J. (1963). Personal communication.
18. HUGHES-SCHRADER, S. Meiosis Without Chiasmata in Diploid and Tetraploid Spermatocytes of the Mantid Callimantis Antillarum Saussure. *J. Morph.,* **73**: 111-42 (1942).
19. IYER, V. N., and SZYBALSKI, W. *In vivo* Cross-linking of the Complementary DNA Strands: the Molecular Mechanism of the Mitomycin Effect. (In preparation).
20. JACOBS, P. A. In Discussion of a Paper 'Chronic Myeloid Leukaemia' by Baikie, A. G. *Scot. Med. J.,* **7**: 100 (1962).
21. JACOBS, P. A., HARNDEN, D. G., BUCKTON, K. E., COURT BROWN, W. M., KING, M. J., McBRIDE, J. A., MacGREGOR, T. N., and MACLEAN, N. Cytogenetic Studies in Primary Amenorrhea. *Lancet,* **i**: 1183-89 (1961).
22. KING, M. J., GILLIS, E. M., and BAIKIE, A. G. The Polymorph Alkaline Phosphatase in Mongolism. *Lancet,* **ii**: 661 (1962).
23. LA CHAPPELLE, A. DE: Cytogenetical and Clinical Observations in Female Gonadal Dysgenesis. *Acta, Endocr., Supp.,* **65** (1962).
24. LENNOX, B., WHITE, H. St. C., and CAMPBELL, J. The Polymorph Alkaline Phosphatase in Mongolism. *Lancet,* **ii**: 991 (1962).
25. LEVAN, A. and HSU, T. C. The Human Idiogram. *Hereditas,* **45**: 665-74 (1959).
26. LINDSTEN, J. *Lancet* (1963, in press).
27. McKUSICK, V. A. On the X Chromosome of Man. *Quart. Rev. Biol.,* **37**: 69-173 (1962).
28. MOORHEAD, P. S., MELLMAN, W. J., and WENAR, CHARLES. A Familial Chromosome Translocation Associated with Speech and Mental Retardation. *Amer. J. Human Genet.,* **13** (1): 32-46 (1961).
29. MORISHIMA, A., GRUMBACH, M. M., and TAYLOR, J. H. Asynchronous Duplication of Human Chromosomes and the Origin of Sex Chromatin. *Proc. Nat. Acad. Sci.,* **48**: 756-63 (1962).
30. MULDAL, S., and OCKEY, C. H. The Denver Classification and Group III. *Lancet,* **ii**: 462-63 (1961).
31. NACHTSCHEIM, H. The Pelger Anomaly in Man and Rabbit. *J. Hered.,* **41**: 131 (1950).
32. NEEL, J. V., and SCHULL, W. J. The Effect of Exposure to the Atomic Bombs on Pregnancy Termination in Hiroshima and Nagasaki. Washington, D.C. National Academy of Sciences, National Research Council. Publ. No. 461, 1956. pp. iii and 241.
33. PATAU, K., THERMAN, E., INHORN, S. L., SMITH, D. W., and RUESS, A. L. Partial-trisomy Syndromes. II. An Insertion as Cause of the OFD Syndrome in Mother and Daughter. *Chromosoma,* **12**: 573-84 (1961).

34. ROTHFELS, K. H. and SIMINOVITCH, L. The Chromosome Complement of the Rhesus Monkey (Macaca Mulatta) Determined in Kidney Cells Cultivated *in vitro*. *Chromosoma*, **9**: 163-75 (1958).

35. RUSSELL, L. B. Genetics of Mammalian Sex Chromosomes. *Science*, **133**: 1795-1803 (1961).

36. RUSSELL, L. B., and CHU, E. H. Y. An XXY Male in the Mouse. *Proc. Nat. Acad. Sci.*, **47**: 571-75 (1961).

37. RUSSELL, L. B. and SAYLORS, C. L. Induction of Paternal Sex Chromosome Losses by Irradiation of Mouse Spermatozoa. *Genetics*, **47**: 7-10 (1962).

38. SASAKI, M. S. and MAKINO, S. 1963. The Demonstration of Secondary Constrictions in Human Chromosomes by Means of a New Technique. *Am. J. Human Genet.* (in press).

39. SCHIMKE, ROBERT T. Adaptive Characteristics of Urea Cycle Enzymes in the Rat. *J. Bio. Chem.*, **237**: 459 (1962).

40. SNELL, G. D. An Analysis of Translocations in the Mouse. *Genetics*, **31**: 157 (1946).

41. STEWART, ALICE, WEBB, JOSEFINE, and HEWITT, DAVID. A Survey of Childhood Malignancies. *British Med. J.* **1**: 1495-1508 (1958).

42. SZYBALSKI, W., ERICKSON, R. L., GENTRY, G. A., GAFFORD, L. G., and RANDALL, C. C. Unusual Properties of Fowlpox Virus DNA. *Virology* (in press).

43. THERMAN, E., PATAU, K., DEMARS, R. I., SMITH, D. W., and INHORN, S. L. Iso/telo-D_1 Mosaicism in a Child with an Incomplete D_1 Trisomy Syndrome. *Portug. Acta Biol.* (in press).

44. VOGT, M. and DULBECCO, R. Steps in the Neoplastic Transformation of Hamster Embryo Cells by Polyoma Virus. *Proc. Nat. Acad. Sci.*, **49**: 171-79 (1963).

45. WELSHONS, W. J., and RUSSELL, L. B. The Y-Chromosome as the Bearer of Male Determining Factors in the Mouse. *Proc. Nat. Acad. Sci. U.S.*, **45**: 560-66 (1959).

46. YERUSHALMY, J. On the Interval Between Successive Births and Its Effect on Survival of Infant. I. An Indirect Method Study. *Human Biology*, **17**: 65 (1945).

47. ZLOTNIKOFF, M. A Human Mosaic. *J. Her.*, **36**: 163-68, (1945).

CHAPTER II: GENETIC MARKERS IN CELL CULTURES

Part 1

Summary of Technical Problems

by Dr. Harry S. Eagle

Neel: This morning it seems that it might be appropriate for Dr. Eagle to summarize some of the outstanding technical problems which confront us in dealing with human cells as we would deal with bacterial cells. After that, Dr. Gartler will lead the discussion on marker traits. We felt that the kind of information which Dr. Eagle will summarize would have a lot of bearing on our discussion regarding marker traits.

Without trying to influence unduly the course of this discussion, I would suggest that we let Dr. Eagle proceed with a minimum of interruptions, because some of the problems that will come out of his presentation we will get to tomorrow.

Eagle: Or perhaps later today. Dr. Neel thought it might be a good idea to summarize, as he says, some of the technical aspects of culture. I am afraid that most of what I have to say is platitudinous to most of you who work with cell cultures; nevertheless, it might be helpful to point up some of the present deficiencies in our technical procedures.

As you all know, and contrary to what has been said by some workers in the field, not all cells can be cultured. Whether one begins with a trypsinized suspension or with explants, most cell cultures are not recognizably the functional cell of the organ from which they were derived. This, of course, limits us greatly in the isolation either of differentiated cells with chemical markers or of cells with genetically determined biochemical defects, and which are expressed only in a specific organ.

The second point I want to make is that although a good deal is known with respect to the nutritional requirements of cells, very little is known with respect to their metabolic activities. The amino acid metabolism of cultured cells has been delineated in some detail, but almost nothing is known as to the biosynthetic pathways involved, for example, in lipid metabolism or carbohydrate metabolism, and the synthesis of macromolecules involving lipids and carbohydrates.

The reason for the protein requirement of cultured cells is still unknown. We do not yet know the actual role of the protein; and, although various cells have been isolated which can do without protein, it is required by the generality of cultured cells. It obviously has multiple functions. It does promote attachment to glass in monolayer cultures, but it also has a nutritional role. Holmes at Wilmington (44) has some interesting and unpublished data which suggest that there is, indeed, a diffusible material which he has isolated from protein, which has many of the growth-promoting properties of the serum alpha-globulin fraction. This is, however, still very much in the experimental stage.

As I said a minute ago, with only a few exceptions, differentiated and functioning cells have not been successfully maintained in serial culture. The exceptions are few, indeed. One of them is Fischer's (86, 87, 61) mast cell tumor, which continues to elaborate heparin and serotonin in dispersed cell culture. There are two cultures isolated by Sato and Buonassisi (8), at Brandeis, one of which is an adrenal tumor culture and the other a pituitary tumor culture, both of which continue for many months to elaborate organ specific hormonal agents. It is, perhaps, relevant to point out that all three of these differentiated functioning cultures are from tumors, and this may be more than coincidental.

Dr. Ephrussi (26) has succeeded in culturing pigmented cells of chick iris epithelium, which, in serial culture—Boris, how long were you able to carry this out?

Ephrussi: Eight months.

Eagle: —which, under appropriate conditions, have continued to elaborate pigment. These exceptions suggest the possibility that if we knew more about the factors determining the perpetuation of function, we might be able to achieve more than has so far been possible in the development of a library of differentiated functioning cells.

In this same connection, also, I should like to point out that we as yet do not know the nature of the metabolic controls which are operative *in vivo* to limit the growth rate of most tissues, and which are apparently released in cultured cells, to the degree that their generation time is anywhere between 16 hours and 4 days, enormously rapid in relation to the generation time of most cells *in vivo*.

As was mentioned yesterday, the phenomena of enzyme repression and end-product inhibition which have been shown to be so important as metabolic controls in cultured bacteria have not been found as regularly operative in cultured animal cells. As a matter of fact, I know of only two examples of such controls. One is what Bob DeMars (15) mentioned yesterday, the repression of glutamine synthetase by glutamine in serially propagated cells (heteroploid), and the other is the reported inhibition of purine metabolism by the provision of adenosine or guanine as reported by Magasanik and McFall (69). We have not observed end-product inhibition or repression in a wide variety of biosynthetic reactions in culture, and they do not appear to be generally operative in cultured human cells.

One can regulate the rate of cellular growth by the same tricks which have been used in bacteria, by some chemostat or cytostat arrangement. With a continuing input of fresh medium into a culture, either at a controlled rate or at a controlled and limiting concentration of an essential metabolite, one can indeed control the growth rate, and arrive at generation times of anything between 16 hours and 8 days (13).

A third point I would like to mention is something we all have been plagued with, the so-called transformation of cultured cells. These may take many forms. They include the obvious morphological transformation of an epithelial culture to a fibroblastic culture, the reverse transformation of a fibroblastic culture to an epithelial culture; there is the reported malignant transformation of cells deriving originally from normal tissue; and there are the transformations involving a change in the karyotype of the cells. These several changes are often, but not necessarily, associated.

The cause for these transformations is as yet unknown. The role of PPLO, and the possible role of adventitious viruses, remain to be assessed.

Another possibility, which I hope will be discussed today, is that we are dealing with mutational events in somatic cells which confer a selective advantage on the mutant. It is difficult to exclude the possibility of a cellular contaminant introduced, as has happened frequently in the past, in any laboratory in which multiple strains are carried.

I would like to point out that, although most of the things we heard yesterday relate to diploid cells, there are a number of serially propagated heteroploid cells, and that these two kinds of cells differ markedly in the way they behave in culture.

In general, the diploid fibroblasts grow more slowly. Most heteroploid lines can be divided ten-, twenty-, or even a hundred-fold; while these diploid fibroblasts can usually not be divided much more than four-fold. In general also, diploid cultures are difficult to get going in suspension culture; they clone with difficulty; and they are reported to have a limited lifespan. It is the last, in particular, which is of tremendous interest, because if it is true that these diploid cultures either transform or die, one may reasonably ask what it is which determines that death. Is there really a built-in senescence factor?

Finally, one of the most obvious differences between cultured cells and cells in organized tissue is that of population density. In organized tissues, we are dealing with a population density of 100 million cells per milliliter, while even in heavy cultures, we are dealing with population densities on the order of 100,000 to 500,000 cells per ml. This tremendous dilution of cells in the medium cannot fail to have important effects on their economy. It cannot fail to promote the loss of metabolite intermediates and cofactors to the environment and must have important effects on the metabolism of the cell, perhaps contributing to the fact that cultured cells in general do not carry out the specialized functions of the organ from which they were derived, assuming that one has, in fact, cultured the specific functioning cell.

The loss of essential metabolites to the medium, with resulting important effects on the biochemical behavior of cultured cells, has in fact been observed in many biosynthetic reactions (23) and can be illustrated by cystine and glutamine. From the very beginning, these two amino acids have appeared to be essential for all cultured cells, in spite of the fact that they are not required *in vivo* for nitrogen balance by any animal yet studied.

In fact, however, all cultured cells so far examined are capable of synthesizing cystine by the classic pathway, involving the formation of homocysteine from methionine and of serine from glucose, their conjugation to cystathionine, and its cleavage to give cysteine and homoserine (24). However, the intermediates and the formed cystine itself are lost to the environment in culture in amounts which exceed the biosynthetic capacity of the cell, so that it dies before the concentrations in the medium and in the cellular pool can be brought up to metabolically effective levels.

At appropriately high population densities, the cystine requirement disappears. The medium can then be conditioned, and the concentrations of the intermediates and of cystine itself brought to the necessary minimum level compatible with cellular function and growth, before the cells die.

The absolute level at which cystine no longer becomes essential is a function of the precursors which are provided. If the cell is given only methionine and glucose, the population must approach the saturation level of 200,000 to 500,000 cells per ml, before the cells are capable of growing in a cystine-free medium. If the cell is provided with preformed homocystine and serine, the critical population is reduced to something like 10,000 cells per ml. If one gives cystine, one cell will grow in a billion volumes of fluid.

Glutamine and glutamic acid are another example of population-dependent requirements. We have always been puzzled by the fact that glutamine, which occupies so central a role in cellular metabolism and which is nutritionally essential for growth in culture, nevertheless does not appear to be a nutritionally essential amino acid in the whole animal. This also is a population-dependent requirement.

If one begins with a cell which has no problems in going from glutamic acid to glutamine, such as monkey kidney epithelium, which without prior adaptation has a high initial level of glutamine synthetase, and in which the block to survival is merely the synthesis of glutamic acid, then with such a cell, at very high population levels, on the order of 500,000 cells per ml, glutamic acid and glutamine are no longer essential amino acids. Work in progress suggests that this may be true also for cells which, by adaptation, by exposure to high concentrations of glutamic acid, have developed a high glutamine synthetase level.

Stern: May I ask you one question about your comments regarding possible senescence with cultured cells? It seems to me the fact that these cells in the body would have permitted the body to persist means that there is no innate senescence, but it is, rather, a senescence factor under these culture conditions. Could you elaborate on that?

Eagle: In using the word "senescence," I did not, of course, mean to imply that this is related to the senescence of the whole organism. The point nevertheless could be made that the number of cellular generations which these cells undergo in the course of six, twelve, or eighteen months' cultivation *in vitro* is consistent with the number of generations which they would undergo in the whole animal in the course of the lifetime of the animal, in view of the greatly reduced generation time *in vivo*. I don't want to make this point. I don't believe it. But the point can be made.

McKusick: I was going to ask, could we have a definition of serially propagated cell cultures versus diploid cells?

Eagle: No, this was a slip on my part. They are both serially propagated, but one may distinguish between the slowly growing diploid cells, which do eventually die in the hands of most workers, and the heteroploid, rapidly growing and indefinitely growing cultures. The latter can be divided, as I said, tenfold, fiftyfold, a hundredfold, grow indefinitely, and are heteroploid. The others are euploid, grow slowly, and can be divided to a relatively limited degree.

McKusick: Wouldn't better terminology be "heteroploid" and "diploid," then, for the two types of cells?

Koprowski: I think there was an attempt made to have the American Tissue Culture Association decide on the nomenclature of different tissue culture systems. I do not think the various proposals have been put to a formal vote, but I was not present at the meeting, whereas Dr. Chu was.

Chu: Actually, this was proposed by Dr. Hayflick from your institute. [Laughter]

Koprowski: His was only one of the motions filed with the Association, and I do not know whether his or any other proposal has been finally decided upon.

Chu: It is a matter of definition, just as Dr. Eagle has pointed out to us. There are two terms proposed by Drs. Hayflick and Moorhead (40): "Cell strain," to describe diploid cells, and "cell line," referring mostly to heteroploid, fast-proliferating cells.

Crow: Do you have any suggestions on how to keep those terms straight, as to which means what?

Szybalski: I am afraid that I would always forget which is which.

Koprowski: The cell line is immortal and the cell strain has a limited lifetime in tissue culture.

Ephrussi: Yes, but where is the limit? Is it six months or eight months?

Koprowski: This is, I think, a very clear limit.

Steinberg: You know what it is after you've lost the culture. [Laughter]

Eagle: A priori, you would not know that a given diploid line does not have the potential of indefinite survival. To me, this appears an artificial and perhaps meaningless distinction. It gives the words "line" and "strain" meanings which they do not now possess.

Billingham: Are any exceptional lines of cells known that have faithfully retained their initial normal diploid karyotype throughout a long history of propagation *in vitro?*

Eagle: I know of none.

Gartler: These are lines which, in terms of chromosome number, have remained diploid, but usually contain an abnormal chromosome or two, as for example in the pig lines of Harris and Ruddle (37). I believe this is also true of the hamster lines, which are supposedly diploid. Dr. Herzenberg, as I recall it, aren't your lines diploid?

Herzenberg: No, I never said that. These lines are aneuploid.

Gartler: I see. Anyway, I think, although some lines apparently do have diploid numbers, there is always a question as to whether or not they are really normal; in fact, in most cases, they apparently are not.

Herzenberg: There may be some interest in these lines of Harris and Ruddle. If there is, if there is some chromosomal abnormality which is maintained indefinitely, and you don't get aneuploidy as a result of this, I think, perhaps, there is something of interest here. It is not clear, because it appears in general that once you have aneuploidy, you don't have anything stable at all, but you have a continually changing karyotype situation.

Bayreuther: I would not say that this is necessarily true. It is generally accepted that there are species differences in regard to karyotype stability under *in vitro* conditions. There seems to exist a gradient. The mouse karyotype seems to be the least stable one—with differences in different strains—then follow the hamster, man—the rat being the most stable in this respect. The pig could belong to the same group as the rat.

Lejeune: With human beings, we have had the experience that we can keep cell lines for more than one year without the karyotype changing. But I must add that we are doing this with small explants, and we transfer the explant itself, and that is probably related to the population size; in fact, we do not transfer the new-grown cells themselves, but we transfer the explants. I would point out that after a year the explant becomes very small, and most of the time we have lost the line altogether. But, in between, there was no change of the karyotype, so that could be related to the fact that the explant was still a kind of body tissue in a particular medium.

Renwick: Could Dr. Koprowski tell us anything about the Wistar human cell line or strain?

Koprowski: What should I tell you about it?

Renwick: Is it diploid?

Koprowski: According to Moorhead, Saksela, and Levan, the culture of fibroblasts obtained from human embryos always retain their diploid character. Regardless of its origin, this system can be maintained under tissue culture conditions for 50 subcultures or for approximately 120 generations before dying out. The factor involved in the senescence of the cells is, at present, unknown. It is impossible to "transfer" the aging factor from a dying culture to one which is growing vigorously. No infectious agent has been isolated from the culture at the stage of senescence and, at present, it is a puzzle why the culture dies out.

Although human cells in culture always retain their diploid character, the same cannot be said about cells obtained from other mammals. I am not familiar with a single tissue culture system which maintained either morphologic, karyologic, or biologic properties of "normalcy" if it was originally started from an animal organ. I am familiar with most of them, and with one more, of growing different embryos in different laboratories, and the observations were the same. If you grow under these conditions—and they are different from those mentioned by Dr. Lejeune, in that it is not a transfer of the fragment but it is just splitting of the whole culture—they die.

I would much like to echo what [Bayreuther] has said, that it is somehow related to species, because only in man can you with great ease maintain such cultures in the diploid state, and afterward, they will, of course, die—after fifty or sixty generations.

Renwick: Does anybody have data on the relative length of life in culture of embryo cells compared with adult, say, "old man" cells?

Eagle: We are starting, in relation to this problem of so-called cell senescence, a long-range pedestrian job of deliberately growing some of these cultures as slowly as we can, and other parallel cultures as fast as we can. After, let's say, a year, the one culture would have been through, perhaps, a hundred cell generations, and the other on the order of 500 or 4000 cell generations. This would tell us whether the death of the culture is indeed related to the number of cell generations, or whether it, instead, involves some environmental factor. Anticipating the possibility that this really is inherent in the cell, we are starting to study embryos and adults of varying ages, to see whether the life span of the cell *in vitro* is at all related to the age of the individual from whom it was isolated. I have no confidence that anything will come out of this.

Herzenberg: Do you have any comment on the question of the optimality or how good your conditions are for growing cells of varying types, Dr. Eagle? The conditions which have been devised so far have been based mainly, I believe, on your work with a number of established cultures. These have become almost mandatory conditions for growing cells, with very minor variations.

As an example, I just heard from Dr. Greenfield (32) at the Cancer Institute of the NIH that by using the astounding kind of conditions, to a tissue culturist, of 50 percent oxygen, he is able to maintain parenchymatous liver cells functioning, although not growing, for a period of a couple of days at least, which is very much better than anybody else has been able to do. He can separate the cells and prevent them from leaking out their enzymes, and maintain their metabolism.

Now, he is a physiologist, apparently, and he says that the liver uses about half of the oxygen supply of the organism, the intact organism, so this is not too unlikely a kind of requirement for oxygen on the part of liver cells. Most of us would tell our students, "No, keep the oxygen out. You must use air and CO_2"—a very minor difference.

Eagle: Well, as you know, we have never developed a medium as such. We have just looked for the growth requirements, beginning with these nondiploid, rapidly growing cells. For these rapidly growing heteroploid cells, it is apparently the case that the minimum requirements essential for growth are, as you say, the optimal requirements, providing a growth rate which is essentially maximal, and which is not further increased whatever you add. Nevertheless, even for such heteroploid cultures, at low population densities one specific metabolite becomes essential, namely, serine.

If you try similarly to clone the slowly growing diploid cells, again using a "minimal" medium, with only essential growth factors, one finds that the minimum population level at which most of the cells will grow, instead of being on the order of 100 cells per ml without serine, and one cell per 10 ml with serine, is on the order of several thousand cells per ml.

Self-evidently, at these low population densities something as yet unknown is required for survival, which is not required at large population densities; and Leonard's point is well taken. I think there is a large area here for study.

If this is true for a diploid line which is already established in culture, it must be all the more true for cells which have not yet been cultivated. It is quite possible that we may find specific nutritional requirements for certain cells which have so far resisted cultivation.

Billingham: Is it known whether cells explanted from an animal of an inbred strain thrive as well as similar cells obtained from a hybrid or outbred donor?

Eagle: I know of no such data.

Herzenberg: We have been culturing cells from mice, and this is not a study which is intended for that purpose, but we have been able to grow cells routinely from any strain we have tried. They grow for a while, however, and then they stop in the usual way that you find with mouse lines, and then they transform, if you are patient enough. Then, they will grow indefinitely. But we have been able to start cultures from each mouse strain we have seriously tried.

Billingham: Have you ever cultured cells from hybrids to see whether they will keep on growing?

Herzenberg: We grow them from hybrid lines as well.

Billingham: And there is no difference?

Herzenberg: I wouldn't say there is no difference, but there is not an obvious one.

Szybalski: This senescence phenomenon appears to me as one of very great biological importance, but on the other hand it doesn't seem to make any sense. There should be, therefore, some very critical experiments performed. I just wonder whether anybody has done the following experiment: to take an explant, grow it for a while, and then divide it into two cultures A and B. A should be frozen and put away and B should be propagated until it reaches a state where it starts to die out. Then, you thaw culture B and prepare three cultures A, $A + B$ and B, and compare those three. The $A + B$ mixture would be a very important one, because it would demonstrate whether there is any extracellular interaction between "senescent" and "young" cultures.

Koprowski: These experiments were published.

Szybalski: Where A and B were mixed?

Koprowski: No. Tissue culture originally obtained from a female embryo was mixed during its phase of senescence with a luxuriously growing fibroblast culture obtained from a male embryo. No reciprocal transfer of characteristics was observed. On many occasions cells kept in a frozen state were thawed out and propagated in tissue culture. On every occasion senescence and death were observed.

DeMars: I heard Hayflick discuss this work this summer, and these cultures are subject to a mysterious rule, which is that, regardless of the regimen of freezing and thawing, the thing that determines the time when they die is the number of transfers.

These cultures are transferred in a very regular way, on a one-week cycle. The population would be divided in half, and then fed on a certain program and then subcultured again, by a 1:2 dilution. I think the magic number is somewhere around fifty of these operations which lead with startling regularity to death of the culture.

The important thing to keep in mind here is that the thing that seems to be important is the number of transfers, because anybody who has cloned a culture and then propagated the result knows, in terms of cell generations, a culture that is cloned and then propagated several times already exceeds, in terms of its number of cell generations, the number of cell generations leading to the death of these cultures studied by Hayflick; so the senescence phenomenon here may not be directly related to cell generations, accumulation of genetic damage, or what have you.

Koprowski: I would say "not known," rather than not "directly related," because these experiments have not yet been done.

DeMars: All right; but, for the moment, there is no obvious connection to the number of cell generations, but, rather, to the number of operations.

Eagle: One caveat there, Bob. When one divides a culture in half, especially these diploid cultures, one has no assurance that all the cells sit down and propagate: 50 twofold divisions every week are a *minimum* of 50 cell generations; but it could be 100 or 150.

DeMars: I would agree with that completely, and I also would not subculture in that way, just because you lose so many cells. I agree with Dr. Szybalski, that it is mysterious, but I think that a very clear experiment could be done.

Szybalski: What is your experience about "petering out" of diploid cell cultures?

DeMars: We lose our cultures after about a year, but after many more cell generations, apparently, than represented in Hayflick's experiments.

Koprowski: Why do you lose your cultures after a year?

DeMars: I wish I knew. [Laughter]

Ephrussi: There is no doubt, it seems to me, that there is an impressive body of data showing that there is difficulty in propagating cells indefinitely. Now, whether this is a real phenomenon of senescence or the result of fortuitous causes, nonfitting environment and so on, is a real problem.

I would like, though, to warn against this too easy acceptance, by the tissue culture people, of the idea that this is an inexorable law, and I would like, in the first place, to use something which is usually not regarded as entirely scientific reasoning, because it is teleological. However, I want to remind you that, in fact, we are all Darwinists, evolutionists, and selectionists—and that the selectionist reasoning *is* teleological reasoning. I mean, we all say: "It is not surprising that wild type gives rise predominantly to deleterious mutations, because what is in nature is the best." So teleological arguments are not to be sneezed at altogether.

When you think of these strains and lines, as Hayflick calls them, you must remember that they differ essentially in gene dosage. In the "cell lines," no new genes have been added, but rearrangement of the diploid genotypes have resulted in new gene dosages and imbalances. Under the artificial conditions of *in vitro* culture, this becomes, for some reason, an advantage; yet, it is hard to believe that what has been established in nature, through the living world, the diploid cell, is deliberately so balanced that it will survive only a certain number of cell generations and no longer. I am aware, of course, that one could get around this by a number of arguments. I am sure that Dr. Crow could think of some. [Laughter] I mean arguments that would be logical from the evolutionary point of view.

I want to emphasize that this *can* be done, but, then, the evolution of cell lines will have to be regarded ultimately not as an inevitable process, but a predetermined goal; and this, I hate to admit.

I think that when we talk about cell culture the emphasis needs to be put on the many unknowns, beginning with the very brutal handling that we give the cells. Dr. Eagle very nicely pointed out a number of things, such as the effect of cell density, which are very far removed from those in nature, *in vivo*. I would like to give you in a few words an example which I have followed within the last few weeks and which shows how some fortuitous causes come into play.

I have been carrying, for the purpose of our work, now for over a year and a half, one of Earle's mouse strains—or, I should rather say lines. [Laughter] That is the so-called high cancer-inducing strain, NCTC 2472. It has some very nice chromosomal markers. When we received this strain, we established its karyotype and compared it with that given in a publication of several years ago from Earle's laboratory. We found that although some small rearrangements had occurred, the karyotype was *grosso modo* unchanged, i.e., it was stable, with a modal chromosome number of 55.

We have now worked with this line for over a year and a half, and this is one of three strains which we have succeeded so far in mating, so it is one of the pillars on which our activity is based. We are reexamining it periodically, and very carefully and, for over twelve months, found it very stable.

Now, I want to define it a little more. This is a hypotetraploid line, with several rearrangements. It does constantly throw some "doubles," that is, some cells with a modal number of 110 chromosomes instead of the usual 55. During the first year in my laboratory, the populations of this line contained somewhere between 5 and 10 percent of "doubles." This was no bother, and we did not feel we were in danger of losing the line.

The striking fact is that there were apparently very few, if any, intermediates between the 55 type and the 110 type. We did not make very many accurate counts on cells with high chromosome numbers, but it is clear that there were very few intermediates, and the higher types had no selective advantage.

To my very unpleasant surprise, about two months ago, we noticed, in examining this strain, that it was being invaded by a cell type with a modal number of 90 chromosomes. Well, this was a cause of great alarm, because the cells with 55 chromosomes which are the indispensable tool for our mating experiments, ended up by being somewhere near 20 percent of the population instead of 95, all the rest of which was composed of cells with approximately 90 chromosomes; so we undertook a number of things to try to modify the conditions (temperature, medium, serum, and so on) so as to give a selective advantage to the cells with 55 chromosomes, before resorting to cloning, because cloning of this strain is extremely difficult.

To make the story short, none of these measures was effective. What really happened was that in the cultures which were kept in the usual medium the 90 chromosome cell-type suddenly started going down, and we are back now to where we were. We have not changed a thing. This just shows what may go on under "controlled conditions." I say that we control 1 percent of the conditions, and we really don't know what the other 99 percent are. I think that it is the accumulation of accidents like this that is the cause of the extinction of cell strains. Every tissue culturist knows that he has difficulties from time to time and starts tracing them. We think of distilled water, or the detergent, or the cleaning woman, and so on.

DeMars: Stop, please! [Laughter]

Ephrussi: You know what happens when we start analyzing. Before we find the culprit, if we ever do find it, everything straightens out and the cultures are going well again. This is the usual accident, which does not lead to destruction of the culture, but, I think, within 50 passages in 6 to 12 months, there is just enough time for two accidents to coincide in time, and that is the answer.

Gartler: I might add that we have had the experience, in working with something over 70 skin biopsies, that almost the only ones that have failed to start have been from very old people.

Chu: May I also add to this point. In successfully starting a culture, cells derived from younger persons may be easier to grow than those from older persons. However, individual differences may mask the age effect. For example, we have cultivated *in vitro* cells from foreskins of many newborn babies. There was practically no age difference, but the growth rate was quite variable.

Gartler: Have you worked with human material and if so, what ages were the oldest subjects?

Chu: About 80 years old.

Lejeune: In my laboratory, we have some idea, because, often, with the children and the parents, it turns out just roughly that to obtain a good karyotype, it must grow about one week in the cases of the child and two or three weeks in the case of the parent. While I would not say this is a good statistic, at least it is something.

Billingham: When you were culturing skin from older mice, in your experiments, did you take into consideration the influence of variation in the phase of the hair growth cycle?

Chu: No, but we have routinely checked the somatic chromosomes by ear or tail biopsies and the variation of hair thickness on these sites is not much.

Patau: I would like to turn Dr. Ephrussi's teleological argument the other way round.

Ephrussi: I said you could.

Patau: Of course, you know it. I should think there is almost bound to be an optimal generation length for any given species, because if it were too long, it might amount to a serious lack of evolutionary plasticity of the species.

Ephrussi: That is exactly the kind of argument that I thought could be adduced.

Patau: For that reason, there might be a selective premium on some mechanism that enforces senescence, so the idea of senescence is not implausible. Of course, once the reproductive capacity of the organism has stopped, this would not apply any more, but a delay of further deterioration would, except for special cases, hardly be in the interest of the population, since it would delay the elimination of useless competition. That such delay would be to the advantage of the older individuals themselves would naturally not affect selection.

Ephrussi: But reproductive capacity could be prolonged, too.

Patau: Yes, but that would again increase the average generation length. It could well be that a mechanism of senescence has been selected for.

Stern: May I bring in an organism very distantly related to this? Eudorina is an organism similar to Volvox, with which you are familiar. Volvox consists of very many cells, a colony-like organism, but Eudorina has only 32 cells. It propagates in two ways: one, asexually, by dividing each of these 32 cells in fast divisions five times, building up new colonies of 32, but also sexually, by forming new gametes. Hartman made an attempt to find out whether sexuality was necessary to keep this organism growing continuously, or whether the asexual process was sufficient, too. In other words, is it related to the case of senescence?

In each case, of course, it is a very simple photosynthetic organism, which can be grown completely in inorganic culture medium with very specifically determined artifical light, for instance 12 hours dark and 12 hours light, and so on. Hartman was able to keep this organism growing for many, many years, purely asexually; so there was no senescence in this primitive, potentially sexual organism.

Szybalski: Well, just as in *Escherichia coli,* which is potentially sexual and grows indefinitely.

Ephrussi: There is an Ascomycetes, Podospora, which has been studied by Rizet in France, which very definitely will not survive beyond a certain number of generations without sexual reproduction. Vegetative propagation results in a type of senescence, which, incidentally, can be affected by some gene mutations. But the main factor determining the ability of a strain to be propagated vegetatively is cytoplasmic and the modalities of its transmission make one strongly suspect that a virus is involved; so it is very hard to say what it really is.

Atwood: While we are citing examples, there is a very old one in Neurospora. Sheng (91) isolated a mutant that seems to have a fixed lifetime in terms of number of transfers or amount of growth that it can make before it stops. He calculated, for the dilution hypothesis, and concluded that it grew enough so that one could not have even one molecule of anything that was in the original spore, so the diluting-out hypothesis is wrong.

Renwick: The *simple* diluting-out process.

Atwood: Yes. The character segregates normally as a chromosomal locus. It is rejuvenated by crossing. It can also be rejuvenated by heterokaryosis.

Szybalski: What is the mechanism of this phenomenon?

Atwood: The mechanism has never been solved, but I say that here is an organism that normally has indefinite growth, which, by one mutation, is changed into one that has a mysterious kind of fixed lifetime.

Szybalski: I mean, we have to think about any mechanism.

Atwood: The phenomenon is real. [Laughter]

Szybalski: Could you invent some formal mechanism which would explain this phenomenon? E.g., there could be a series of dilution phenomena. First, there would be dilution of type A of catalyst molecules, the supply of which stops under the particular growth conditions. As long as at least one A molecule is present, a large pool of B type molecules is maintained in the cell. When the last molecule A disappears, the pool of B molecules would begin to be diluted out. The presence of the pool of molecules C is in turn dependent on the presence of at least one molecule of B. If life of the cell depends on the presence of at least one molecule of C (or D, or E . . .), you could easily explain the quantitative aspects of this "senescence" phenomenon by this complex dilution mechanism.

Neel: Perhaps, now that we have had this very fine introduction into the philosophy, the techniques, and the mystique of tissue culture, we can move on to begin to discuss the various types of marker traits, which can be followed in culture material. I am sure we are going to keep coming back to the issues which have been raised so far this morning, but let's move along to our marker traits.

Introduction to the Study of Markers in Cell Culture

by Dr. Stanley M. Gartler

Gartler: There are three requirements for effective formal genetic analysis in any system: markers, recombinations, and directed transfer of hereditary material. As we have already heard from Dr. Eagle's discussion there are a number of technical problems inherent in all culture material which are serious obstacles to the rapid development of a mammalian somatic cell genetics field. However, definite advances have been made in the past few years, and our purpose will be to summarize and evaluate this progress. Today we shall try to survey the various markers that have been reported as usable at the cell culture level, and tomorrow we will move on to a consideration of the possibilities of hereditary transfer and recombination in cell culture.

There are at least two ways in which one can go about trying to obtain markers for cell culture work. One is to begin with known *in vivo* mutants—that is, start cultures from individuals with known genotypic and phenotypic differences and attempt to study these differences at the cell culture level. This approach has the obvious advantage of starting and working with genetically known material. On the other hand it has the disadvantage of usually involving normal cell cultures, which as we have just heard, have considerable technical difficulties.

The other basic approach to cell markers is to begin with a cell population of the established cell type, and attempt to produce variant lines by the simple techniques that have been used so successfully in microbial genetics.

Both of these approaches have been used, and a number of reports have appeared, describing a variety of different cell lines. These reports cover antigenic characters, differences in various enzymatic activities, variation in resistance to purine analogues and differences in viral susceptibility, for example.

In order to try to survey these reports in a fairly interesting manner and to avoid this being a simple cataloging session, I thought we would spend the first part of it on a more or less thorough discussion of the studies of the known *in vivo* characters in cell cultures. I have asked a number of the people here, who have done the original work in these areas, to act as discussion leaders in these different areas. I don't mean to try to formalize the presentations, which is obviously impossible here, but I thought, in this way, we might be able to channelize the discussion about these different markers and thereby make the discussion more meaningful, both to ourselves and to the readers of the proceedings of the conference.

I might give you some idea of what I have in mind. We will start with Dr. Herzenberg who will present his work on the H-2 antigen in mouse cells *in vitro*, and then go on to Dr. Krooth, who will discuss his very interesting work with acatalasemia and galactosemia. Then, I want to go from this area to my own work on glucose-6-phosphate-dehydrogenase in cell culture.

I would like to call on Dr. Herzenberg to begin with his comments on antigenic markers in cell culture.

Study of the H-2 Locus in Murine Cell Cultures

by Leonard A. Herzenberg

Herzenberg: I might say that most of this has been given in a formal presentation a few months ago* at the Gatlinburg (Oak Ridge) symposium (41), so I don't think a formal repeat of this would be at all in order. I would just like to start the discussion. I don't think we have to keep it at all formal as far as I'm concerned. I think everybody should pop in, as they have been doing.

[Slide] We have here an impressive chart, impressive because you won't be able to understand it, and anything we can't understand is impressive, or, perhaps, repressive.

Koprowski: Could we have the lights out?

Herzenberg: Yes, but you're not going to see much more of it, I'm afraid.

Koprowski: You're right. [Laughter]

Szybalski: Is this Egyptian or Assyrian?

Herzenberg: What I have up here, actually, is a chart summarizing the work that has gone into the immunogenetics of the H-2 locus, or the H-2 chromosome region in the mouse.† This covers a period of some twenty-odd years now, involving a large number of people, especially George Snell and Jack Stimpfing at Bar Harbor, the late Peter Gorer, Bernard Amos, Gustavo Hoeker in Chile, and others.

The H-2 (Histocompatibility-2) locus in the mouse, which really could be just called an isoantigenic locus, determines antigenic differences between individuals which can be detected by other individuals

---

*Parts of this work were supported by USPHS research grants, AO-2700 and C-4681.

---

† A revised nomenclature for H-2 antigens is now in preparation by George Snell and others and will undoubtedly be published.

in the same species. One of the ways in which this has been studied is by the grafting of tissues; therefore, histocompatibility. It could just as well be called a blood group locus, because it determines antigens located on the red blood cells.

There are a large number of alleles, certainly in excess of **26**, at this point which have been found in different inbred mouse strains, or, in some cases, in individual mice, which have then been bred to get strains. Some of these may have arisen by crossovers (for example H-2^g) between some of the existing alleles. The allele is, of necessity, somewhat inexact.

Let me describe this in general. The H-2 locus is actually a region of the chromosome that has been found to have crossing-over to the extent of about 1 percent in the mouse, which is a very high level. Therefore, it is a large region of the chromosome. This locus determines a series of distinguishable antigenic components, distinguishable on serological bases, in general. These antigenic components are described by letters, which were in the body of the table, and, on the right-hand side, we have the particular strains in which these were found.

The matter of interest to us here is, first, if these antigens could be shown to be maintained on cells growing in culture indefinitely, they could be used as genetic markers. These would be true genetic markers in the sense that the characteristics that we can examine will be determined by a typical Mendelizing unit in the mouse. We have shown that, indeed, these antigens persist indefinitely, in culture on all cells we have looked at. The oldest cells that we have looked at are now six years old. The H-2 antigens are present as well on the C3H cells that Earle started in 1940.

The question now is, how can we detect these antigens on individual cells, so that we can do true genetics in culture? A variety of methods present themselves immediately, and several of these have been worked with and explored, with reasonable degrees of success. A detailed report has been published (10, 11).

If one has a cell which is appropriately sensitive to the killing action or cytotoxic action of antibodies in the presence of complement, one can detect the antigen on the cells by the fact that the cells are killed. It is perfectly straightforward. It turns out that cells of lymphoid origin are most sensitive to the cytotoxic action of antibodies and complement. We have obtained a number of antigenically marked cell lines in culture (or cell strains—I'm not sure which), which are indefinitely propagatable at this point. Is it a strain?

Gartler: No, it is a line.

Herzenberg: They are killed by appropriate antibody and complement.

The efficiency of killing with ML-388—we have worked with this line for the longest period—is about 99 percent, under the best conditions.

Koprowski: What did you mean by "lymphoid origin?"

Herzenberg: In this case, this is from a methylcholanthrene-induced lymphoma. Originally, it was a histocytic cell, according to the pathologists, and then it became more of a macrocytic-looking cell. Is that right? At this point, if you make a Wright stain of it, it has a large nucleus and a little bit of cytoplasm around it.

Eagle: How many discrete antigens are you dealing with in a specific type of culture?

Herzenberg: In this particular case, we have been dealing with a cell that arose from a homozygous mouse, a mouse homozygous for the H-2^d allele. We have shown that the killing is exclusively, or almost exclusively, due to antisera directed against antigens determined by the H-2 alleles. There are lots of other antigenic differences between these cells and other cells, but the killing is specifically due to H-2. We can show this in several different ways.

Now, within the H-2 complex of antigenic components, we have been able to get killing with so-called monospecific sera. I say "so-called," because all this means is that by serologic means, sera have been fractionated by absorption or by suitable immunization and then absorption, so as to react with only one *known* component.

It has been the history of all immunogenetic investigations that the more you look at a single component, the more you can break it up into a large number of components. What the antigen or antigenic component in this case is, at the molecular level, I wouldn't care to say. I don't think we can really come to any conclusions on it at this point. There are always the two conflicting possibilities: one, that an antigen component is a specific region of a molecule, and the other, that it is a reflection of the complexity of the serum which is used to detect it; in other words, there is a whole series of different antibodies, and the antigenic component is, in a sense, defined by the antibody which reacts with it. I don't know if I am just confusing us more, but the point is that we cannot make any conclusions at the molecular level as to what we mean by an antigenic component at this point.

Szybalski: Does this 99 percent efficiency mean that if you plate a hundred cells, you get one colony which is growing?

Herzenberg: It means that if you have a hundred colonies growing, without selection, you have one colony growing with selection.

Szybalski: Yes, and this one colony is now different, or is it just a survivor?

Herzenberg: No. I'll get to that. It is not different as yet.

Ephrussi: Excuse me, but what is the cloning efficiency?

Herzenberg: It varies between 30 and 50 percent.

Steinberg: An H-2 allele produces more than one known antigenic factor. Is the killing due to only one of these, or do you require more than one of them, or is one more efficient than the others?

Herzenberg: It is determined by more than one antigenic component. You can get killing with one or two or several. I am not prepared to say what the relative efficiency of killing is with the various ones, because what you mean by having antibodies against a particular component is that you take a complex serum and fractionate it, or else you prepare sera in different mouse strains and you cannot directly compare a particular antibody in one strain with another.

McKusick: What is known about the chemical nature of the antigen? Did I understand that this is a lipoprotein in nature rather than a polysaccharide?

Herzenberg: The evidence at this point is not at all compelling. Everybody has jumped on the bandwagon of assuming that this antigen is a lipoprotein.

All that can be stated with certainty is that the antigenic activity, determined by the inhibition of hemagglutination (in other words, the absorption of hemagglutinating antibodies), the induction of hemagglutinins, or, based upon another serologic test, the enhancement phenomenon in mice, is located in a lipoprotein-rich fraction. It is just a shift of orthodoxy, without any real basis. I might say I may be responsible for this, because we have published the first paper (42) in which we found it was a lipoprotein fraction, and we did not conclude it was lipoprotein, by any means. Everybody else has now jumped onto this (38).

We are dealing with an antigen which we really don't know anything about as to its chemical structure. We know very little about the molecular configuration, antigenic components, or antigenic factors, if you wish, which are determined by this region of chromosome in the mouse. Nevertheless, we can detect the antigens on cells in culture, and one more very significant thing, I think, is that in either meiotic situations, or particularly in meiotic situations, crossing over or genetic recombination between these various components has been observed in a reasonable number of cases at this point, probably about a dozen, and a crude linkage map is being developed, particularly by Stimpfling at Bar Harbor, at present.

This is based upon the very naive, but possibly correct, and, I think, only possible kind of hypothesis, that the arrangement of these components can be made in linear fashion; that is, perhaps, there is some direct relationship between the genetic map and the antigenic components here. I say this is naive because we have no information about the molecular structure of the antigen, and there may be a series of steps between the gene product and the antigen in this case. One cannot, with justification, make a direct analogy between, say, the structure of hemoglobin and the structure of the gene, and the problem here.

Now, we say we have a selective system, so far, with respect to these antigens in culture, which is not a very highly efficient process. After one passage of this sort, where we pick up one colony out of a hundred which grows after selection, still in this case it has the original antigenic composition. If we carry this selection over 14 passages, somewhere between the eleventh and the fourteenth passage, we end up with a mixture of cells, some of which are no longer killable by serum and complement and others of which are still as sensitive as those we started with.

Eagle: Excuse me, Leonard, but I am a little puzzled here. If you are dealing with a multiplicity of antigens, all involved at the same H-2 locus, is your selection done with an antiserum to one of this complex of antigens, or to the entire complex?

Herzenberg: It is with an antiserum directed against a number of the components, neither all of them nor one. It is against, in this case— it is an antiserum prepared by injection of tissues. I should, perhaps, have said this in the beginning. All the antisera we are working with are sera prepared by injection of tissues from one mouse strain into another. They are never prepared against the cells that are cultured. We are dealing with antigens which are exactly equivalent to the antigens found on the cells in the original animal, as far as the reaction with antibodies at least is concerned.

The antisera in this case are all prepared in one mouse strain that carries the H-2^b allele, against tissues from mice carrying the H-2^d allele, and we have made use of the coisogenic strains of Snell, which differ genetically only by the allele, or essentially only by the allele, carried at this particular locus, the H-2 locus. They are genetically identical, within practical limits, except for the H-2 locus. These sera, therefore, are relatively clean with respect to antibodies against antigens other than H-2.

We are not selecting, therefore, against a single antigenic component, certainly, at this point. As I said, after 11 to 14 repassages with constant selection, we ended up with a mixture, a mixed population of cells, resistant and nonresistant to the cytotoxic action of serum and complement. These were then cloned out. We cloned many times before that, looking for this, but at that point they were cloned out, and we did end up with stable cultures of cells resistant to the killing action of the antiserum and complement. We have a number of parameters by which the sensitive and resistant cells are different. However, the resistant cells do still have the H-2^d antigen, but in lesser amount per cell.

This is not a contaminating cell because of that fact alone. These cells will still form a tumor when inoculated into a mouse of the H-2^d phenotype. They have not gained as far as we know an antigenic difference, which prevents them from growing in animals having the H-2^d genotype.

Ephrussi: Excuse me, but it seems to me that there is good evidence that the antigenicity controlled by this locus in quantitative terms, does decrease in particular, with ploidy.

Herzenberg: Yes.

Ephrussi: Are these by any chance cells with higher ploidy?

Herzenberg: We have looked at them, and they are not grossly different in ploidy. We have not counted individual chromosomes, but we have not gone from a diploid or near-diploid to a near-tetraploid.

Gartler: Does the resistant line clone as well as the parent line?

Herzenberg: They clone with about the same efficiency. There are a number of things which are different about them. They grow a little more slowly. The cells are larger. The amount of antigen per cell surface area is about one-quarter to one-eighth as much. They have this difference in morphology, I think, in both clonal and individual cells, in gross appearance (11).

Eagle: How do you interpret their resistance now to the antigen?

Herzenberg: I would probably interpret it on the same basis as Möller (72) interprets the relative resistance; I mean Möller in Klein's laboratory—on the same basis as he interprets the resistance of sarcomas, or the relative resistance of sarcomas and carcinomas relative to lymphomas, that there is less antigen surface area, and you don't get as much complement bound which lyses the cells, but this interpretation is not relevant, I think, to genetics specifically.

I might say I admit that this was simply a model which we had available for seeing whether any of the methodology might work. Briefly, other ways of picking up the antigens on the cells with which we are working in mass cultures are absorptions or neutralization of antisera with these cells (10). If the antigens are present on the cells, we can immunize the mice with these cells and, by appropriate genetic control, we can show which antigens are there. These are rather crude methods and not very useful for genetic purposes. A promising nonselective technique is labeling the cells with fluorescent antibody methods. We can label these cells by reacting them first with mouse antiserum and then with fluorescein-conjugated rabbit antimouse-gamma-globulin.

You get very nice ring reactions, provided you keep the cells alive. This technique, again, has been described by Möller (73) for tumor cells and tissue cells, and it works reasonably well for culture cells. I say "reasonably well." It is not perfect.

It is essential that the cells be kept alive for the staining to be specific and clear, and it is just this property which we want to have here, that you don't kill cells unless you add complement. The antiserum alone is not toxic. We are hoping, therefore, although we have not yet done this, to pick up stained and unstained cells, or small clones, and see what sort of differences we have here.

But now, the main object of our tooling up—and this has been a long tooling-up procedure, of preparing all sorts of different mouse antisera in sufficient quantities and getting a number of different cell lines growing in culture—our main interest now is to work with cells derived from F-1 hybrids or from heterozygous animals, in the same way as the Kleins have been working with tumors *in vivo* in mice, selecting for losses of particular antigens or antigens determined by particular alleles in mice. We wish to do this in culture.

Let me just say why. The first cells which we have available, which we could grow, as I said, were homozygous, to start out with. This is if they were diploid. If they were aneuploid in culture, we don't know how many doses of this d allele we have in the culture cells. We may have two or three or maybe even more. Conceivably, we could have one, but I think this would be less likely.

If we start out with a cell, however, which is heterozygous, that is, H-2^d over something else, then we can select against H-2^d, and we will need only a single change to find the loss of the antigen. This is what Klein has done in the mouse *in vivo*, and he has been very successful in showing that with the so-called heterozygous tumors, he can get loss of the antigens, determined by one or the other of the alleles in the heterozygote, by grafting the tumors back into one of the parental strains which made the original heterozygote. You can put such a tumor back into a mouse which has the H-2^s homozygote state, and the tumor will not grow. These cells will not grow in such an individual but will be rejected by the homograft reaction, unless a change to loss of H-2^d occurs in some of the cells, and, indeed, this happens all the time in his material.

An H-2 allele determines a whole series of antigenic components. In the mouse, using the homograft reaction, it is not possible to dissect these components very far. He can, in one particular case, dissect the H-2^a allele into essentially what is d and k, and show loss of either k alone or d+k in such a situation. He has interpreted this as possibly being due to mitotic crossing over in these cells.

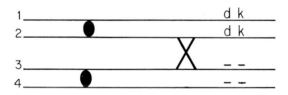

Figure 27. See text.

For example, let's consider a diploid cell which is heterozygous, we will say, in this case for d and k, arranged in this order along the chromosome (Fig. 27). If mitotic crossing over occurs between chromatids 2 and 3, and then chromatids 2 and 4 go to the same pole at segregation, that cell will have lost both d and k. If, however, crossing over of the same chromatids were to occur but *between* d and k, then the cell will have lost k but not d. In order to lose d without losing k, you have to have a double crossover. Since Klein finds loss of only k or loss of d and k, and never loss of d alone, he favors the hypothesis that the loss is due to somatic crossing over.

Atwood: What is the relative frequency of loss of both to loss of k?

Herzenberg: They are not very different from each other.

Atwood: Well, then, it must mean that either the hypothesis is wrong or d and k are very close to the centromere. [Laughter]

Herzenberg: Yes. There is another possibility; that is—and I suppose that we ought to be sophisticated enough to realize that double crossing over in small regions is not very rare at all. It seems to be an increased frequency of crossing over, very close to another crossover, a sort of negative interference.

This is purely an interpretation, and we are far from the actual possibility of proving it at this point. But, in culture now, if, indeed, there is some sort of linear arrangement of the antigenic components, we might have, say, the antigenic components, A, B, C, and D, in a given cell, in the heterozygous state. Our intention is to select with an antiserum directed against one or just a few of these components, and, hopefully, detect the true variants or true losses in progeny cells, and then check to see what other nonselective antigenic components are lost at the same time. This is, again, simply a hope for the future, and, perhaps, for a little more immediate future than it was two years ago, but there is no experimental evidence to add on it at this point.

We now have at least two of Klein's lymphomas growing as lymphocytic cells in culture, growing in suspension, unfortunately; they do not attach to the glass. They are nice, round cells, and you put them back in the animal and they form a tumor, and you put them back in the culture and they grow in culture. They still maintain their heterozygous antigens. They have not been selected at all. But cloning is difficult with them because they do not attach to the glass.

Bayreuther: Can't you overlay them with agar?

Herzenberg: I am sure there are all sorts of tricks one could apply. But, every time you try to apply a new trick in culture, it takes you six months to get it to work properly.

Stern: How far are d and k on the meiotic crossing over map? Is that known?

Herzenberg: There are twelve crossovers or so known at this point, six of them published and six of them just told to me. The statement cannot be made with any certainty. The whole region is said to undergo about 1 percent crossing over.

Stern: But there is no special reason to believe that d and k are extremely far away?

Herzenberg: These have been shown to be crossovers.

Atwood: There is one point that might be relevant to this. If these come from crossovers, then, the allele that was with them has become homozygous, probably, and this means that it would be lost, then, less frequently than it was lost before, when it was with the original d and k. Is that true or is it not?

Herzenberg: In Klein's experiments?

Atwood: Yes. I wondered if you had looked for that.

Herzenberg: You mean, the allele that is with them should be homozygous in another cell?

Atwood: The cell that has lost both d and k at once by crossing over should be a homozygote for the other allele.

Herzenberg: For s, yes.

Atwood: Yes, for s, and then it would be lost much less frequently than s is lost in the original heterozygote.

Herzenberg: Yes. In fact, if they should start with a cell derived from homozygous mice, then, they have never selected a true loss variant. They can select false-positives, as they call them, but in all cases these have turned out not to be true loss variants.

Atwood: Well, then, that makes this test even better.

Herzenberg: But I don't know if they have looked at these kinds of—yes, it would make the test better, but whether they have actually looked there, I don't know. I don't think they have published on them.

Neel: Can we go back to Dr. Stern's point, that if, already, there are some twelve crossovers between d and k, and if the chromosomal region involved in these antigenic properties may extend some distance beyond your markers then the actual region involved may have considerably greater potentialities for crossing over, if you test for the right antigens.

Herzenberg: No, there weren't 12 crossovers with d and k. There have been some 12 crossovers all together between different components in the H-2 system. With this information, it is becoming possible to assign a unique sequence of the components. It is a tremendous job to look for crossovers here. What you have to do is to set up an F-1 cross between two individuals, and then test the progeny of the cross with a whole battery of antisera. The mouse hemagglutination system is not the most ideal system to work with, so they have to try them at a variety of antisera concentrations and be absolutely sure of their results in each case.

Neel: But is it fair to say that most of these crossovers have been discovered accidentally rather than systematically?

Herzenberg: The first one was discovered accidentally, but Stimpfling is now looking for them systematically in two particular crosses.

Neel: So the frequency of recombination might be considerably higher than the 12 known cases to date would imply?

Herzenberg: Not considerably.

Renwick: In Klein's work, in the surviving cells which are, presumably, homozygotes for 2^s—has he tested for dosage factors? That's the same point Dr. Atwood was mentioning.

Herzenberg: Yes. They published on this (55), trying to reach the conclusion that it is not hemizygous but is homozygous; that it does have more antigen than the heterozygous cell does. I have had a lot of experience with mouse serology, particularly using the hemagglutination method which they have to use, and I would be very loath, and I am sure they would agree, to accept these conclusions completely; that it is very difficult to tell a twofold difference in the amount of antigen per cell, because it is just a twofold dilution, you see, and everything is done by serial twofold dilutions, so the difference between whether you see a weak agglutination or you see none in the final tube of the agglutination series—

Renwick: As far as it goes, it is consistent with homozygosity, is it?

Herzenberg: Yes, it is consistent with it.

DeMars: Do your selective methods or typing methods actually lyse the cells, or do they just become rounded and sit there and fail to divide, or what happens in your culture?

Herzenberg: In some cases you can see them lysing, but not all of them.

DeMars: Is it quickly?

Herzenberg: Yes, they lyse within ten to fifteen minutes.

DeMars: That's too bad.

Motulsky: Is there any change in the titer or the level of antigen in the primary cultures, as compared with when they become permanent, or have you tested this at those stages?

Herzenberg: There isn't a very large difference between the amount of antigen on the cells that have been in culture for six years and those put back into an animal that grows the tumor, when you look at the tumor cells. There is not much difference, comparing the amount of antigen on these ML-388 cells that have been in culture for six years and another tumor arising from the same animal, at this time.

Koprowski: But you actually do not have primary cultures of normal origin. We are only discussing cells of tumor origin.

Herzenberg: Well, we have primary cultures of normal origin, but they are not terribly useful because we can't kill them, so far. We have them, and they stain with fluorescent antibodies, but our primary aim at this moment is to select differences.

Motulsky: But you say all of these lines, if you let them sit, become permanent type?

Herzenberg: Yes.

Motulsky: When they become permanent, do they then show the properties of being lysed by the antiserum-complement system?

Herzenberg: The two that we have, that are round cells deriving from these lymphomatous lines, do. They are still sensitive. But fibroblasts are not sensitive.

Motulsky: How many different H-2 alleles have you worked with at the cell-culture level so far? How many have you taken?

Herzenberg: Four, but one is a sort of combination of the other two; that is, a combination of d and k, so it would be three.

Szybalski: Does this mean that you have four independent selective systems at this time, or how many selective genetic systems do you have?

Herzenberg: One is no good at all. The anti-b is not a good selective system.

Sybalski: How many good selective systems do you have?

Herzenberg: Three, but, as I say, again, one of them is not very good. Actually, there is a multiplicity, when you really mention it, because the allele d determines a series of antigenic components, and we have shown that we can kill with fractionated sera, with sera directed against just one or a few of these components; so that it is just a matter of how many different fractions of sera we can make. But you can function—

Szybalski: What is the selective efficiency of this system? About 1 percent? Did I understand you correctly?

Herzenberg: In one passage?

Szybalski: Yes, but I am thinking more along the experimental designs as normally employed in microbial genetics. Do you know anything about spontaneous mutation rates in this system?

Herzenberg: As far as antigenic loss goes?

Szybalski: Yes.

Herzenberg: Well, we have been working. At this point, we have data on these things only with the homozygous cell, and we have found none, as you notice, that have actually lost the antigen. There is a decrease in amount, which we ascribe to—

Szybalski: Does this mean that the cells have mutated and have changed to heterozygotes from homozygotes?

Herzenberg: I don't think so. The cell type has changed. It is probably just a fairly large change, and may be due to a single kind of primary change which we have no idea what it is, but it results in these cells which are different in several ways, as I showed you at the beginning, and are resistant to the killing action of the serum. But they are not true antigenic losses, which is what we want to work with.

Szybalski: What I am really asking is whether, at present, your system is ready for real *quantitative* type of genetic experiments?

Herzenberg: It is practical for one kind of experiment right now, and that is what we are doing now; that is, starting with heterozygous tumors, selecting against just one of the alleles, a whole allele, which is the most sensitive system, and seeing if we can't get a complete loss of antigen in the same way that Klein has gotten in the mouse. I'm just following on his coattails.

DeMars: The nicest way to nail down mitotic recombination here would be if you could find the twin spot. In the culture environment where the cells are fixed on the glass one can work as with Drosophila. This is the reason for my original question. If you start with cells that have double heterozygosity in repulsion ($\frac{a+}{+b}$) one sort of segregation following recombination would yield the $\frac{a+}{a+}$ and $\frac{+b}{+b}$ homozygotes. These segregants would form colonies side by side and each colony would have lost one of the antigens if enough growth had occurred following segregation. If you select against the antigen of one cell type then the reciprocal segregant would survive. Furthermore, if the selective treatment is such that the cells selected against are morphologically altered but not killed then both cell types might be recoverable and subject to further examination.

For instance, could you grade your selective treatments, so that, instead of lysing the cells, they just became rounded or sick-looking? This would allow you to scan the culture and find the patches of cells that look perfectly fine.

Herzenberg: Bob, this is what we intend to do with the fluorescent antibody, to allow small clones to develop, and stain them. They are not killed by that. We know this. They are not killed by just antibody, once we leave out the complement. You can look at them without killing them.

DeMars: Fine. Then you will be able to look for twin spots.

Szybalski: Would their frequency be reasonably high for this type of experiment?

Herzenberg: I don't know. Based on Klein's material, it is, yes.

Neel: Before we leave the material which has just been presented, I wonder if I could ask Dr. Herzenberg about the kind of problems that he thinks can be attacked with this system of his.

Herzenberg: Well, the first one is the question of whether gene processes or genetic processes can, indeed, be studied in somatic cells in culture; that is, can you find true gene mutations in culture? Can you find mitotic crossing over in culture? Perhaps, we don't have to question any longer whether it is possible to get exchange of genetic material from one cell to another. One has to develop markers for this and ways of studying the markers in individual cells. Is this satisfactory for the record?

Renwick: Wouldn't you add segregation in general, not just somatic crossing over?

Herzenberg: Yes

Neel: Could you distinguish between mutation and somatic crossing over?

Herzenberg: On paper, yes, very easily. [Laughter]

Neel: I wasn't thinking of the paper demonstration.

Herzenberg: As yet, we have no evidence of either occurring for sure in culture, so I don't see how we can distinguish between these things —I mean, experimentally, between things which we have not found yet. No, I don't mean to be facetious, but if you were to find, for example, selecting against one of the antigenic components here, others obligatorily changing at the same time in some cells, and then you selected for another one and other ones changed at the same time, you might, if it was really always the same kind of change and you couldn't build up any kind of a linear sequence on the basis of this, then you might expect all these changes were mutational changes.

If, on the other hand, you found that it was easier to build up the linear sequence from the changes that build up, you might suspect that these were due to somatic crossing over or mitotic crossing over. You could look for the twin spots, as Dr. DeMars has suggested; that is, you should look for the reciprocal type. If you find it, then, this would prove that you had mitotic crossing over.

DeMars: I think it is important here to keep in mind two things. First, in order to establish a sequence with mitotic recombination, several markers on the same arm of a chromosome will be required. This will take many more markers than are now available and lots of time before they become available.

That is why, in my own thinking about this, I have assumed that we were going to have just one marker to work with. You can formally distinguish between nondisjunction, mutation, haploidization, and mitotic recombination in a rigorous way using just one marker, provided that you rig the scheme so that you can recover the twin spot.

Second, it is not enough even to find the reciprocal crossover type in a population. If you can show that the two reciprocal types arise side by side, and if you can make a chromosomal analysis of the two segregants and rule out nondisjunction, you can also rule out mutation and haploidization. That is why I asked the question concerning your ability to detect and characterize the reciprocal type when you select against one of the serologic types.

Herzenberg: You have two kinds of twin spots.

DeMars: You can have two kinds of twin spots, as Dr. Stern pointed out, and one marker is enough to give you the twin spots that you need.

Neel: But, with the amount of migration in these cultures, if there are "twin products," are they going to stay side by side?

DeMars: You were seeing a greatly magnified microscopic view, but on a macroscopic scale, they would be close enough.

Ephrussi: Twin spots (in the genetic sense) are the obligatory result of the process being explained here. But there is no necessity at all that there should be geographical localization, as there is on the integuments of Drosophila.

DeMars: Well, they don't have to be like that [clasping hands]; they can be like this [intertwining fingers]. How are we going to get that in the record? [Laughter]

Chu: There are two facts that may be helpful to supplement Dr. DeMars' comments. The first point is that all the mouse chromosomes are acrocentrics. So we have only one arm to worry about. The second is that with the knowledge of sex-linked antigens in the mouse I guess one can make use of the hemizygous state.

Herzenberg: They are not usable yet.

Chu: Well, I was just asking the question.

Herzenberg: They were found just a few months ago, by very long graft rejection; I mean, the only evidence for it is the rejection of grafts, after thirty or forty days, I believe.

Renwick: How do you distinguish between mutation and haploidization with one marker? I don't think you can (except by chromosome studies), unless you have a marker like the H-2 complex.

DeMars: If it is haploid, I don't suppose you can, very readily. I would be very happy to find either one. But you can certainly make a good formal demonstration of mitotic recombination in this material, provided you have the proper selective scheme.

Renwick: If you have a locus such as Dr. Herzenberg is working with, you have effectively got multiple loci to work with; that is, he has so many mutant sites on the one locus that he has the equivalent of a large number of loci to play with.

Ephrussi: I would like to point out that sometimes it does help to see things, and while we speak of twin spots, I think that our chances of detecting them in a visual manner would be greatly enhanced by the use of epithelial tissues. That is where you have a slight chance of seeing really geographically separated twin spots. That is one thing.

The other thing to which I would like to call your attention is something much less sophisticated, and therefore less fashionable, namely pigmentation. Pigmentation would be a very good visual marker; in fact, we are planning to try the visual detection of hybridization by using two strains of mouse iris, which have no pigment for different genetic reasons, so that cell fusion (which we are interested in) would result in the appearance of pigmented spots on a colorless background.

Neel: I might say that, some years ago, I looked for a somewhat different kind of twin spot, namely, to see whether in a Negro known to be a carrier of the gene for albinism, to see if we could find twin spots of albino and somewhat darker tissue, because there is some evidence that the albinism gene in the Negro is a diluter of pigment. It was a forlorn hope.

Gartler: I thought we might spend a few minutes on the work that has been carried out attempting to detect the ABO antigens in human cell culture. I don't know if anybody here has worked with these markers at the cell culture level and if not I will briefly review this area. Has anybody here worked with the ABO markers in cell culture?

There are three interesting papers on this subject (43, 51, 56). Högman (43) reported that he could detect the ABO antigens in the first cultures that grew out of fetal kidney and lung tissue explants. In the primary culture, roughly 50 percent of the cells exhibited a mixed cell agglutination reaction for the appropriate antigen. However, after a short period of time, the cells lost their reactivity. Apparently, only the epithelial cells in the culture exhibited any reaction, and as fibroblast-like cells overgrew the culture, all reactivity was lost. In this regard, it is of interest to note that Dr. Herzenberg mentioned that while his fibroblast cultures maintained antigenic specificity, they were not lysed in the presence of antiserum and complement as were the nonfibroblast cultures.

Herzenberg: I believe that is irrelevant because different cell types in the mouse are known to have different sensitivities to the cytotoxic action of sera, whether or not it is culture.

Gartler: Kodani (56) has just published a report essentially confirming Högman's work. That is, that the ABO antigens are detectable early in the culture history and that they disappear after a short time in culture. He has made one additional observation of interest. Cells may pick up an antigenic specificity from the serum in which they are cultured: for example, O cells may exhibit a weak A reaction when cultured in A serum.

Renwick: The work which George Le Bouvier (63) did very much confirms this, along the same lines. He found, using mixed agglutination techniques, that there was a decline in the proportion of cells which showed the antigen among those that were sticking to the glass.*

As far as I know, he believes that most of the cells that showed the antigen were epithelial in type. These tests were all done on cultures derived from foreskin, and it is clear from some other work he did that the cultures can contain cells of different types, all looking similar, but having, for instance, different viral sensitivities. He has no evidence that a given cell or its clone loses its antigen, whereas he has evidence for artefactual selection against antigen-carrying cells during subculture, the selection arising when the medium, with its suspended cells, is discarded prior to trypsinization.

Gartler: The only other work I know of along this line is that of Kelus, Gurner, and Coombs (51) who, several years ago, typed the HeLa culture. The blood types of the individual from whom the HeLa cells were obtained are known. She was MN-positive, and they were able to show MN reactions, using rabbit anti-MN.

Renwick: I think it is important to point out here that he could not safely distinguish whether it was M or MN. It was an "MN-type antigen" (51).

Gartler: And I think her blood type was MN, and this was still present on the HeLa cell culture.

Renwick: I believe that isn't so. The MN group of the donor of the HeLa line is not known. Coombs has been misquoted, I am sure, many times. I don't think there are any of these blood groups which he did which were really specific in the sense of distinguishing between two different antigens of the same system. Coombs and his collaborators were able to show an MN type antigen; they were able to show H antigen which belongs to the ABO system, and they were able to show the Tj^a which is present in practically everybody and is

---

* Afterthought: He found that among the cells which did not stick, after trypsinization, or which came off the glass, the proportion of antigen-carrying cells was much larger. These were maintained in roller-tube cultures for up to three weeks, but did not establish themselves on the glass and eventually degenerated.

nonspecific. As far as I know, there is really no definite evidence that two antigens of a single system could be distinguished at that age of a tissue culture.

Herzenberg: Actually, I think that Dr. Gartler is correct here, that the patient was MN, and they did detect, with rabbit serum, M and N specificity. If there is any antigen which I bet would be more likely to be maintained for a long period, of the commonly known blood group antigens in man, it would be the MN.

Renwick: The MN grouping in red cells is pretty reliable, but MN grouping in tissues by mixed agglutination is not so specific (83).

Neel: Why would you bet that one would persist?

Herzenberg: Because I think that it is found on cell membranes of a variety of tissues. It is a messy one, in that M goes to N. But I think, and Coombs would agree with this, that although it is messy to work with, he has the strong impression, as the cytologists continue to insist, that the M and N are found in a variety of cell membranes throughout the organism.

My bet for kinds of antigens that you would want to find persisting in cultures would be those that fit the following requirements: one, that they be on white cells, generally speaking, and, two, that in species where you can work with the situation (and, perhaps, in man, you can do this as well), it be clearly histocompatibility antigens. In other words, you could induce isoantibodies against them.

Renwick: I think that the easiest antigens to work with would be those that you know are still present; in other words, use the long-term cultured cells as your antigen stimulus, and see what antiserum you can produce from those, instead of doing what has been previously done—looking in culture cells for antigens which you knew beforehand did exist in the individual.

Atwood: The genetic basis for this is known, whereas any antigens that you revealed newly on old lines are not known.

Renwick: But you can then go to the original family again and use the antiserum produced from your culture.

Herzenberg: What are the essential prerequisites? If you want to work with human antigens, you have to be willing to utilize human beings, with tissue cells. If you work with rabbits, I think, you're going to run into all sorts of difficulties.

Bayreuther: One system that has not been mentioned here is the polyoma virus induced cell antigen, discovered by Sjögren and Habel (92, 33). This new antigen is present in tumors induced by polyoma in mouse and hamster cells *in vivo* and *in vitro*. The genetic basis for this new antigen is unknown. The antigen is exhibited in cells that do not produce any virus or any constituents of the virus. After longer periods of *in vitro* cultivation the antigen can be lost. These cells maintain, however, their neoplastic properties. This is a new field, just opening up. R. Bases has done some *in vitro* work in Dr. Dulbecco's laboratory. Applying techniques similar to those used by Herzenberg, Bases prepared antisera against cell membranes or whole tumor cells induced by polyoma. The presence of the new antigen— presumably surface—is revealed by the fact that the transformed cells are specifically sensitized to the killing action of complement by the antiserum. This killing is measured quantitatively by the loss of the colony-forming ability of single cell suspensions.

Ephrussi: Did you say that the polyoma antigen can get lost, without loss of neoplastic character?

Bayreuther: Yes.

Ephrussi: Is that loss of the antigen detected at the culture level or at the cell level?

Bayreuther: On the cell level. These cells can be cloned with high efficiency. Exposure to antiserum does not sensitize them to the action of complement.

Herzenberg: That doesn't mean necessarily they have lost the antigen, as we have found. They still have the antigen. They just have a little less of it.

Bayreuther: That is quite possible. Bases has different lines showing different degrees of loss. Some of them seem to have lost the antigen completely.

Eagle: As shown by what? By killing or fluorescent antibodies?

Bayreuther: By killing and fluorescence.

Eagle: Because Herzenberg's data show the fluorescent antibodies do it.

Ephrussi: Do you think the karyotypes correlate with these gradual losses, or what? Has this been looked for?

Bayreuther: That has not been looked for.

Eagle: If you put this antigen-free transformed cell into the animal and it forms a tumor, has the tumor regained the antigen?

Bayreuther: No, it does not. It seems not to induce immunity either.

Ephrussi: You mean, using it for rejection and then challenging the animal?

Bayreuther: It does not induce immunity. Tumors with the antigen are not rejected, when the animal had been previously challenged with a high number of killed cells free of the antigen.

Koprowski: Perhaps one should immunize against polyoma and then compare the results of challenging the animals with each of the two kinds of cells: cells with the antigen and cells without it.

Herzenberg: Isn't it true that the only evidence that the antigen is truly lost and not just inactivated biologically, in terms of the cell being allowed to be killed or rejected, is the fluorescent antibody? Is that conclusive?

Bayreuther: Yes, it is conclusive.

Herzenberg: I might just mention that, technically, we find that the fluorescent staining is certainly not an all-or-none process. About 5 percent of the cells from populations that are positive do not stain, but we cannot pick out these cells. They are not antigenically stainable. Their mixed progeny is stainable, again, which, I assume, is just some sort of a technical reason why these cells are not staining, an inability to demonstrate the phenotype.

Gartler: But, in this case [Bayreuther's], I assume, it is a population difference which fails to show the reaction, not just a small percentage of the cells; so this is quite different.

Ephrussi: Is there any correlation between strength of antigen-antibody reaction, in this case, or by tests, say, of your antiserum plus complement? In other words, is there a correlation between that and the growth phase of the culture, or the growth rate?

Herzenberg: No. We have looked for this, and we have not found any. I won't say there isn't any, but we have not been able to find it. We have not been able to find a particularly sensitive period or a particularly resistant period.

Eagle: Boris, why do you ask the question?

Ephrussi: Well, I am asking the question because I think there is very little systematic study of the different growth phases when, for example, claims are made that cells derived from a well-known organ necessarily lose their specific differentiation and enzymatic activity. Very little account is taken of the fact (or of the possibility, at least), well known in microorganism, that a number of enzymes really build up only during the stationary phase. For many reasons people work chiefly with the exponential phase, during which many enzyme systems are at the minimum.

I personally would expect that, during the exponential phase, you would find the cells to contain all the enzyme systems required for the process of cell duplication. However, when it comes to specific activities connected with differentiation, you would look into the nonubiquitous enzyme systems, and these may very well be elaborated just in the stationary phase. In so far as the antigens are concerned, I don't know whether there is a cycle in the culture, too.

Renwick: An illustration of what you indicate is known in human cells. The quantity of cell-bound acid mucopolysaccaride is greatest in slowly growing cells, I believe (74).*

Ephrussi: This could be expected as well on the basis of altogether vague indications in the old tissue culture literature, but much better, say, on the basis of Gale's work on bacteria, which showed that there is a cycle of elaboration of a number of enzyme systems, which come up, really, at the end of a long growth cycle. I myself published a study about ten years ago on the synthesis of cytochromes in yeast, showing that the whole growth cycle, except the last two generations, goes on at the expense of glycolysis, and that cytochrome oxidase is elaborated only at the very end of the growth cycle, when growth slows down and switches from the exponential to the stationary phase.

Billingham: Do you get that sort of effect with your retinal pigmentation?

Ephrussi: Yes, very definitely, I think, because pigment formation is very clearly inversely proportional to the growth rate.

Eagle: Yet, this is not true for at least two of the lines which continue to function well in culture, those studied by Sato and Buonassisi (8). The reason I asked Klaus [Bayreuther] the question about what happens when you put it [polyoma-altered cells that have lost polyoma antigen] back in the animal is that their adrenal culture loses its capacity to respond to pituitary hormones after x months of culture. If these cultured cells are then reimplanted into the animal and produce a tumor, and that tumor is recultured, the capacity to respond to pituitary hormone is restored, as if the cell had somehow been recharged.

Herzenberg: Or, perhaps, the culture had been recharged.

Ephrussi: Exactly. In this case, you really don't know whether there is not some interaction with something coming from the organism into which we implant.

Herzenberg: Or selection. He had not ruled out selection.

Eagle: No, he has not ruled out selection. I asked him that specifically.

DeMars: It might be worth while, since we are immediately going to talk about biochemical defects of the cultured cells, to give some

---

* Afterthought: The *total* production of acid mucopolysaccharide, however, shows the opposite effect—it is maximal in rapidly growing cells (Morris, 74).

examples of what Dr. Ephrussi means, and I think that I can show two slides that will make the point.

We have been studying a number of enzymes in cultured cells, and we have been very prissy about it, in the sense of asking ourselves what an enzyme determination means with these cells. I will be very brief about this.

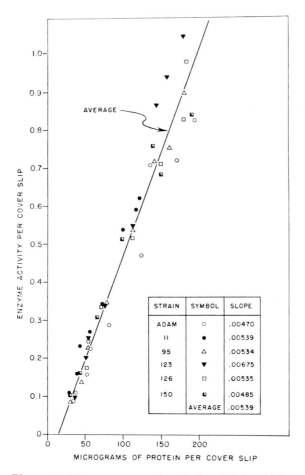

STRAIN	SYMBOL	SLOPE
ADAM	○	.00470
II	●	.00539
95	△	.00534
123	▼	.00675
126	□	.00535
150	◘	.00485
	AVERAGE	.00539

Figure 28. The appearance of acid phosphatase activity during the growth of six strains of diploid human cells. The graph relates total enzyme activity per culture to total cell protein per culture at different points during growth and shows that acid phosphatase is formed at constant specific activity throughout growth.

We took into account variations in enzyme activity during the culture cycle, and we have found so far two different patterns relating enzyme activity to growth during the propagation of the cultures. The first case involves acid phosphatase, which is almost always considered to be an ill-defined collection of enzymes. I think this may be unjustified in the case of the cultured human cells. In any case, it exemplifies an important rule.

These experiments are done by making a series of replicate cultures on coverslips and then assaying the enzyme activity directly on the dry monolayers. Samples of coverslips are taken daily for making determinations of enzyme activity and total cell protein.

Figure 28 shows one experiment with six different strains of cells: two normal male, two chromosome 18 trisomy, and two normal female. Each point represents duplicate determinations of enzyme activity and of total cell protein at a given stage of the culture cycle. The samples were taken daily.

You can see that for acid phosphatase, these points form a beautiful straight line, and the six strains represented here form a remarkably homogeneous group. We can make a ratio of total activity to total protein and define the enzyme specific activity.

In determining enzyme activity in this case, if you do the whole experiment and then derive the slope of the curve, you get one estimate of specific activity. If you do what people often do, which is to take the culture at some single, poorly defined stage, usually when it is pretty heavily grown, you can get pretty much the same estimate of specific activity.

Things are not as simple for beta-glucuronidase, which is shown in Figure 29. This is exactly the same kind of experiment. Mrs. Gorman in my laboratory has been studying this enzyme. Again, we have a variety of euploid and aneuploid strains. The same experiment is performed, with daily determinations of total enzyme activity and total protein. You can't make straight lines with these curves, and, in particular, in some experiments, when the cultures have gotten near the maximum density, you can get steep rises in total enzyme activity without a commensurate rise or, indeed, any net change in protein content of the culture.

In another experiment, many replicate cultures were made, and one set of them was handled in the usual way, which is having the medium replaced daily to provide the maximum growth rate. The other sets of replicate cultures were fed in, in this way, for zero days, for two days, four days, and then transferred to a medium that had been taken

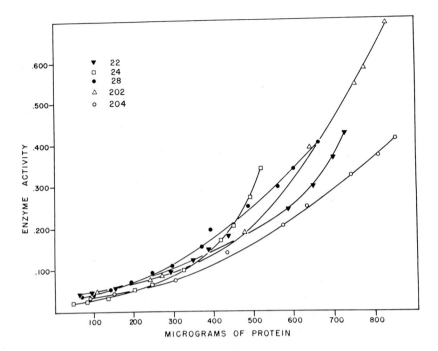

Figure 29. The appearance of beta-glucuronidase activity during the growth of five strains of diploid human cells. The experimental technique and manner of graphical presentation are as for the determinations of acid phosphatase described in Figure 28. These curves show that the specific activity of beta-glucuronidase increases significantly during growth of the cultures.

From Jean M. Marsh, and Robert DeMars, "Acid Phosphatase Activity in Cultivated Human Cells," *Experimental Cell Research* (1963).

from cultures of maximum population density, so-called used or conditioned medium. In such a medium the cells do not grow very well.

The cell protein showed almost no change in the used medium, but there was a steep rise in beta glucuronidase activity.

This is very different from acid phosphatase. With acid phosphatase, if you don't get a change in protein content, either a lowering or an increment, you do not get any change in acid phosphatase. Here, [in the case of beta glucuronidase] big changes in enzyme activity can accompany little or no change in total protein.

The other thing is that this will, of course, remind people of the work reported by Cox and Pontecorvo (14), working with cultures derived mainly from foreskins. Alkaline phosphatase behaves very much in the same way in response to used medium, although I don't think they have published experiments of exactly this sort. But the formal aspects of the problem are the same, I think.

Mrs. Gorman has gone one step further. She has asked herself: "Does this represent the unmasking of protein that is already there but enzymatically inactive, or does this represent or depend on the synthesis of new protein?" She has used puromycin, which is a specific inhibitor of protein synthesis, and, under conditions where protein increase is blocked by puromycin, you cannot elicit these steep rises. You freeze the protein content and you freeze enzyme activity.

I think, therefore, in a general way, these are related to the remarks of Dr. Ephrussi, because, under the ordinary conditions of cultivation, beta-glucuronidase is found in substantial amounts only when the population has almost or actually stopped increasing. We have no idea of what beta glucuronidase is used for by the cells, nor do we have any idea what alkaline phosphatase is used for by the cells, but, in both cases, these enzymes are characteristic of the maximum stationary phase of the culture.

If you take a population like this, that has built itself up, and then subculture it, it does not maintain, or it does not start out with a high level. It is back where it started, and it goes through the whole process again. It is not a question of selection for high enzyme cells. It is a recurring cycle of low relative rate of enzyme formation and then higher relative rate of enzyme formation, conditioned in some way by what the cells do to the medium, apparently, or, maybe, what the medium does to the cells. We don't know.

Ephrussi: However, in the case of the cytochromes, we have shown rather clearly in our paper, I believe, that the cycle is an effect of glucose, and that, by decreasing the glucose, one can prevent the cycles from occurring.

DeMars: In this case, we are not having glucose repression; that is, if we lower the glucose content of the medium down as low as we can, beta glucuronidase still goes—

Ephrussi: I was not trying to suggest that it necessarily is glucose, but I mean it may be as simple as that with respect to some other constituent.

DeMars: Well, we always invoke glucose. If you have had experience with microbes, you always worry about glucose.

Ephrussi: Oh, sure.

DeMars: So we worry about it, too, and it isn't important here.

What seems to be important is that a variety of treatments that slow the growth of the cells boosts the relative rate of glucuronidase formation. For instance, lowering the concentration of serum in the culture medium slows the growth of the cells and accelerates the rate of glucuronidase formation. Lowering the glucose content slows the growth rate of the cells, but does not boost the glucuronidase formation.

Eagle: How about the omission of amino acid?

DeMars: We have not done this as yet.

Renwick: One question arises from Dr. DeMars' comments, which I know he has thought about. Is this effect of used medium a nonspecific increase of a large number of enzymes, due to some nonspecific effect on a certain batch of metabolic processes or is it due to the accumulation in the medium of, let's say, some substrate which induces these enzymes fairly specifically?

I want to make only one comment on the work of Cox and Pontecorvo (14). I looked at the electrophoretic mobility of the alkaline phosphatase in the induced cells, and all the bands were increased, roughly, tenfold in the same proportion, so, in the case of alkaline phosphatase, we can add a little bit more than just one enzyme to the total number of inducible enzymes.

DeMars: I think I might add some general comments. The different shapes of the curves that relate enzyme activity to growth in the cases of acid phosphatase and beta glucuronidase indicate that the definition of rather small differences in specific activity, differences as small as twofold, may require more than precise determinations at some arbitarily chosen, single point of the culture cycle. In addition, repeated determinations throughout the culture cycle may be necessary.

Now, Dr. Herzenberg asked me one question, which I did not take up at the time; that is, in the straight-line curves for acid phosphatase activity as a function of growth, the best straight lines fitted statistically almost never passed through the origin, that is, zero enzyme, zero protein. They always passed through the protein axis, in a way which can be interpreted in the following manner:

At the beginning of the growth of these cultures, that is, immediately after subculture, the cells act as if they had lost enzyme activity that was present just before subculture, without a commensurate loss of total cell protein.

Now, he is very familiar with this phenomenon, and I think that many people are now; that is, that the procedures we use in subculturing these cells often lead to losses of not only amino acids or other metabolites of low molecular weight, but as well to losses at least of activity and probably of substance, of high-molecular substances, such as enzymes. In the case of acid phosphatase, these cells act as if half of the acid phosphatase activity were lost relative to the total protein content upon subculture. This happens with beta-glucuronidase, also. It is even more striking when one looks at the gamma glutamyl transferase of HeLa cells, for there, we can boost the activity to a maximum by growing them in the absence of glutamine. If we subculture cells with the maximum level of this glutamyl transferase enzyme, and then examine the enzyme activity relative to the total protein content of the inocula, as soon as possible after the cells have attached, which means within several hours, one finds that if one uses small inocula, one has lost as much as 90 to 95 percent of all of the enzyme activity that was present initially. Nevertheless, these small inocula grow very well and quickly recover their enzyme levels.

In the case of the enzyme in the HeLa cells, the loss of activity, or the apparent loss of activity, is a function of the size of the inoculum. The relative loss, therefore, is smaller, if you increase the size of the inoculum. But when one uses inocula so great that many of the cells fail to attach, one never recovers more than half of the activity that one puts in the bottle to begin with.

There is, then, another lesson here, I think; that is, in making enzyme determinations with these cells, there is a real premium on either avoiding the physical manipulation of the cells, either with scraping, centrifuging, or suspending them, trypsinizing them, and so on, or, if this cannot be avoided, then, one must have very reproducible procedures for manipulating the cells.

Chu: May I just ask a technical point? What kind of method do you use for subcultures—scraping or trypsinization?

DeMars: We use trypsin regularly.

Chu: Do you know about the effect of trypsin on cells?

DeMars: On enzymes, also. That is not a problem here. We can rule that out, that trypsin has inactivated the enzyme in the cells.

Gartler: I think we ought to go on to the next topic. Dr. Krooth will take over now.

Study of Galactosemia, Acatalasemia, and Other Human Metabolic Mutants in Cell Culture

by Dr. Robert S. Krooth

Krooth: I find, to my great relief, that about 50 percent of my comments have already been made. I shall therefore give a more extemporaneous discussion than I had anticipated. I don't mean, incidentally, to suggest that I had already thought of everything that was said. That is far from true. [Laughter]

The principal points that were made earlier were that most cell lines or strains fall into one of two groups: the "propagated lines," and the "euploid lines." We have already discussed Hayflick's terminology for this. My own terms are just an arbitrary way of putting it. We also have discussed briefly the fact that there is some evidence to suggest that cultures move from one category into another.

Herzenberg: In both directions?

Krooth: At least from euploidy to aneuploidy. It has been the experience of our laboratory, and a number of others, that at least among human fibroblasts of benign origin, the spontaneous change from euploidy to aneuploidy, if it occurs at all, is a rare event.

The other general comment, that I should like to enlarge on for just a moment, is one that was mentioned by Dr. Eagle and others; namely, that cell lines in culture, whatever their category, as a rule, cannot be shown to resemble their presumed tissue of origin. Therefore, when one attempts to pick diseases which will persist in cultures of these euploid fibroblasts, one soon discovers a limitation: There are many interesting human enzymes which are known to be affected by genes but which apparently do not occur in the cultured cells.

The question arises, which genetic diseases of man can one follow in cultures of euploid fibroblasts? I think there are several criteria for selecting appropriate diseases.

If one knows that the enzyme is one which does occur in cultures of normal euploid fibroblasts, then, one is in a strong position, assuming that the enzyme which occurs in the fibroblasts is structurally identical with the one that is disturbed *in vivo* by the action of an abnormal gene.

Another criterion is, since only a limited number of enzymes have thus far been studied in these euploid fibroblasts, that the enzyme which is disturbed by the gene should be an enzyme which in the normal person is ubiquitous. In other words, the enzyme which the gene deprives of its activity should be an enzyme that occurs in virtually all the tissues of the body, so that it does not appear to depend upon which way the cell is differentiated; the enzyme is present, regardless.

A third criterion that seems useful is this: The genetic disease should remove enzyme activity from all, or almost all, of the cells of the body, for there are several human enzymes which have the property that, although they can be shown to catalyze the same reaction, they are structurally and even immunologically different in different tissues; so it is particularly important that the abnormal gene remove the activity of the enzyme from virtually all the tissues of the body. If this condition is met, it suggests that the enzyme disturbed by the gene is one that is indeed ubiquitous; the same protein everywhere.

In practice, one difficulty arises: No enzymes have been examined in literally all the tissues of the human body, and it is even hard to find enzymes that have been examined in a great many. What I use is a rule of thumb, and I would not care to have to defend this rule, that if an enzyme is present in a white blood cell or, for that matter, any peripheral blood cell, and is also present in some parenchymatous organ other than spleen, the enzyme is ubiquitous. I have not done a large survey of the literature to show that this is truly a universal rule, but it seems to work. Perhaps, by the end of this conference, I shall be the proud owner of the world's largest collection of exceptions to this rule. [Laughter]

In Figure 30, I should like to show some examples of diseases which appear to involve ubiquitous enzymes. The quality of evidence in each case that the enzyme or protein involved in the disease is ubiquitous varies from item to item. For example, the inclusion of Wilson's disease is based on the hypothesis put forward by Uzman, which may not be correct, as indicated by the question mark.

Bearn: At least put two questions marks.

Gartler: Three.

Krooth: Yes. We have attempted to test Uzman's (110, 111) hypothesis in cultured cells. Dr. Paul Altrocci and I were not able in preliminary experiments to find consistent differences in the cell protein between patients with Wilson's disease and patients with an unrelated group of diseases. This list is far from exhaustive, and I shall come back to it later on.

We have been particularly interested in galactosemia and acatalasemia, whereas Dr. Gartler has worked on the glucose-6-phosphate dehydrogenase system. I hope he will review his work for us later on today.

I think, of all the diseases on this list, by far the most interesting is orotic aciduria (45). Rodney Howell, Jarvis Seegmiller, and I have done a little bit of work on the heterozygote, although not with very conclusive results. The disease appears, on the basis of clinical evi-

```
"UBIQUITOUS" GENETIC DISEASES

1. CYSTATHIONINURIA

2. OROTIC ACID URIA

3. WILSON'S DISEASE (?)

4. ESSENTIAL FRUCTOSURIA
   WITH HYPOGLYCEMIA

5. GALACTOSEMIA

6. ACATALASEMIA

7. ZWISCHENFERMENT GENES

8. CERTAIN OTHER SACCHARIDURIAS(?)
```

Figure 30.

dence and on the basis of enzymatic studies (93) on the father of the one patient who was studied, to be a defect in either orotodine-5'-monophosphate pyrophosphorylase or orotidine-5'-monophosphate decarboxylase. Only about 25 percent of the normal activity with respect to these enzymes was found in the erythrocytes of the parents of the patient. On the basis of clinical studies on the patient himself, which are unique in many respects, it seems quite probable that the patient was unable to biosynthesize uridine. This was determined not by direct enzymatic assays or clinical studies using isotope recovery but, rather, by inductive reasoning. I won't take the time to recount the argument, but it is really quite convincing.

When this patient became ill for any reason—the patient died at age two-and-a-half—he would lose his appetite, much as any other child; he would then, one thinks, diminish his dietary supply of uridine, cytidine, deoxycytidine and thymidine. Since he could not biosynthesize these compounds, he presumably depleted his body stores.

Clinically, one observed that when the child got sick, his white count and red count would fall to very low values. This could be reversed most strikingly by feeding, or otherwise administering, the patient mixtures of uridylic and cytidylic acid. Under such therapy, the white and red blood cell count would go up.

Well, I have devoted some time to this because it does seem to me at present to be the most interesting of all these metabolic errors for genetic studies using cell culture.

McKusick: Why did the patient die, if this was such a treatable condition?

Krooth: Shortly after discharge from the hospital, the patient was obliged for a time to discontinue his dietary nucleotides, for these produced severe diarrhea. He contracted chicken pox and, in the course of this illness, developed some of the more bizarre complications, including varicella pneumonia.

Gartler: Bob, how many families with orotic aciduria have been reported?

Krooth: One.

DeMars: Wasn't there one reported in England, also?

Krooth: As far as I know, no. But it is conceivable that a patient could have been reported without my noticing it. Smith, Sullivan and Huguley (93) assayed the erythrocytes of fifty consecutive patients (with unrelated diseases) for these two enzymes, and they report that they found one patient whose red cells had heterozygous levels. It is therefore possible that this disease is much more common than is generally realized. Many relatively rare diseases, once clearly described, emerge as being more common than was previously thought.

Herzenberg: What enzyme did they assay and where?

Krooth: They assayed both the pyrophosphorylase and the decarboxylase, and the assay was done on hemolysates.*

Herzenberg: And they were both low?

Krooth: Yes. The reason they are both low is unknown. As I pointed out earlier, the exact site of the enzymatic block is not known.

Stern: How about the mother?

Krooth: The activities of the two enzymes were reduced in her hemolysates also (93). The assumption that this disease is due to homozygosity for a recessive gene is based on two lines of evidence: First, enzyme activities were reduced (compared to normal) in hemolysates

---

* Added: Fallon, Lotz, and Smith (28) have now shown that orotidine=5′= monophosphate decarboxylase is diminished in the leukocytes of heterozygotes.

from the parents and two out of three sibs of the patient (93). Second, the parents were blood relatives (45).

I really did not intend to take so much time on this, which is already in the literature. Howell, Seegmiller, and I found that cultured fibroblasts from the patient's father put C^{14} from orotic acid into $C^{14}O_2$, with specific activities that averaged about one-fourth normal, but we had a great deal of day-to-day variation in our results that we could neither explain nor control. We, therefore, think that our data are not too helpful, although they are suggestive. I do think, on a priori grounds, one might expect to see this disease persist in culture and to be a most useful genetic tool.

Szybalski: Do the cells require uridine to grow?

Krooth: The father's cells did not. Presumably, the patient's would.

Szybalski: You did not test the patient?

Krooth: No. Unfortunately, the patient died before the disease was published. It would be most exciting if anybody could get cells from one of these patients into culture.

This list is probably incomplete, because Williams *et al.* (120) reported that the glucose-6-phosphatase activity in intestinal cells is reduced in relatives of patients with the glucose-6-phosphatase form of glycogen storage disease, that is, Cori's Type I. Similarly, Hülsman *et al.* (46) and Williams and Field (119) have reported that, in patients with the phosphorylase-deficient form of glycogen storage (liver) disease (Cori's Type VI), they find reduced phosphorylase activity in the leukocytes of affected patients; so this disease also might be susceptible of study, using cell cultures.

Gartler: Wasn't there a report some time last year that the lesions in Hartnup disease also showed up in intestinal mucosa?

Krooth: I was not aware of that. That is interesting and encouraging. As I say, this list is still quite limited, and all of these diseases, or at least most of them, have the property of being extremely rare.

Renwick: Maple syrup urine disease is another one, isn't it?

Krooth: Perhaps.

Neel: Some people are mystified by your reference to "maple syrup" urine disease. Would you care to elaborate?

Renwick: It is just that the urine smells of maple syrup. That is why it is called maple syrup urine disease.

Krooth: I do not want to say that almost any disease is a bad candidate. I have simply put down the ones that seemed to me at the moment to be most promising.

I thought, now, I would briefly review some of our own work on galactosemia and acatalasemia. The investigations on galactosemic cells in culture were performed in collaboration with Dr. Arnold N. Weinberg, now of the Massachusetts General Hospital. A more detailed account of these studies is given elsewhere (58,59). Galactose is acted on by a specific kinase, galactokinase, and also, to some extent, by hexokinase, and is converted to galactose-1-phosphase. Then, galactose-1-phosphase reacts with UDP glucose in the presence of a specific transferase and the galactose is substituted for glucose on the nucleotide. Then, UDP galactose is acted on by a specific epimerase, which converts UDP galactose to UDP glucose.

In forty patients whom Kalckar (49) has studied, the block in every case described was at the transferase.

Szybalski: Are there any clinical cases of galactokinase or epimerase blocks?

Krooth: I don't think any clinical cases of blocks involving the other two enzymes have been described. There are mutants of them, of course, in *E. coli.* Dr. DeMars, if I may quote him, has put forward the intriguing suggestion that there might be blocks involving the kinase which would not be clinically apparent. This is something that, so far as I know, nobody has looked into.

I might just also point out that patients with galactosemia are able, after about the age of two-and-a-half, to utilize galactose to a quite significant extent, and this utilization can be augmented by the administration of progesterone (80) and menthol (25).

The mechanism for this appears to be another enzyme, thought to be confined to liver, and first described in mammals by Isselbacher (47). It has been shown to appear in rat liver as the rat matures. The reaction catalyzed is between galactose-1-phosphate and UTP to yield UDP galactose, and pyrophosphate. Hence, the enzyme is a pyrophosphorylase. The reaction exemplifies one of the differences between the biochemistry of man and unicellular forms, such as *E. coli.* By this alternative pathway, the mature liver seems to be able partly to obscure the cellular phenotype of the rest of the organism.

McKusick: Are the pathological effects in galactosemia due to the galactose-1-phosphate? Then, is this the reason one would not expect phenotypic effects from a kinase mutation?

Krooth: Not all the steps in the pathogenesis of this disease are perfectly clear. It has been suggested that accumulations of galactose-1-phosphate in the lens, the gut, and elsewhere render this compound particularly likely to be troublesome. It has been recovered from the cataracts of animals fed high doses of galactose and, also, I think, it is supposed to exhibit an inhibitory effect on phosphoglucomutase. In

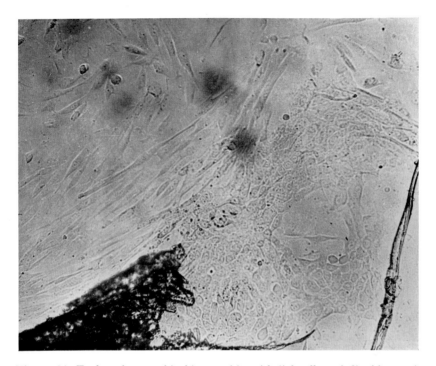

Figure 31. Explant from a skin biopsy with epithelial cells and fibroblasts migrating from it. Original magnification 75x
Reprinted from (59) by permission of the *Journal of Experimental Medicine*.

addition, it has been suggested that the hypoglycemia produced, presumably through insulin, by the hypergalactosemia may be responsible for some of the damage to the central nervous system.*

In answer to your second question, I think, possibly, Bob DeMars could answer this better, but I believe that one of the reasons kinaseless mutants might be spared symptoms is that there may be two enzymes which will do this reaction: hexokinase and galactokinase. It is conceivable that a person could miss galactokinase and not get ill, as was pointed out to me by Dr. DeMars.

Returning now to our own work, cell lines were developed from skin biopsies on two patients with galactosemia, the heterozygous mother of one of these patients, and five controls.

Figure 31 shows an explant with fibroblasts which have come out of it. In addition, you can see epithelial cells which have been ex-

* A review of theories concerning the pathogenesis of galactosemia is given by Isselbacher (48).

foliated by the explant. In practice we were not able to recover the epithelial cells on subculture, and all our experiments were done with the fibroblasts. Chromosome studies were performed in collaboration with Dr. J. H. Tjio on all but one of these lines, and the cells were consistently euploid, in the sense that approimately 95 to 98 percent of them were diploid and most of the remainder were tetraploid.

The cell lines were developed in Eagle's (22) minimium essential medium, supplemented with sodium pyruvate, the nonessential amino acids, and NCTC 109, and 12 percent pooled human serum. In our growth experiments, we omit the NCTC 109 and we use dialyzed rather than whole serum. I might just make a comment about the pyruvate which we added to the serum. This compound was prepared by Dr. Leon Levintow, by the method of Price and Levintow (82). We have found that the purity of the pyruvate is surprisingly critical. It must be prepared from triply distilled pyruvic acid, neutralized in the cold, and so on. Without such pyruvate, it is not always possible to get the normal cells to grow in galactose—we now think that we know the reason for this—as well as they do in glucose.

Figure 32 shows one growth experiment. JDU is a galactosemic line

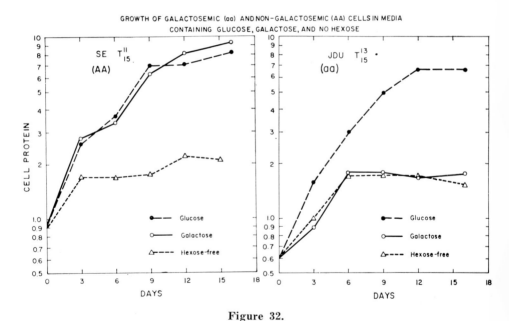

Figure 32.
Reprinted from (59) by permission of the *Journal of Experimental Medicine.*

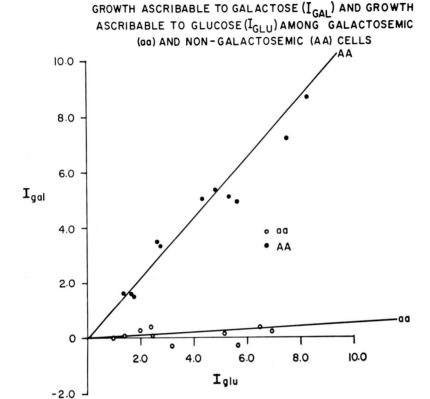

Figure 33.

Reprinted from (59) by permission of the *Journal of Experimental Medicine*.

and SE is a control line. The dark line connecting the open circles shows the growth of the cells in medium which contained 100 mgms percent galactose. The dotted line, with the closed circles, shows growth in medium containing 100 mgms percent glucose, and the line connecting the triangles shows growth in medium which was hexose-free. One unit of protein is equivalent to about 0.1 mg of bovine serum albumen.

Under the conditions described, we found that there was an equal growth of all our control euploid lines in glucose and galactose. However, in the case of the galactosemic cell line, although we continued to get adequate growth in glucose, the effect of the two genes for galactosemia appears on these graphs to pull the galactose curve down from the glucose curve to the hexose-free curve.

Szybalski: Hexose-free or no hexose added?

Krooth: Both. The medium was glucose-free when tested with glucose oxidase. Dialysis of the serum appears to eliminate at least the measurable glucose.

In Figure 33, we have attempted to measure that part of the growth of these cells which could be said to be ascribable to either glucose or galactose. What we did was to take our final cell protein, in glucose, say, minus the final cell protein in medium that was hexose-free, and divided it by the initial cell protein. This gives us a quantity which we feel we can say is the growth *ascribable* to glucose. We call this quantity "I_{glu}." We then compute in an analogous way, the growth which is ascribable to galactose and called it "I_{gal}." Figure 33 shows I_{gal} plotted against I_{glu}; in other words, the growth ascribable to galactose against the growth ascribable to glucose. In this graph, each experiment is a single point. The nongalactosemic cells [AA] appear to fall on one line [indicating on board] and the galactose cells [aa] on another one.

We cannot be absolutely certain that the slope of the galactosemic line is exactly zero. Our galactose was prepared by double-crystallization in alcohol as described by Kalckar *et al.* (50), who has told us that a trace of residual glucose may still remain. In addition, we were not as vigorous as we are now in washing these cells. We were afraid to wash them too much in those days for fear that we would injure them.

ISOTOPE EXPERIMENTS

	LINE	"AGE" (DAYS)	M-NUMBER	TISSUE OF ORIGIN	R (1)/(2)
	(AA) MI[4]	27	16	MARROW	0.6
	(aa) JDU[4]	27	10	MARROW	0
	(AA) Be[7]	65	8x10[3]	SKIN	0.4
	(AA) RCU[4]	79	32	SKIN	0.3
AA	(AA) Be[11]	72	2x10[5]	SKIN	0.3
	(AA) Be[20]	160	3.8x10[12]	SKIN	0.3
	(AA) SE[8]	71	9.6x10[3]	SKIN	0.3
	(aa) BY[4]	56	10	SKIN	(0)
aa	(aa) JDU[6]	55	240	SKIN	0.01
	(aa) JDU[9]	119	9.6x10[4]	SKIN	0
	(aa) JDU[17]	192	2.3x10[10]	SKIN	0
Aa	(Aa) MAD[4]	68	40	SKIN	0.09
	(Aa) MAD[(5+6)]	76	128	SKIN	0.09

Figure 34.

Reprinted from (59) by permission of the *Journal of Experimental Medicine.*

Line	Age (Days)	Subculture Number	R
LBR	34	4	0
JDU	428	25	0
BE	441	35	0.2

Figure 35.

Szybalski: Does this slide show essentially the same as the previous one; are they inhibited by galactose?

Krooth: It suggests that they do not use galactose for growth.

I thought I would proceed with the summary of our work on galactosemia. Our other kind of data came from radioisotope studies on the cells. Whole cells were incubated with galactose-1-C^{14} and glucose-1-C^{14}. Equal aliquots of cells from the same flask were incubated simultaneously with each of these compounds, and the carbon dioxide was collected and counted for C^{14} activity. We then computed a ratio, which we called R, of counts in carbon dioxide collected when galactose-1-C^{14} was the substrate to counts in carbon dioxide collected when glucose-1-C^{14} was the substrate.

Figure 34 summarizes most of our data from the isotope experiments. The cell lines are designated by letters. The time interval between the date of the biopsy and the date of the experiment is the "age" of the line. The M number is a crude estimate of the minimum number of times that these cells had increased in culture up to the time of the experiment. The ratio, R, for the control cell lines, was about 0.3. The ratio for the galactosemic cell lines was about zero. One donor [MAD] was the mother of patient JDU, the galactosemic patient. The mother's ratio was about 0.09, which is intermediate between the abnormal homozygotes and the controls.

We also developed a cell line from a sternal marrow aspiration on both a control and a galactosemic patient, and the results are about the same, except that, for some reason, the control cells in the case of this line developed from marrow had an increased ratio of counts from galactose to counts from glucose compared with the lines developed from skin.

We kept two of our lines in continuous culture for about fourteen months. At the end of this period, the cells were pretty sorry looking, and their growth rate was barely measurable. As shown in Figure 35, we found that the R ratio for our control line was now 0.2, a value recovered in three separate determinations, so that there was a suggestion, the significance of which we cannot evaluate, that possibly the R ratio fell slightly as the line became very old. This slide also contains data of about a third galactosemic cell line (LBR) which we recently developed.

I might say that these values were, of course, rounded off. In point of fact, some of the galactosemic cells did put a significant number of counts from galactose into carbon dioxide as compared with background. The figure varied between about 1/100th to 1/5000th the value which was obtained in the normal cell lines. Actually, it was just one determination that was about 1/100th.

Renwick: How can you be sure that the galactose did not contain a very slight trace of glucose?

Krooth: I can't say categorically that it did not. The galactose-1-C^{14} we used was obtained by my coauthor in this work, Dr. Arnold N. Weinberg, from the National Bureau of Standards. He chromatographed it and found it pure. In any case, the possibility of it containing minute traces of glucose is one which we really cannot rule out.

Renwick: Was it chromatographed for the detection of C^{14}?

Krooth: That is, was it counted?

Renwick: Yes.

Krooth: It was counted after the addition of cold glucose; no radioactivity was detected over the glucose spot.

I thought that I would briefly summarize the work we have done on a second inborn metabolic error, acatalasia, which is a disease characterized by congenital absence of the enzyme, catalase. It is inherited like an autosomal recessive. The enzyme, catalase, catalyzes the decomposition of hydrogen peroxide into water and oxygen.

One should emphasize that this reaction is how one identifies the enzyme and measures its activity, but whether this is the *in vivo* reaction for which cells normally use the enzyme is at present unclear.

Our work was done in collaboration with Dr. Rodney R. Howell of the National Institute of Arthritis and Metabolic Diseases, and Dr.

Howard B. Hamilton of the U.S. Atomic Bomb Casualty Commission. Our findings are set out in greater detail elsewhere (Krooth, *et al.* 60). The disease (total absence of catalase) is one which, in the homozygous state, has thus far been described only in Japan. I think that Dr. Hamilton and his associates now have a Korean family in Japan in which the disease also occurs. Our specimens came from Japan, from biopsies which were performed at Hiroshima, and which were sent to us by air at the National Institutes of Health.

Before very briefly presenting our data, I might comment on the clinical manifestations of the disease.

Szybalski: One moment, please. Were the children born after or before the bomb?

Krooth: Our patients would both have been born before the detonation.

Neel: But the patients did not live in Hiroshima, in any event.

Szybalski: I am sorry; I thought that Bob referred to Hiroshima.

Krooth: Yes, I did. The biopsies were performed there. I don't know where the patients were when the bomb went off.

I feel rather inept in discussing the clinical manifestations of this disease, because I personally have never seen an affected patient. We just received these tiny particles of tissue and I base my comments on what I have read (103, 104, 75, 122, 105).

Apparently, however, about half the patients, who are homozygous, have severe recurrent gum infections that are rather indolent. These infections can be shown in most instances to be due to anaerobic organisms, such as the anaerobic streptococci and *Clostridium*. Several of the patients have actually developed gangrene of the gums. In most of the patients thus far described, removal of the teeth prevents these infections from recurring. Once these patients are edentulous, they seem to get on quite well.

The other half of the patients, who have been found to lack the enzyme, have no known clinical symptoms at all. They do not have a history of the gum infections and they do not have to have their teeth removed. They seem to enjoy good health.

Gartler: There is no difference in the level of catalase depression in that group?

Krooth: So far as I know, again, from reading the literature, there is no evidence that catalase activity is present in either group by enzyme assay. I believe that Dr. Takahara and his associates (106) have now attempted to detect the enzyme immunologically. The presence of a cross-reactive material is being investigated in their laboratory.

Stern: When you have somebody with acatalasemia who has no clinical symptoms and who has affected sibs, the acatalasemia-affected sibs also have no clinical troubles?

Krooth: I don't know.

Neel: This is the impression, but, you see, the first cases were picked up because they presented a clinical problem, and it is only now that it is being realized that a good many acatalasemics, maybe even greater than half, will not have any serious clinical problem. Some of the acatalasemics now being discovered by the systematic study of the families of affected persons have minimal or no symptoms.

Steinberg: The families that were picked up have heavily affected individuals, but no others were found who were mildly infected?

Neel: Sometimes.

Steinberg: May both types occur in the same family?

Neel: That's right.

Krooth: The heterozygotes, thus far, seem to be perfectly well clinically and to be free of symptoms.

The catalase activity of the red cells of a control population in Japan and of the red cells of heterozygous persons indicates that the heterozygotes possess enzyme activity that is about 44 or 45 percent normal (105). The assays which have been done on red cells are apparently extremely precise, with a very small coefficient of variation. The homozygotes, of course, have no detectable erythrocyte catalase.

In addition to erythrocytes, a number of other tissues have been examined in homozygotes, and the catalase activity in these tissues cannot be demonstrated, either.

We developed cell lines from one homozygous patient, one heterozygous patient, and eight control individuals. Euploid fibroblasts were again used, and catalase activities were determined spectrophotometrically, by the method of Beers and Sizer (2). The assay involves attempting to follow the decomposition of hydrogen peroxide over a period of one minute, by following the fall in optical density at 240 millimicra. Our data are summarized on the next slide.

Figure 36 shows the presumed genotypes with the number of lines of each genotype which was tested, and the total number of determinations performed. One can see that the means differ rather sharply from each other. The standard error of the mean is also given. The coefficient of variation for the nonacatalasics was about 20 percent. The differences between the means are highly significant.

TABLE IV

SUMMARY OF DATA ON CATALASE ACTIVITY

Presumed Genotype	No. of Lines	No. of Determinations	Mean Catalase Value	Standard Error of Mean
c^*c^*	1	7	0	All Values Zero
Cc^*	1	15	211.2	± 14.0
CC	8	38	762.0	± 21.0

$$\frac{Cc^*}{CC} = 0.28$$

Figure 36.

Reprinted from (60) by permission of the *Journal of Experimental Medicine.*

FREQUENCY WITH WHICH SPECIFIED VALUES OF CELL CATALASE ACTIVITY WERE OBSERVED
FREQUENCY
15
12
9
6
3
c*c*
Cc*
CC
0
100
200
300
400
500
600
700
800 and above
CELL CATALASE ACTIVITY

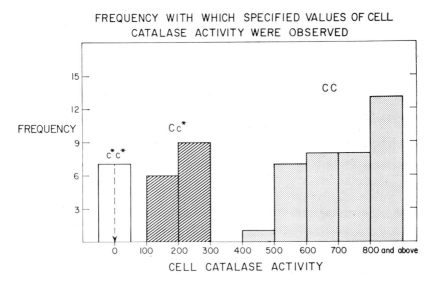

Figure 37.

Reprinted from (60) by permission of the *Journal of Experimental Medicine.*

We included in the control series one American donor of Japanese origin, since both the patients with the abnormal gene were Japanese, and he fell close to the center of the distribution for Europeans.

The ratio of the enzyme activities of our heterozygote to our normal homozygotes was 28 percent, as compared with a population mean of 44 percent when erythrocytes, rather than nucleated cells, were studied. However, we had to use an entirely different assay system to cope with the lower levels of catalase with which we were dealing. I doubt if much can be made of this difference.

Figure 37 gives the frequency distribution of catalase activities. The abscissa measures micromoles of hydrogen peroxide decomposed per hour per milligram of cell protein—a virtual quantity which we obtained by multiplying by 60, since we actually compute the fall in optical density only for the first minute. Catalase activity in the cells of our homozygote was undetectable by our assay. The variation in different determinations on the heterozygote is shown. There is no overlap between the three phenotypes.

Although we have a frequency distribution, it should be emphasized that for two of the phenotypes, the genetic sample was of size one— only one individual in each case. Determinations were then done on different bottles of cells from the donor, and it is the frequency of determinations falling within the specified ranges that is graphed. Population studies with fairly large samples on the erythrocytes of persons having each of the three genotypes indicate that there is no overlap, although I think that a second gene has recently been found where the heterozygote overlaps the normal homozygote, but I shall comment about that later.

DeMars: Do you disrupt the cells in any way for this assay?

Krooth: Yes.

DeMars: How, exactly, is it executed?

Krooth: The cells are washed three times in phosphate buffer and are then sonicated with a Millard probe sonicator. The vial containing the cell suspension is put in ice, and the sonic energy is delivered in four pulses of 30 seconds each. The probe is allowed to cool for 30 seconds after each pulse. The temperature under these conditions has not gone above 10°C in the vial containing the cell suspension.

We studied the effect of a number of variables on the cell catalase, such as subculture number, the age of the cell line as defined previously, and also the estimated number of times the cells had increased as of the moment of the experiment. We did not study the variable that Dr. DeMars discussed, namely, the effect of life cycle of the cell

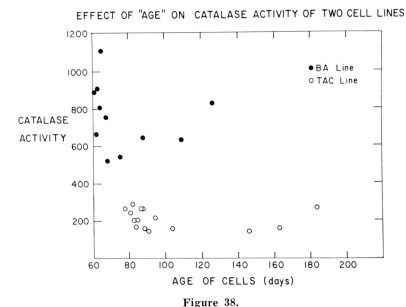

Figure 38.

Reprinted from (60) by permission of the *Journal of Experimental Medicine*.

on catalase activity. All of the bottles on which enzyme determinations were done were bottles which had generated a confluent monolayer and were fully grown. We did do experiments keeping the cells in such bottles alive with frequent feedings for up to five days after a confluent monolayer had formed, to see if the "aging" of the monolayer affected the catalase activity. Apparently, it did not.

Figure 38 summarizes our results on one parameter—age of the cell line itself.

Herzenberg: Is that total activity per bottle or per milligram or what?

Krooth: Activity is expressed as micromols of hydrogen peroxide decomposed per milligram of protein per hour, which is the ordinate in Figure 38, while the abscissa is time in days. A heterozygous line and a normal one are shown. There is a suggestion from this graph that, possibly, the catalase activity of the normal line and of the heterozygous line falls a bit with age, but the effect is not statistically significant, and it does not appear striking. At least over a time period of 180 days, the age of the line does not seem to obscure discrimination between the cellular phenotypes.

Gartler: How does the catalase activity in established cell lines compare with the activity here?

Krooth: Catalase activity in established cell lines has been studied by this same method by Lieberman and Ove (65); in fact, we finally picked this method because of their work. It was of the same order of magnitude. The LP-8 subline of HeLa cells ranged around 700 by their method in our laboratory.

Szybalski: Is it the hydrogen peroxide, the selective agent?

Krooth: We worked on this question for some time. In our experiments we overlayed the cells with varying concentrations of hydrogen peroxide (in buffered saline) for 15 minutes. We were not able to add hydrogen peroxide to the medium, because there was some evidence that in this mixture, it was reduced by certain of the nutrients, so we were obliged to add it to a solution of inorganic salts, and because of the protein and other requirements of the cells, we could do this for just a short time.

Over this 15-minute period, we were unable to find a concentration of hydrogen peroxide which would kill the acatalasic cells and not the normal cells. It was very easy to find a concentration that would kill them both. The problem here is that when you have an enzyme whose *in vivo* function is unknown, it can be difficult to challenge cells lacking the enzyme in an appropriate fashion.

Herzenberg: Heavy radiation sensitivity, in the presence of oxygen?

Krooth: This was something which we wondered about, since hydrogen peroxide has been implicated by some people in the biological action of ionizing radiation, but we have done no relevant experiments.

Szybalski: Anyway, to pick up differences in both cases, you would need a good quantitative system with high cloning efficiency, which would permit plotting nice survival curves. Is your system amenable to such a quantitative approach?

Krooth: Well, nice cloning is—

Herzenberg: Maybe, you could put the peroxide in some agar, so you didn't have so much mixing and sloshing around in the diffusion and so on, so the cells that got rid of it would survive and the others, in the other area, would not.

Krooth: What we tried to do, for precisely that reason, was to grow the cells under an agar overlay. However, our efforts were not very successful. It seemed a little harder for us to do this with the euploid fibroblasts than for our colleagues in the same laboratory, virologists who were using HeLa cells. Then, we took filter paper discs, impregnated them with various concentrations of hydrogen peroxide and put them on the agar. It didn't work. We did not get repeatable results, and even in experiments that looked fairly clean, we could not distinguish between the two cell lines.

Stern: I wonder why the heterozygote has so clearly less than 50 percent activity? I wonder whether the acatalasemic cells produce some protein which is not affected as catalase, but which competes in some fashion with the synthesis of catalase?

Krooth: That is an interesting thought. The people who did some of the original work on this disease in Japan—and I think Dr. Neel was an author of this particular paper—were interested in the possibility that the 44 percent mean they observed in erythrocytes differed from 50 percent. Dr. Takahara and his associates (106) have extracted catalase from human erythrocytes, made an antibody to it, and then reacted the antibody with material from acatalasic cells. They did not find any evidence of a cross-reacting material.

Neel: Dr. Stern, that 44 percent may not be a valid difference from 50 percent, because these are bloods that were collected in the field and had to be brought back to the laboratory for testing.

We think that this may be some loss of catalase activity in the 24 hours that it took to get them back to the laboratory.

Stern: But in Dr. Krooth's cell work, he gets only 28 percent.

Neel: Yes, but there is another point about that. That is based, of course, on one specimen. In the heterozygote, even though erythrocyte catalase values do not overlap with normal, there is a considerable range, and we don't know how much of this is technical and how much is biological. But he could, by chance, have picked up an extreme deviate in the case of his one specimen.

Krooth: The catalase activity of the hemolysate from our heterozygote was about 40 percent of the Japanese population mean reported by Takahara, *et al.* (105). I am not sure in this case that 28 percent differs significantly from 40 percent. For one thing the assays on the hemolysates were done titrimetrically, whereas the cell culture assays had to be done spectrophotometrically (because of the smaller quantities involved). In addition, as Dr. Neel points out, our assay was done on cells from only one heterozygote and eight control donors.

Stern: When considering cases in which a heterozygote produces less than half of the normal amount of the substance, I think of hemoglobins, where we had 60 to 40 percent, on the average; 60 percent normal hemoglobin and 40 percent sickle cell hemoglobin. This, as you may point out, may not be real, but at least it is inclined to be in the other direction.

Neel: We discussed that very point in the paper where these erythrocyte results were presented, because it was so clear. If it is true, it is of considerable theoretical interest, but we just can't be sure it is a valid effect.

Gartler: Bob, have you tried any mixing experiments with the galactosemic and normal cells, to see what you could pull out, whether you could pull out a wild type from a population of galactosemics?

Krooth: No, we haven't. You mean, mix them and clone them?

Gartler: Yes.

Krooth: I don't seem to be very good at cloning these cells, and this really is something I am going to have to try to get better at.

McKusick: What is the evidence for there being a second form of acatalasemia?

Krooth: There was one family that was discovered and worked on, I think, by Dr. Hamilton and Dr. Neel. Am I correct? Perhaps, Dr. Neel would care to answer that.

Neel: I could speak very briefly to the point. This is a still undescribed family from Hiroshima, where there is acatalasemia in two sibships, affected persons having zero catalase values. However, some individuals who must be carriers, by virtue of being a parent of an acatalasemic, have values that fall within the normal range. If one plots the catalase values of the whole family, and it is an extensive one, instead of obtaining the expected bimodal curve, we get a unimodal curve skewed to the left. We are in the midst of a statistical approach to obtaining a mean carrier value from this curve; while I hesitate to quote a precise value yet, it is clear the mean value will be significantly higher than in previously studied families.

McKusick: On that point, may I ask if you know yet whether there is cross-reacting material in this family?

Neel: No. Dr. Takahara made the immunological studies, Bob mentioned; it has been very difficult to produce an antibody specific for catalase.

Crow: To go back to the question that Dr. Stern raised, one of Dr. Steinberg's Drosophila mutants, from his prehuman days (to use Dr. Stern's vocabulary), seems to me to be relevant to this question. This is a mutant, *pearl* I believe he called it, which when combined with other pigment-producing alleles causes them to produce less than they otherwise would.

The simplest interpretation is that this allele produces a substance that combines with the substrate, but doesn't convert it very efficiently into the product, and thus competes with other alleles utilizing the same substrate. In fact, in this case, you showed—

Steinberg: I'm glad somebody read that paper! [Laughter]

Crow:—that it did have some slight pigment-producing activity, because in a heterozygote with a deletion it produced some color.

Steinberg: Well, it was more pigmented than white; the homozygote, if anything, had less pigment than the heterozygote with white. Is that right? I have forgotten that altogether.

Ephrussi: I probably missed something when Dr. Krooth mentioned the technique for these things. Are you using sonicates?

Krooth: Yes, sir.

Ephrussi: Is there any inhibition of enzyme activity in mixtures of sonicates from normal and from homozygote?

Krooth: No. We have done that, and I won't take the time to show the slide, but we have done it both ways. In fact, we have done it three ways. We have mixed the sonicates from the abnormal homozygote and the normal, and we get the activity we would expect from the component activities. We also mixed crystalline bovine catalase with the abnormal homozygote sonicate, and, again, observed what we would expect from the component activities. We also mixed the heterozygote and the normal, with similar results.

Ephrussi: In other words, there is no interference?

Krooth: We cannot find any.

DeMars: Were these mixed during the sonication procedure itself?

Krooth: No, sir.

DeMars: This is not completely impertinent. [Laughter] The sonication makes peroxides, and, if you have a strain low in peroxidase in the extract, it might be more susceptible to the killing effects.

Szybalski: I wonder whether you were using AET during the sonication? AET is used for preventing radical formation.

Krooth: No. I may say the mixing was done after sonication, not before.

Herzenberg: There is another example of Professor Stern's point, a very recent one, which, perhaps, will become more important. In heterozygotes for gamma globulin allotypes in rabbits, Dray (20) just reported that you can change the ratio of the two types of allotype globulins. In this case, development of the heterozygous offspring of a homozygous mother immunized against the paternal allotype led to a greatly decreased level of paternal-type gamma globulin in this offspring. This disparate level, Dray reports, maintains for at least a year.*

* Afterthought: (Herzenberg) We have recently found an allelic pair of gamma globulin isoantigens (allotypes), Gg-1, Gg-2 in mice which can be used as markers of antibody-forming cells. This provides a useful system for studying changes in product ratios of two alleles under selecting conditions within an animal.

Eagle: I would like to say a few words about the variant strains which are reported to have one or another biochemical deficiency which, at first sight, would seem to be very good markers, but I don't think they are quite as useful as they appear to be.

In all cases but one that we have examined so far, these apparent selections are partial only, and the inability of the cell to synthesize a given metabolite and to grow in the absence of a given metabolite disappears.

Herzenberg: These are stable lines?

Eagle: Yes, these are stable lines, long-term cultures, not diploid.

Ephrussi: But are these from the original marked animals, or is the marker introduced *in vitro?*

Eagle: I will show you in just a minute. I have a slide that summarizes most of these that I have been able to cull from the literature.

Szybalski: When you say "partial," you mean the so-called "leaky" mutants. Am I correct?

Eagle: Yes. My interpretation of what is happening here is admittedly not rigorously proved, but it is reasonable.

If one tries to clone any of these serially propagated cultures in the minimum medium which will permit the growth of large inocula, then, at, e.g., 50 cells per ml, only about 10 or so will grow out and, with a total of 10 cells, usually none will grow out.

If you add serine to the medium, all the cells will grow out—again within the limitations of cloning efficiency.

At the critical population which will permit cloning in an initially serine-free medium, one finds that the concentration of serine in the medium builds up to that level which, added to the medium, would have permitted the growth of small inocula. It is therefore a reasonable inference that large inocula grow because they are able to build up the concentrations of serine (and of the derived glycine) in the medium to the minimal effective concentration before the cells die of the specific deficiency.

Haff and Swim (34) at Western Reserve isolated a line of rabbit fibroblasts which would not grow in a minimal medium unless he added serine. This fibroblast has proved to differ from the generality of cultured cells in degree rather than kind. The critical population density at which serine becomes unnecessary, instead of being tens or hundreds of cells per ml, is on the order of 150,000 cells per ml. Below this level, the cells cannot build up the concentrations of serine and glycine in the medium to the minimal concentrations necessary for survival and growth.

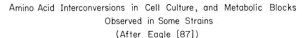

Amino Acid Interconversions in Cell Culture, and Metabolic Blocks
Observed in Some Strains
(After Eagle [87])

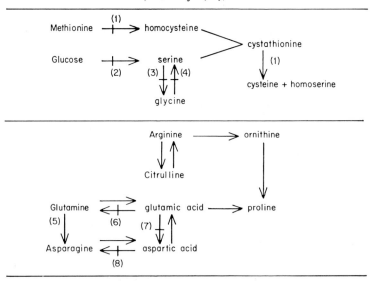

(1) Too little produced for cell survival except at high population densities.

(2) Partial block in rabbit fibroblast RT 6.

(3) Partial block in monkey kidney cells.

(4) Possible block in patient with hyperglycinemia.

(5) Apparently complete block in Walker carcinosarcoma 256, Jensen sarcoma, mouse leukemia L−5178Y, and MDAB hepatoma.

(6) Normally low activity, inadequate for survival of most cell lines, unless induced by high concentrations of glutamic acid.

(7) Possible block in Jensen sarcoma and mouse leukemia L-5178Y.

(8) Block, partial or complete, in Walker carcinosarcoma 256 and mouse leukemia L-5178Y.

Figure 39.

This is the general pattern we have found in almost all of the so-called variant lines which have been reported.

Figure 39 summarizes amino acid interconversions, as they have so far been found in cell culture. As I mentioned earlier, all cells can make cystine from methionine, but the amounts made are so small that the cells die unless the population density is increased almost to saturation, on the order of 200,000 to 500,000 cells per ml.

Swim's fibroblast has a partial block in the formation of serine from glucose. Monkey kidney cells in primary culture have a requirement for glycine and are partly blocked in the conversion of serine to glycine.

This block is also population-dependent, and monkey kidney cells will grow in the absence of added glycine, if the inoculum is on the order of 100,000 cells per ml. In this specific case, the actual block is not at the enzyme level, but at the level of the cofactor. There apparently is a partial block in their capacity to reduce folic acid, which is present in the medium, to the metabolically active cofactor, which is some form of reduced folic acid. If reduced folic acid is added to the medium, glycine becomes nonessential.

Now, I put this in with all reservations, because this may or may not be the case. This is the case that von Neuheim and Barton Charles have reported from Hopkins, a case of a child with hyperglycinemia, with enormous levels of glycine in the blood, in which they have shown, in some as yet unpublished experiments, that if they inject labeled glycine, the label appears in the blood serine to a much lower degree than in the case of normal controls.

We have this culture going, and we are just beginning some experiments to see whether this metabolic block is present in skin cells or whether its presence is perhaps limited, for example, to the liver, in which case, as Dr. Krooth has pointed out, it is not amenable to study in culture, so far.

Most cells can make glutamine from glutamic acid, on exposure to high levels of glutamic acid. Dr. Lockhart (66) found a variant cell which was unable so to adapt, and Dr. DeMars told me yesterday that he has isolated a large number of such variant cells which do not adapt to glutamic acid.

DeMars: Not a large number, but others.

Eagle: This group of variant cultures is extremely interesting. McCoy (68) at Oklahoma reported that the Walker 256 carcinosarcoma had an absolute requirement for asparagine, over and above the usual requirement for glutamine. This is the only example we have found so far of a specific amino acid requirement which is absolute, in the sense that it does not disappear at a sufficiently high population density. We have not yet done the labeling experiment to see whether this is, indeed, an absolute block in the ability of the cells to make asparagine from glutamine.

There are other lines which can use aspartic acid for asparagine synthesis, but cannot convert glutamic acid to aspartic acid, and yet, other lines which cannot convert aspartic acid to asparagine.

I mentioned this morning that, in fact, neither glutamic acid nor glutamine is required for the growth of cells. If a cell begins with a high level of glutamine synthetase, the small amounts of glutamic acid which it can make from glucose and an as yet unknown source of alpha amino nitrogen, suffice for cellular growth. These are the reported amino acid blocks, all but one of which turn out to be a partial: but perhaps they can be used as biochemical markers, even so.

I would like to ask to what degree this group thinks these ordinarily amino acid-requiring strains, which have a partial biosynthetic block, can be used as useful markers?

Szybalski: The selective or the nonselective markers?

Ephrussi: Yes, nonselective.

DeMars: One of them was amenable to some selection; that was the strain that couldn't grow very well in the absence of glutamine. The strain called S3R1, when put in high concentrations of glutamic acid, would not grow, where the parent strain would.

Eagle: But that was not an absolute block.

DeMars: No, that was an absolute block if you characterize the phenotype in terms of ability to grow in that special circumstance. I studied that mutant strain carefully, and that strain could form glutamine synthetase and it could accelerate the rate at which this enzyme is formed, if you remove the glutamine. However, in order to get it to grow at all and form enzyme at the accelerated rate, one had to give it a bit of glutamine to get it started. Once you initiated growth with a very small amount of glutamine, then, you remove the glutamine and the so-called mutant strain could then be propagated in the absence of glutamine. Its rate of enzyme synthesis was less than the maximum rate of enzyme synthesis of the parent strain. We might say that both strains formed unit amounts of enzyme in media containing glutamine.

In the absence of glutamine, the parent strain would accelerate this rate, between 10- and 15-fold. The mutant strain would accelerate only five- or six-fold; so it was not a complete block in enzyme synthesis. The closest we got to finding out what was wrong with that strain was that it had to have a larger amount of glutamine in order to get started. The parent strain also had to have a small amount of glutamine initially in order to grow subsequently in its absence. This could be shown by starving the parent strain for several hours in a medium free of glutamine and glutamic acid. If then provided with 20 millimolar glutamic acid it failed to grow unless initially provided with as little as 10^{-5} molar glutamine, which could be omitted from the medium once growth had begun.

It was a partial block and seems to be very relevant to what you are saying about leakage of low molecular-weight metabolites.

The phenotype of the strain with the relatively increased requirement for glutamine was amenable to selection using an auxotrophic selection technique. In a medium containing glutamic acid, but not glutamine, the parent strain, which was able to grow, died if aminopterin was present. The glutamine-requiring strain, being unable to grow, survived the aminopterin-induced thymine shortage and could be efficiently recovered after aminopterin was removed and glutamine was added to the medium.

I think, therefore, in the appropriate conditions, these partially blocked strains can be used very well. You can get a sharp distinction in phenotypes that are selectable. Their utility will be limited by our ingenuity. In that case, we were able to select for this pseudo-auxotrophic mutant.

Eagle: There is one more strain which I did not put on this slide because it does not relate to amino acid metabolism, and that is the classic strain of Earle, the now famous fibroblast, which, unlike other serially propagated long-term culture cells, cannot utilize galactose. In that cell the block has been shown by Maio and Rickenberg (70) to be due to the absence of demonstrable epimerase activity. It is therefore a different block than in the case of the galactosemic cells, and one which their data would indicate to be an absolute block. If that is the case, it might be a very useful cell for marker studies.

Ephrussi: I have a parenthetical question, since Dr. DeMars referred to the equivalents of the penicillin technique. Has anybody succeeded in establishing something like this for *in vitro* grown cells?

DeMars: I'll send you a reprint (17). Dr. Szybalski uses the technique regularly in his work, using different phenotypes. Isn't that right?

Szybalski: Correct!

DeMars: In clearing out the background for certain mutations, you apply the thymine starvation technique; so I don't know if I should discuss this.

Gartler: Dr. Bearn has been doing some interesting work on the maintenance of the isozyme patterns of lactic acid dehydrogenase in cell culture, and this would be an appropriate time to present that material.

Bearn: I am rather hesitant to discuss it, because it is very much work in progress and we have only just become interested in this general area. Things are in the exploratory stage, and we are still very ignorant. But, at least, I thought I might tell you how far we have got, and then I would like very much to have people's comments.

We have been interested in lactic acid dehydrogenase for a number of years (112, 113). This enzyme occurs in different molecular forms and falls within the category of an isozyme. We thought it might be of interest to see whether tissues grown *in vitro* would show qualitative alterations in their isozyme pattern. If they did, our long-term aim would be to try and modify the pattern (81, 114).

Muscle from a 22-day rabbit embryo contains all five isozymes. The second slowest band is usually split. By 27 days the most rapidly migrating band decreases and in adult tissue you simply get a single band in the cathodal region (isozyme 5). Rabbit liver shows a similar series of sequential changes.

In the developing rabbit heart one gets a very different picture, because, although you start off with all five bands in the 22-day-old embryo, as development progresses the more slowly moving bands are lost and one ends up, in the adult, with only the most rapidly migrating band (isozyme 1). It then seemed of interest to see whether the sequential changes observed in the intact organism would also occur under *in vitro* culture conditions. Naturally, within a very short time, all the cells whatever their tissue of origin began to take on the appearance of fibroblasts and if one could get hold of a biochemical handle which would indicate differentiated function it would be useful. Now, if you culture rabbit muscle you find that you tend to lose *in vitro* those same bands that were lost *in vivo*. In general, the picture is similar to the *in vivo* changes, although a little less marked. Rabbit heart, which you will recall, became more anodal during embryological development becomes, under the tissue culture conditions we employed, more cathodal. At 35 days for instance, the anodal bands are already becoming fainter and the maximal activity is in the slower bands. It must be stated that all the levels of enzymatic activity must be equalized before electrophoresis. One can summarize by saying that after a period of prolonged tissue culture, whatever the species used, chick, rabbit, or man, the isozyme pattern changes in a similar fashion. But, and this seems quite clear, the species' specific pattern is retained and so one could easily tell by doing an isozyme pattern whether the fibroblasts in any particular bottle were from chicken, rabbit, or man.

I think there may well be advantages in following qualitative differences rather than quantitative, and, although of course one will still be bedeviled with all sorts of problems, this sort of approach, which is also being used in other laboratories (9, 77), may prove helpful.

Eagle: These dispersed cells are rabbit embryo?

Bearn: Yes.

Gartler: You haven't followed them any longer than thirty-five days?

Bearn: So far, no.* I expect that they will finally continue the sequence they started.

Gartler: I believe that Paul and Fottrel (77) reported on cell culture esterase patterns.

Bearn: I think in his system there were no changes whereas ours did change.

Study of Glucose-6-Phosphate Dehydrogenase Mutants in Human Cell Culture

by Dr. Stanley M. Gartler

Gartler: I thought I would take a few minutes to go over some of our work on the study of glucose-6-phosphate-dehydrogenase (G6PD) variations in cell culture.

Essentially, the basic results are very similar to what Dr. Krooth reported for galactosemia and acatalasia. For those of you who may not be up-to-date on the story of G6PD variations, I will very briefly review the picture.

This is a sex-linked locus, for which a number of different alleles have been found, most of them resulting in marked deficiencies of G6PD activity. The first mutant allele was detected in Negroes and was related to the sensitivity of those particular individuals to primaquine. The phenotypic effect of this mutant allele is to lead to a G6PD level in the red blood cell of about 15 percent of normal without any appreciable lowering of leucocyte G6PD activity. The Mediterranean Caucasoid mutant allele leads to almost zero activity in the red blood cell and to a G6PD level in the leucocytes of about 15 percent of normal. Another G6PD mutant is associated with congenital nonspherocytic hemolytic anemia. In this case the enzyme has been shown by Kirkman (54) to be structurally altered. It is labile but can be stabilized by TPN. Other alleles also exist as for example, those which are activatable by normal red cell stroma and those which are not.

---

* Cells have now been kept for over three months and have maintained the expected sequence.

Motulsky: Did you imply by your data a lack of activator in the Mediterranean conditions?

Gartler: No. The work I am referring to is by the Israeli group, that claims that in some of their deficients, activity is restored by incubating hemolysate with stroma or normal cells. There is also the recent report from the South Pacific (52), which indicates that there are two further varieties of mutants with regard to activation of mutant activity by incubation with normal red cell stroma.

McKusick: Stan, did you mention the electrophoretic bands?

Gartler: I'm sorry. You are much more familiar with the details of that variant than I am; why don't you describe the phenotype.

McKusick: Some 35 percent of American Negro males have a fast-moving electrophoretic band on starch gel, stained by histochemical methods, and this is also sex-linked, contrary to what Boyer at first thought. This variant he calls Type A (5). All glucose-6-phosphate dehydrogenase-deficient Negroes are Type A, so the two seem to be very closely linked, or may represent a double mutation at the same locus—

Neel: And in females?

McKusick: The female can be typed. The heterozygote can be typed.

Renwick: Only in white cells. It has two bands in white cells, but it is not so easy to demonstrate these in red cells.

Bearn: I wonder, can it be done in red cells?

McKusick: Kirkman, I believe, finds that he can type them in red cells (53).

Gartler: We were interested in the G6PD system for two reasons. One, since the enzyme is present normally in all tissues of the body, we thought that we should be able to use it as a marker for cell culture. Also, since it is involved in the shunt pathway and the formation of ribose, we thought it might be approachable selectively, although we have not been successful in this respect.

We took skin biopsies from individuals with different types of this deficiency and assayed the resulting cultures for G6PD activity. The biopsies included three of the Mediterranean Caucasoid variety, one Negro, and one associated with congenital nonspherocytic hemolytic anemia.

Gartler: We also analyzed four cultures from individuals heterozygous for the Mediterranean variety of deficiency. In Table 2 are shown the enzyme activities in these cultures. These assays were performed after cultures had become well established and the values reported here are the means of at least three determinations at different times on each culture. As we shall see, the G6PD level changes somewhat during the culture history and in general the values given here are maximal values. It is worth pointing out that the differences between normals and Mediterranean deficient cultures are comparable to the *in vivo* leucocyte differences. As was mentioned, Kirkman has shown that the G6PD in the mutant associated with congenital nonspherocytic hemolytic anemia is quite labile and can be stabilized by TPN. We found that the G6PD activity in crude extracts of our culture from such an individual behaved in the same way. This is shown in Figure 40. Essentially, then, the basic properties of these various alleles *in vivo* have been maintained in cell culture.

TABLE 2

Mean G6PD activity in all cell lines studied. Reported as change in optical density /min /mg. protein. N = normal; H = heterozgous; D = deficients. Assayed at approximate peak of culture G6PD activity.

N						H				D			
										Med.	Var.	Cong.	Nonspher.
Fs	Mad	Mal	1D	9	H	MM	3	4	5	Pur	Md	2	Bell
.126	.123	.109	.121	.122	.110	.050	.125	.120	.046	.008	.025	.026	.028

DeMars: Is there a primaquine-sensitive type represented on these?

Gartler: The Negro variety is the one usually referred to as Primaquine-sensitive and this type has normal enzyme activity in cell culture. As I have mentioned, in a Negro G6PD deficient, the red cell activity is about 15 per cent of normal, while the white cell activity is very close to normal. Thus one would not expect to be able to work with this type in cell culture. The Mediterranean type which is associated with favism is also susceptible to primaquine.

Motulsky: Yes, they are all susceptible to primaquine.

Gartler: Is the one associated with congenital nonspherocytic hemolytic anemia susceptible to primaquine?

Motulsky: I think it has been studied, and it is.

Gartler: In that case, they are all susceptible. The cells in culture do not seem to be susceptible to selection by primaquine, or related substances, at least under the system we have tried.

DeMars: I have also wanted to know whether cells cultured from a primaquine-sensitive person of the classical sort, of the type found

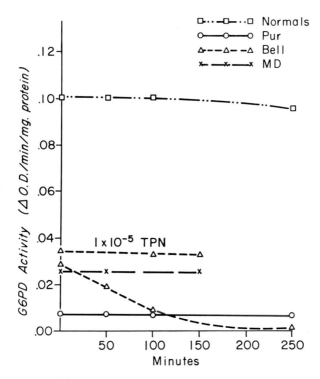

Figure 40. Stability of G6PD activity in normal and various deficient lines.

among Negroes, would manifest the mutant phenotype in cultures of skin cells?

Gartler: You mean lowered glucose-6-phosphate dehydrogenase activity?

DeMars: Yes, a primaquine-sensitive.

Gartler: We started off with Negro cultures, and we were not able to find any obvious difference between normal and deficients so we did not pursue this.

We also investigated the possibility of interactions between various extracts of normal and deficient cultures. In general we have no evidence for any sort of activation or interaction between the extracts of these cultures. However, I don't believe these results are necessarily applicable to the stroma activation story in red blood cells, since we are clearly dealing with a different cell type.

We have also studied cultures (three were started from patients of Dr. E. Beutler) from several heterozygotes for G6PD deficiency in the hope of obtaining information on the question of whether a culture heterozygous for a sex-linked marker consisted of one or two populations. We first tried a histochemical approach to this problem, though with relatively little success. We were able to demonstrate statistical differences between normal and mutant cultures histochemically. However, the possibility of using the method to distinguish between the one and two population hypothesis seems remote. Even after a relatively long incubation period (one hour), normal cultures had a number of unstained cells, while after relatively short periods of incubation (15 minutes), deficient cultures already exhibited some stained cells.

Renwick: How long do you have to incubate those?

Gartler: These were incubated for half an hour. You can get some reaction very quickly, within a few minutes, and, if you use phase contrast, the granules appear very quickly.

DeMars: What do you do to the cells to carry out the staining?

Gartler: We simply remove the growth medium from a coverslip culture and add incubation medium.

DeMars: Untreated cells?

Gartler: Yes.

DeMars: You don't mix them or treat them with anything?

Gartler: The cells? No. We tried fixed ones and we found that the best results were with untreated cells. After the cells reach a fairly high density, we wash off the medium, and then put them in our incubation mixture, which consisted of the nitro-B-T, G6P, TPN, and buffer.

DeMars: I am just a little concerned about the ability of the glucose-6-phosphate to get into the cells readily, unless you do something to those cells.

Gartler: I was told by many people that G6P could not get into the cells, unless, of course, you froze them or interfered with their permeability in some way. But the controls without glucose-6-phosphate plus iodoacetate are always negative. Furthermore, if you use glucose instead of G6P, the reaction is much slower. I don't know whether this proves that G6P gets in or not, but it certainly proves that G6P is more effective than glucose for this purpose.

DeMars: I was just concerned about the variability in the reactions of your individual cells. You might sharpen the uniformity of the reaction by cell treatment.

Gartler: Well, we tried various procedures such as freezing the cells but, in general, the fastest and the most uniform was simply leaving the cells intact.

Atwood: This is a microorganism carryover, this idea that phosphorylated things can't get in.

Szybalski: This is not a carryover from microbiological studies. Small phosphorylated molecules do not enter into mammalian cells.

Atwood: They don't? Well, they got into his.

Szybalski: They do not have to enter as the intact phosphorylated moiety. The 5-fluorodeoxycytidine (FCdR) moiety enters the bacterial cell more efficiently when supplied in the form of 5-fluorodeoxycytidylic acid (FCdRP) than in the form of FCdR, but FCdRP is first dephosphorylated on the cell surface (64). Apparently, FCdRP is more resistant to the extracellular catabolic enzymes and thus serves as long-acting repository form prior to its conversion to FCdR, which is then taken into the cell and rephosphorylated. We have observed also that 8-azaguanylic acid is two to three times more inhibitory on a molar basis against our cell lines than 8-azaguanosine.

Gartler: Do you mean that the phosphate is taken off and then put back on?

Szybalski: Oh, yes, I am sure that phosphate is taken off and then put back on.

Gartler: Then, I would think that glucose would do just as well in the system.

Szybalski: Not quite, because, as I have described before, FCdRP is a more efficient inhibitor than FCdR, although the phosphate group is taken off the FCdRP.

Herzenberg: Are we sure, though, that there aren't some examples in mammalian cells where the phosphorylated compound has been shown fairly conclusively to get in?

Szybalski: Are you referring to the paper by Tomizawa and Aronow (109)?

Herzenberg: Yes.

Szybalski: I have some doubts about the conclusions based on this experiment, since we were not able to obtain comparable results with our IMP-pyrophosphorylase-deficient cell line mutants (D98/AH). Our D98/AH mutant lines cannot utilize IMP (inosinic acid) and are indifferent to 8-azaguanylic acid.

Atwood: What about pinocytosis?

Herzenberg: Their data (109) were very convincing, and I think we have to keep an open mind on this.

Szybalski: Experimentally, it would be very nice to have cells which could utilize intact phosphorylated intermediates. But how could these poor cells stay alive while at the same time they would be leaking out into the medium all their precious phosphorylated intermediates, including ATP?

Atwood: The cells are capable of pinocytosis, so anything at all can get in.

Herzenberg: Oh, sure.

Gartler: These cells are surely capable of pinocytosis.

Herzenberg: Well, that's it, then.

Gartler: I'm sure Dr. Szybalski knows that. I guess bacterial cells are not capable of pinocytosis.

Szybalski: It depends on how you define pinocytosis. Competent cells of genetically transformable bacterial take up large DNA molecules, but reject small fragments of the same molecules.

Gartler: In Figure 41 are graphs of G6PD activity of normal, heterozygous, and deficient cultures showing variation in activity with time in culture.

Though these data do not distinguish between the one- and two-cell population hypotheses they are of some interest to consider in this respect.

From the normals and heterozygotes one may assume that there is selection for high G6PD activity in the early phase of a culture history (to about 100-150 days). Thus, in a two-cell population the wild-type cell would predominate during this period, the G6PD level reached by the culture reflecting the original composition of the population. The differences in levels reached by the four heterozygous cultures are compatible with mosaicism in the starting populations. From the data on normals one may also assume that later in the culture's history there is selection for lower G6PD activity. So in the heterozygous cultures the cells with the mutant gene active would begin to predominate and the culture's G6PD level should drop, the bottom being the level of deficient cultures, which is actually what happens. One might ask if there is any other basis than the evidence offered by these data to assume that there really is a selective advantage for high G6PD activity early in the culture history and an advantage for lowered G6PD activity in the latter part. I believe there is. G6PD because of its central role in the pathway of ribose synthesis and because it is an important TPNH generator, should be a good indicator of growth rate, and in fact is in this case. For the growth rates of the cultures are much faster in the early period than in the later phases.

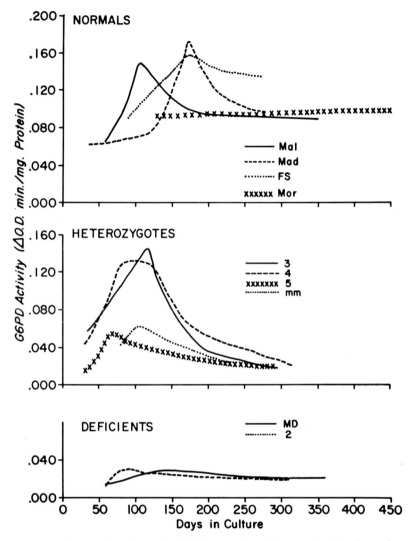

Figure 41. Change in G6PD activity with age of cell culture for normal, heterozygote, and deficient cell culture.

One criticism of the two-cell population hypothesis as far as these data are concerned is that the two heterozygous cultures (3 and 4) that extended well into the normal range at their G6PD peak should then have consisted of only wild-type cells. From their subsequent behavior it is clear that either a small percentage of undetected mutant cells were retained, which is well within the range of the sensitivity and accuracy of our assay procedures, or alternatively the two-cell population hypothesis is wrong.

We might now consider a one-cell population hypothesis with regard to these data. If we assume that in the heterozygous cell we can have combinations of genic activity ranging from 100 percent wild-type activity to 100 percent mutant activity, then we can account for any G6PD phenotypic activity exhibited by the cell. Such a scheme would allow the cell maximum adaptability and I should think would be the choice if a population had the choice to make. One might argue that if this one-cell population hypothesis were true that all the heterozygous cultures should have approached normal G6PD levels at their peak. However, if G6PD level is related to growth rate then one must expect different growth rate patterns from different lines even though they may be identical at one locus.

In conclusion, I would emphasize that these data are simply not strong enough to differentiate between a two- or one-cell hypothesis for the G6PD locus in a heterozygote.

Neel: Stan, could I ask what you would expect if there were two cell types in approximately equal numbers from the beginning?

Gartler: For very early determinations I should expect a value intermediate to normals and deficients and then an increase in activity to somewhat less than the normal peak.

Neel: And then level off considerably higher than your observation levels off?

Gartler: No. If one assumes that there is an advantage to low G6PD activity in the latter part of the culture history, then one can argue that the final level might approach that of the deficient culture.

The other possibility is that the same selective conditions may exist here, and, of course, they could operate in a cell with two types of alleles, which these cells have; that is, we simply just change activity, whereas, in this early period, the wild-type allele is working more and the other one is shut off, and this thing switches in some way.

Eagle: How do you interpret the increase in the wild type?

Gartler: This increase in activity with growth?

Eagle: Yes, at the top of Figure 41, in the wild type.

Gartler: I believe it is related to the increasing growth rate in the early phase of the culture's history. The culture has been sampled over its whole history of growth and sampled every other week, roughly.

Ephrussi: Is the growth included there, or the growth cycle?

Herzenberg: The bottle cycle is not. Would you take a full bottle each time?

Gartler: Yes, we try to use a full bottle, because we have noticed that if we take a bottle where the cells are not fully grown or unhealthy, we may get extremely low enzyme activities, regardless of the culture.

DeMars: I would like to mention briefly one other possibility here. We have found one strain among our diploid collection that exhibited significantly low beta glucuronidase activity. This same strain turned out to be the low man on the totem pole with regard to acid phosphatase activity and with regard to gamma glutamyl transferase activity. This was a trisomic strain, and we hardly thought we would be lucky enough to have the single trisomy affect just those three enzymes we happened to be studying at the time. It turned out that that cell strain, which was of old vintage at the time we did these experiments, had a significantly higher amount of protein per cell than the other strains studied, and it seemed there was a real dilution effect on these three enzymes, so that other proteins, in which these enzymes were not represented, were being produced by the cells in abnormally large quantities.

This might be an accompaniment of the transformation that is occurring or the slackening of growth rate; so that there are all kinds of things that can give these changes in specific activity.

Neel: In the case of this defect, don't we know, in the case of the erythrocyte, that the cell gradually runs out of glutathione? If your cells are reproducing at a slower rate with successive passages—

Gartler: But I don't know if you can compare a tissue culture cell to the red cell, in that sense; at least, I don't think you can.

Neel: I mean, we do know that there are changes in the aging cell —but I am wondering if there is a comparable change here, which might be giving you—

Gartler: These normal cells or cultures definitely age, since they all apparently have a finite life span, and at the same time, as growth rate declines their G6PD activity appears to decrease. In that sense there may be some similarity to the loss of G6PD activity in red cells with aging. However, in cell culture, the drop in enzyme activity with age must reflect a change in the factory which cannot be the case in the red blood cell.

Neel: I know, but are the cells turning over at the same rate from Day 50 to 100 as from 100 to 400?

Gartler: I believe Figure 42 may throw some light on your question.

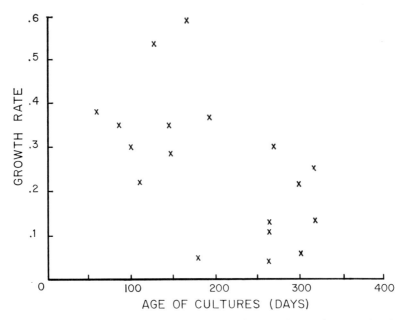

Figure 42. Change in growth rate (relative values) with age of cell culture. Each X represents a growth rate determination on a single culture taken at a particular point in culture history.

The points plotted here are growth-rate determinations on a number of different normal cultures at various times in their culture history. As can be seen, there is a marked decline in growth rate with aging of the cells. These data may either represent an average lengthening of the generation time of all cells in a culture or they may represent the effects of an increasing proportion of cells that fail to divide upon successive transfers. Unfortunately, these data do not permit one to distinguish between these alternative explanations of decreasing growth rate with time in culture of normal cells.

Assuming that the aging process is related to cell generation (i.e., generation time lengthens with each successive cell division), it is of some interest to consider again the G6PD activity curve for the heterozygous culture (i.e., decrease to deficient G6PD levels in the later part of culture history). On the two-cell population hypothesis, we could assume that in the early growth phase the cells with the mutant allele active would divide relatively less often than the cells with the normal allele active. Therefore, at the stage when selection is for low

G6PD activity the mutant active cells will be relatively younger than their competing wild-type active cells and able to grow at a faster rate.

Renwick: One might test the hypothesis by repeating the experiment on a cell strain which was from a known female heterozygote, the two alleles being the deficiency allele, producing mobility-type A enzyme, and the allele producing mobility-type B enzyme. You could test your final product and see whether there was any selection for one or the other X-clone.

Gartler: It would be interesting to see if one could demonstrate those patterns in cell culture.

Steinberg: Could you grow a mixed culture of the homozygous normal and the homozygous deficient?

Gartler: We have not had the opportunity to work with a homozygous deficient culture, although we have had some experience with mixed cell cultures. I might just point out that one could test the two-cell population hypothesis with heterozygous cell cultures if efficient cloning of these normal cells were possible. Cloning early in such a culture's history should lead to two kinds of clones or cultures: one following the normal pattern and the other kind the deficient pattern. Unfortunately, we have not been able to clone our normal cell cultures effectively.

Our experience with mixed cell cultures indicates that the younger cell culture, regardless of its genotype or enzyme level, will overgrow an older culture, which on the basis of our growth rate curves (Fig. 42) is to be expected—the faster-growing culture overgrows the slower one. I think, at this point, where we have been concerned with decreasing growth rates as normal cultures age, we can very nicely turn to the work of Dr. Koprowski, with his SV40 virus, where he has been able to transform such normal cell lines into possibly permanent ones.

Cellular Expression of *In Vitro* Infection
with Oncogenic Virus
1. Simian Virus 40

by Dr. Hilary Koprowski

Koprowski: Dr. Gartler asked me to summarize the results of the effect of a virus called SV40 in human cells in tissue culture. This work was done in collaboration with Dr. Ponten, and the chromosome studies were done by Drs. Moorhead and Saksela. I am not sure whether you are familiar with the agent, which bears the name SV40, but it stands for Simian Virus 40 and was originally isolated from a poliomyelitis vaccine. It was produced in Rhesus monkey kidneys. I have no data on the incidence of SV40 infection among monkey populations, but some people claim that if they collect five pairs of kidneys and grow them as fresh explants in tissue culture, three pairs will be contaminated with SV40.

As you know, many other agents have been isolated from monkey kidney, and we don't know yet how many more may be isolated in the future. This discussion is concerned solely with the SV40 agent, and whether other agents will be isolated under different conditions from other species of monkeys, such as, e.g., the green monkey, has not been settled. The presence of SV40 can be determined by the cytopathic lesions it produces in green monkey tissue culture.

Szybalski: Is this a DNA virus?

Koprowski: They are all DNA viruses: polyoma, SV40, and adenovirus types 12 and 18. The latter viruses were originally isolated from the feces of a patient suffering from a minor infection of the upper respiratory tract.

In our studies, biopsies of buccal mucosa and skin obtained from adult cancer patients or monolayers of fibroblast obtained originally from normal human embryos were exposed to approximately 10^6 $TCID_{50}$ of SV40. Uninfected cultures obtained from the same individuals were kept under the same conditions for control purposes.

Usually, within two to four weeks after exposure to the virus, a cytopathic effect is observed in the cultures and inclusion bodies are seen in the nuclei of the cells. A large fraction of the cell population is not affected by the cytopathic effect, and these cells still retain their fibroblast-like character and follow an organized growth pattern. Within the next one or two weeks, the early transformation pattern is characterized by disorganized multilayer growth of the infected cultures and appearance of foci of epithelial-like cells. These cells are no longer of elongated and cylindrical shape, but are plumper and of polygonal shape with blunt ends. There is an increased mitotic activity in the infected culture at this stage and obvious loss of contact inhibition. The last stage of transformation of the infected culture is characterized by the three-dimensional growth characterized by piling up of one layer of cells over another. Nuclear pleomorphism is accentuated and the nucleus of these transformed, epithelial-like cells has from two to ten nucleoli, in contrast to the noninfected cultures which retain their fibroblast-like character.

DeMars: Are these really nucleoli?

Koprowski: I do not know. It is very difficult to say. They look, in size and staining characteristics, similar to the nucleoli of the normal culture. They are much greater in number.

DeMars: I mean, if you hydrolyze with hydrochloric acid and make a Feulgen stain, do they disappear?

Koprowski: We haven't done that. Complete morphological transformation has been observed as early as five weeks after exposure to the virus and as late as 15 to 18 weeks. However, every single SV40-infected human tissue culture system has undergone transformation.

With two exceptions the virus was always present in the exposed cultures for periods as long as 14 months. However, on one occasion the transformed culture which remained infectious for 25 weeks "lost" the virus without changing its epithelial-like character.

Chromosomal aberrations were observed by Moorhead and Saksela in all transformed cultures. These cultures usually become hyperdiploid, and abnormal chromosomes were always observed. Cultures obtained on four different occasions from one adult donor have shown the presence of a "marker" chromosome during the process of transformation after exposure to SV40.

Eagle: Excuse me, but does this chromosome appear only after the cells have become grossly heteroploid?

Koprowski: The observations here were made on the seventh passage, where they have become heteroploid. This marker chromosome is an acrocentric definitely longer than those of the 13 to 15 group. A most frequently observed effect on virus-infected cultures was "stretching" of the secondary constriction to the point of "breaking off" one arm of the chromosome as shown in Figure 43.

On many occasions the infected transformed cells were inoculated in newborn hamsters subcutaneously and intracerebrally. No growth was observed in any of the animals except for three hamsters which were sacrificed ten days after intracerebral inoculation of tissue cells. A small sarcoma was observed in the brain tissue.

These data are inconclusive because of the presence of virus in the implanted cultures; thus, the animals may have become immunized against the tumor transplants.

Herzenberg: Excuse me, but what was the SV40 tumor then that grows?

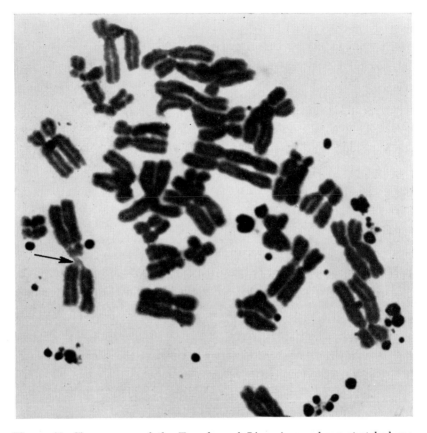

Figure 43. Chromosome of the Transformed Line. Arrow shows stretched secondary constriction of chromosome, probably belonging to group No. 1.

Koprowski: This is a hamster tumor obtained from Dr. Eddy which arose in hamsters injected with SV40. Dr. Defendi, of our Institute, has shown that hamsters injected with SV40 virus become resistant to implantation of these tumor cells.

Two of the human donors received back autografts of their own cells transformed by SV40. In one case, a small nodule was formed at the site of inoculation. Biopsy tissue removed ten days later showed the presence of sarcomatous-like cells. Other nodules regressed within 10 to 15 days after inoculation.

Fifteen other cancer patients received transformed cell and non-infected cell homografts. This produced a violent "foreign-body" reaction within 24 to 48 hours after implantation. In contrast, autografts of noninfected control cultures failed to elicit any sort of reaction when implanted under the skin of the donor.

Lejeune: What was the disease of the patient who was dying from cancer, where you made the implantation of cells?

Koprowski: He had carcinoma of the lung.

Lejeune: Some cases have been reported of people who had sarcomas, and, if you give them just smallpox vaccinations, they develop sarcoma at the point of the virus infection.

Koprowski: None of the patients had sarcomas.

Ephrussi: Do I understand you correctly, that all your transformed cultures go on releasing virus?

Koprowski: Yes.

Ephrussi: Has any attempt been made, similar to Dulbecco's with polyoma, to clone this population and see whether all cells release virus?

Koprowski: Two transformed virus-yielding cultures were cloned. Fifty-two clones grew into cell colonies. Forty-two remained infectious and ten were virus-free. Clones of the infectious cells retained their transformed and epithelial-like character. Ten virus-free colonies looked like normal fibroblasts. Unfortunately, we were unable to determine the karyotype of the virus-free fibroblast-like clonal population, but we have now, as I mentioned before, a transformed culture which does not yield virus.

Szybalski: Were the "transformed" cells cloned? I got the impression that you first obtain a pure clone of the transformed cells and then determine whether it produces again a mixture of the virus-releasing and virus-nonreleasing cells.

Koprowski: Are you referring to cloning the original monolayer?

Szybalski: No, I refer to the cloning of the transformed cells. The question is whether the transformed cells will produce both the virus-free and "virogenic" progenies.

Koprowski: Yes, this could be done.

Szybalski: That was not done hitherto, however?

Koprowski: No.

Gartler: What sort of cloning efficiency were you able to obtain with the transformed cultures?

Koprowski: About 40 to 50 percent.

Eagle: As compared with how much of the original?

Koprowski: One-tenth.

Ephrussi: What kind of cloning technique did you use?

Koprowski: Trypsinized cells were filtered through glass wool and seeded on Petri dishes at a concentration of five cells per ml. Following twenty-four-hour incubation at 37° and removal of the medium, single cells localized under a microscope were separated from the rest of the culture by tightly sealing a glass cylinder to the bottom of the dish with grease. The cylinder was filled with culture medium, and after 10 to 15 days' incubation, the cell colony formed within the cylinder was taken off the glass and transferred to a Petri dish.

Atwood: Were there any fibroblast cells visible at the time the cloning was done, that is, visible in the original culture?

Koprowski: No.

Eagle: These transformed cells would be one of the few cases in which virus-infected cells continue to grow and release virus. Other examples are Rous and myeloblastosis.

Billingham: When you took the transformed human cells and put them into hamster cheek pouch, did you give the hamsters cortisone at the same time?

Koprowski: No. I doubt that it would help because of the presence of SV40 as an "immunizing" agent; presence of SV40 immune serum in contact with the cells prior to inoculation failed to change the results. Probably only very small amounts of virus are needed to immunize against cheek pouch implant.

Szybalski: I wonder whether the possible infectivity of the SV40 DNA (or its distinctive buoyant density in equilibrium sedimentation experiments) could be employed as an index for identification of the fate of this DNA in the host cell? Was this approach tried?

Koprowski: Cells were infected according to Melnick with SV40 DNA, but as far as I know, no transformation has been observed.

Bayreuther: But this is only for the cytolytic interaction.

Koprowski: Green monkey kidney cells were used in this system where, at present, you can only observe the cytopathic effect of the virus.

Szybalski: Was this published, by Melnick?

Koprowski: Do you remember, Klaus?

Bayreuther: Yes, there is one paper on the subject out (30).

Billingham: The very quick reaction that you reported when you put the cancer patient's cells back into him makes one wonder if he was behaving as if presensitized to something or other. Did you by any chance bleed him?

Koprowski: Yes. All patients were bled before implants were made and several had no SV40 antibody.

Billingham: But his serum had no effect on transformed cells *in vitro?*

Koprowski: No, but when the implant was removed from homologous hosts and grown in tissue culture, cells were destroyed by the patient's own lymphocytes present in the culture. Serum seemed to have no effect.

DeMars: There is a fair chance that even cloning these transformed cells is not going to eliminate the virus, and, perhaps, you have to use serum with the cloning.

Bayreuther: This has been done by Shein and Enders (89). SV40 virus was still present in the cultures, although the cells had been cloned and kept under antiserum for more than a hundred days.

Koprowski: In the presence of the immune SV40 serum?

Bayreuther: Yes.

Szybalski: It is my impression on the basis of Dr. H. Temin's work (who is my neighbor at McArdle Memorial Laboratory) that even the Rous sarcoma cells, which seem to be completely free of the extracellular virus, could be induced to produce the virus again, by appropriate treatment. Thus, the potential for virus production seems to be their heritable property.

Ephrussi: Well, Dulbecco was not successful. I am talking of polyoma.

Bayreuther: May I add that Temin's data are doubted. Recent studies show that Rous cells, considered nonvirus releasers, produce Rous virus, however, at a very much lower rate.

Eagle: Are these published data?

Bayreuther: Yes, by R. Ting (108).

Neel: Dr. Koprowski, I think that I missed something in your story. This is a virus recovered from monkey kidney in cell culture, and it has a transformation effect on human cells?

Koprowski: Yes.

Neel: What does it do to monkey cells?

Koprowski: It depends on the species of monkey. The virus produces no apparent lesions in Rhesus monkey kidney, but it causes cytopathic effects in green monkey kidney.

Neel: Yet, it is recovered from what appear at explant to be normal monkey cells; is that right?

Koprowski: Yes, that is correct.

Neel: So this is a temperate phage?

Koprowski: There is no evidence for that. It is perfectly possible that the virus may lyse an occasional cell in the Rhesus monkey tissue culture, and they may be the source of infectious material which we recover in poliomyelitis vaccines.

Neel: But where is this virus when you make your explant from monkey kidney? Is it an established infection in the monkey?

Koprowski: It is obviously an established infection in kidneys of Rhesus monkeys, but it is clear that the epizootiology of the SV40 infection in monkeys roaming loose in India cannot be studied.

Lejeune: But why does the monkey survive?

Koprowski: Men and animals survive most virus infections which may run an asymptomatic course. SV40 need not be an exception.

Lejeune: Because the cells of the monkey die.

Koprowski: The most efficient way to unmask a virus is to grow organs from an infected animal in tissue culture systems.

Neel: This is fine, but where is the virus at the time you make your explant? Intracellular or extracellular, and, if intracellular, well, it sounds like the story of a temperate phage.

DeMars: There have been a number of cases described in the virological literature now with cultured cells, too, poliovirus and others, Western equine encephalitis, where small amounts of virus are continuously liberated during repeated subculture of the cells. In the usual case, especially with Newcastle disease virus, it has been possible to cure the cultures of the virus infection by continuous propagation with antibody present in the medium. In this case, apparently, it isn't working, indicating that maybe the virus actually has a more persistent or intimate relationship with the cells. In those other cases, it seemed to be some sort of dynamic equilibrium between some cells being infected, liberating virus, probably dying, and other cells just going on at a very slow rate, so the other cells could maintain a decent rate of overall multiplication. This case seems to be different, because you can't cure the culture of the virus with antibody and, maybe, not even with cloning.

Crow: What is known in the Rous sarcoma virus about the situation where it carries two different kinds of viruses and, yet, shows the morphology associated with one of them and not the other? This is work with which I know you are familiar.

Bayreuther: Yes, there are two morphology-mutants of Rous. One that makes the transformed cells to be round, the other to be fusiform. When one infects cells with both mutants at the same time, the round phenotype is expressed, but both mutants are produced and released. Cells infected with one can be superinfected with the other, indicating that there is no interference between these two mutants. Such cells again produce both types of virus (107).

Koprowski: To come back to the question of Dr. Neel, Walter Schlesinger and his associates grow out adenovirus from human tonsils removed from apparently healthy subjects. The virus made its appearance only after the tissue was kept for a prolonged time in culture.

Neel: I am not disturbed about the fact that you can isolate viruses from apparently normal tissue. What I am questioning is why, then, the sudden apparent change in the reaction of the kidney tissue to the virus?

Bayreuther: As Dr. Koprowski mentioned, one can explant tonsils into *in vitro* conditions and in many instances no sign of cell necrosis can be seen, nor any virus production be discovered. It took Schlesinger and his coworkers quite a while to work out the right *in vitro* conditions to make cells latently infected with adenoviruses lyse (88). For many other viruses which latently infect tissues, the change from *in vivo* to *in vitro* conditions has been shown to be a shock sufficient to initiate the cytolytic interaction.

Neel: But is the analogy to a temperate phage so very bad?

Bayreuther: It is absolutely out.

Neel: What is the evidence that it is excluded?

Bayreuther: This is the phenomenon of latency. This is Dr. Koprowski's field.

Koprowski: There is no parallel to temperate phage in the virus-animal cell system. As I have mentioned before, it is impossible to know what happens to SV40 *in situ*. It does cause an apparent infection, and it may be present in otherwise healthy kidney cells of the animals. However, it is possible that cells infected with SV40 remain "biologically intact" undergoing mitosis, etc., and the complete virus escaping into the surrounding medium. The parallel with the temperate phage escapes me.

Szybalski: Just as a matter of record, I think that Dr. Temin really believes that there is something analogous to bacterial lysogeny in the case of the—

Bayreuther: In the case of the Rous sarcoma virus?

Szybalski: —In the case of the Rous sarcoma virus. He talked about it at several seminars. He now has lines which do not release any virus at all unless superinfected with a genetically different virus, a fusiform virus. But that is all I know.

Bayreuther: These findings are considered to be inconclusive in their present state. Many technical problems enter here, for example, the use of Rous stocks containing Rous-associated virus, RAV, by Temin.

Herzenberg: For the record, should we have a set of criteria for proving that you have a temperate virus in the mammalian system, and show that these do not fit? I am still not prepared to do this but—[laughter] You were talking about a temperate virus, but there has been no statement as to what criteria will be accepted for such.

Neel: Let's ask Dr. Koprowski.

Koprowski: I promise to prepare such a statement tonight and will attempt to present it during tomorrow's session.

I have been asked to bring you up-to-date on the progress of work related to resistance and susceptibility to virus infection. As you may recall from my report presented to this gathering last year, the resistance of a mouse strain to Arbor B virus is expressed by one gene. Through extensive work on crossing resistant and susceptible strains of mice, we were able to develop a strain "co-isogenic" in respect to the gene of virus resistance but otherwise completely histo-compatible with a C3H mouse. We refer to this strain as the C3H/RRV strain. The West Nile virus which we use as a tool in these investigations will multiply in tissue culture cells obtained from kidneys and heart muscle of these animals, but fails to grow in macrophage culture obtained from their peritoneal cavity. In contrast, macrophages of the susceptible strain will support growth of West Nile virus. There is a complete parallel between cellular resistance and resistance on the whole organism level. Fl hybrids which yield resistant macrophage cultures are fully resistant to virus challenge; macrophages obtained from mice which are susceptible to virus challenge support the growth of virus.

Gartler: Dr. Bayreuther, could you add anything?

2. Polyoma Virus

by Dr. Klaus E. Bayreuther

Bayreuther: In Dr. Dulbecco's group we have been interested in the Polyoma virus mediated neoplastic transformation *in vitro*. Polyoma likens in its physical and chemical properties to SV40, and both of them belong to the same group of DNA-containing viruses, the papova-group (71), which includes also the Shope papilloma virus of the rabbit, the human warts virus, and others, as for example the rat virus, for which oncogenic properties have not yet been reported. Polyoma has a size of 40-50 millimicrons, is a small spherical virus with a coat made up of 42 equal subunits, called capsomeres. Polyoma contains one molecule of DNA, the molecular weight is 6×10^6, the DNA is double stranded and seems to have a ring structure. The buoyant density is 1.30, the thermal stability is relatively high, the half-life time in water is 120 hours at 37°C. The growth cycle is 24 hours, the site of multiplication the nucleus, the natural host is the mouse.

The Polyoma virus-cell relationships are radically different depending on the nature of the cell infected and on physiological conditions. For the sake of clarity these relationships will be subdivided into two major categories: the infective relationship and the non-infective relationship. This classification is based solely on whether infectious virus is released or not.

The infective relationship is best expressed on mouse embryo cells where serial passage of Polyoma brought to light the existence of a clearcut and marked cytopathogenic effect. The existence of a cytopathic effect on mouse cells made possible the development of a plaque assay for this virus (21). The wild population of Polyoma was found to be made up by two plaque mutants, a large plaque and a small plaque mutant. Evidence of the identity of the cytopathogenic and tumor-inducing agents was obtained by the study of the tumor-inducing capacity of single plaque isolates. It was found that such clones were capable of giving rise to the complete spectrum of solid tumors characteristic of that agent.

The studies with Polyoma were for a long time hampered by the lack of a purification procedure that would produce high-titer virus stock of adequate homogeneity. Recently, Winocour described such a procedure. High-titer (10^9 PFU/ml) Polyoma virus lysates can be routinely obtained through the use of tissue cultures made of kidneys from mice about ten days after birth. The virus is concentrated by sedimentation and purified by equilibrium centrifugation in a cesium chloride density gradient. Here crude Polyoma virus fractionates into bands at densities of 1.339 and 1.297 g/ml. The band at 1.3 contains the "full" particles, which are biologically active. Such purified virus-suspensions have a titer of about $10^{10\text{-}12}$ PFU/ml (121). My own investigations showed that the PP:PFU:HAU ratio of such purified large plaque Polyoma suspensions to be $10^7:10^5:1$, for small plaque Polyoma suspensions to be $10^8:10^6:1$.

The noninfective relationship of Polyoma virus with hamster embryo cells was first reported by Vogt and Dulbecco (115). In contrast to the sequence described before in the case of the mouse embryonic cells, it was found that no observable cell necrosis took place following infection with low titer stock of hamster embryo cells. Despite the lack of observable cytopathogenic action, obvious cell transformation was observed. Within two to three weeks following infection with Polyoma virus, hamster embryo cultures undergo a progressive conversion, characterized by the replacement of the normal fibroblastic cells with cells of a new type, having special morphological and growth characteristics. In fact, the normal cells do not grow any further. The cultures of normal cells are essentially "two dimensional." Descriptively, these cultures can be defined as "regulated." On the contrary, the cells of the transformed cultures are much more elongated; they grow at all stages without any regular arrangement; in crowded cultures the cells form a three-dimensional arrangement constituted by many layers of crisscrossing cells. Regulation of cell multiplication and regulation by "contact inhibition" is either absent or ineffective in these cells. When as little as 10^4 of such cells are implanted into young adult hamsters they give rise regularly to tumors at the site of inoculation. The resulting tumors have the karyotype of the graft. In contrast, inoculation of up to 10^7 normal hamster cells, or of Polyoma virus of high titer, does not produce any tumor at the site of inoculation.

We have studied the chromosome cytology in both systems and found different manifestations. When mouse secondary cultures are infected with Polyoma, a certain fraction of the cell population, about 10 percent, remains diploid and keeps on dividing normally, while the remaining 90 percent of the population stop dividing mitotically and become polyploid. Polyploid cells entering mitosis show heavily fragmented chromosomes at metaphase. The breaks are always chromosome breaks. Chromatid breaks have never been observed. In contrast, in the noninfective interaction leading to transformation of hamster and rat cells, chromosome mutations are absent in the early state leading to step I of the transformation.

Koprowski: How do the chromosomal breaks compare to those described in measles? Is this the same type?

Bayreuther: German measles?

Koprowski: Regular measles described by Levan and Nichols.

Bayreuther: I cannot answer your question; I do not know this paper.

Koprowski: Levan and Nichols have reported that up to 70 percent of white blood cells obtained from children suffering from measles infection show chromosome breaks.

Bayreuther: We have found that this process can be interfered with by puromycin, which would indicate that the virus acts via early protein synthesis. We, however, do not know whether these chromosome breaks are precondition for, or a consequence of, the virus synthesis, but I perhaps better continue to describe our work on transformation.

Szybalski: One moment, please. Were these the cells with broken chromosomes, which bred true and which were viable, or am I mistaken?

Bayreuther: No, those cells with fragmented chromosomes are not viable, they do not divide any more, but remain attached to the substrate for longer periods of time.

Szybalski: Are these just eliminated? Are these not converted to so-called "transformed" cells?

Bayreuther: No, they are not the transformed cells, they are excluded from the process that leads to transformation.

Ephrussi: May I ask a question? If I understood you correctly, you have 10 percent diploid cells, and the 90 percent refers to the percent of cells which undergo the cytocidal change. Is that correct?

Bayreuther: Yes.

Ephrussi: We have two lines from the 10 percent diploid cells, and they are converted cells; they do not release virus, but produce tumors.

Bayreuther: Some of them are virus-free; others are in a "carrier state."

Ephrussi: I didn't test it myself, but that is the statement of Dulbecco. Reimplanted into the mouse, they give tumors. Now, at the time I got them from Dulbecco, they were not diploid. They were in the 70 chromosome range. I just wondered whether, really, this double characteristic of nonrelease of virus and neoplasticity by the implantation test, was detected at the time when, as you suggest, the karyotype was still diploid?

Bayreuther: I could not answer that. The cells you have from us were in tissue culture for at least one year before you received them. Nobody knows how they looked chromosomally when they were newly transformed.

Ephrussi: That is what I meant.

Bayreuther: Nobody knows.

Ephrussi: Well, I want to add a very naive technical remark. I am rather new in this business of chromosome studies, but the experience I have had shows me that there are a number of cells undergoing chromosome breakage, if the preparations are made when the cultures turn yellow—I mean they go acid, that is at the end of the growth cycle. This happens particularly quickly and is very difficult to control in cultures which, like the Polyoma-converted cells, lack contact inhibition, because of the terrific growth in several layers.

Bayreuther: No, the cells infected are normal mouse secondary cultures. The chromosomal changes occur within 24 hours. The cells are nutritionally under perfect conditions. They are growing in monolayers.

Eagle: Klaus, I am puzzled. When you began, you said, with the mouse cells, 10 percent could be superinfected. Did you mean—

Bayreuther: I tried to say that about 10 percent of the cells look chromosomally normal. These 10 percent are either not infected at all or are infected but have not entered the cytolytic interaction. Since we have a "steady state" in our mouse cultures, which cannot be explained solely by the high heat stability of Polyoma, I would like to believe that these chromosomally normal cells, which are dividing actively at all times, throw off variants susceptible to Polyoma infection.

Eagle: At what stage does the transformation take place? Somewhere—

Bayreuther: The transformed cells can only come from the chromosomally normal population.

Eagle: As a result of what? I'm not clear yet.

Bayreuther: Well, we really don't know.

Eagle: As to what happens in the transformation?

Bayreuther: We really do not know more; we do not understand the mechanism of transformation.

Atwood: Does the multiplicity of infection make any difference to that percentage, 10 or 90?

Bayreuther: Yes, it does. The percentage of polyploid cells is directly related to the virus input within 24 hours after infection, that is during the first growth cycle. We thought of developing a new virus assay system this way. It would be more sensitive than the plaque assay and very much faster.

Atwood: I think you have to be careful about ascribing chromosome breakage to a highly specific action of the virus; it is caused by various other cytotoxic agents as well.

I wanted to mention some experiments of Nomura (76) which are pertinent to this, although they are in bacteria. You know that phage was supposed to break up the bacterial chromosome, so he wanted to test this directly. The experiment was to infect conjugating pairs in which the Hfr was phage sensitive and the F⁻ resistant. After the host processes in Hfr were turned off by the infection, an intact chromosome segment could be transferred to F⁻. The point is that the host-specific processes are not turned off primarily because of chromosome damage, but the destruction of the chromosome occurs later and is apparently secondary.

Bayreuther: This is possible, particularly in the light of the data of Frankling and Baltimore (29).

DeMars: Is this work of Nomura's you are referring to done with intact phages or with the phage ghost?

Atwood: I am not sure. I think he did it with both. He has worked with ghosts, intact phage, formalin-killed phage, and a colicin which has properties similar to the T6 attachment site.

Bayreuther: We have thought of the possibility that it could be a contaminating substance or agent. But since we got the same results with cesium chloride density gradient purified virus, I think it is excluded. But now I would like to continue with my report about our work on transformation.

As important as the finding is that one can obtain neoplastic transformation by these DNA-viruses in mass cultures, a quantitative assay system for transformation is needed for the study of the mechanism of cell-virus-interaction on the cellular level. Such an assay system for Polyoma has been described by Stoker (94). It makes use of an established line of hamster kidney cells that exhibit, however, already all neoplastic properties. It reacts with morphological changes after infection with Polyoma. Such morphological changes occur, however, also spontaneously. In addition, tumors arise at the site of inoculation when cells of this line are implanted, regardless of whether these cells were infected with Polyoma or not. These and many additional features make the system described by Stoker inadequate. The phenomena studied are clearly of secondary nature superimposed on an already fully neoplastic cell.

Attempts have been undertaken to develop a universal assay system and two quantitative routine assay systems for DNA tumor viruses mediated neoplastic transformation *in vitro* have been established: (1) for Polyoma virus on hamster heart cells and rat embryo fibroblasts, (2) for SV40 virus on hamster embryo fibroblasts. Since both systems are basically the same I would like to restrict myself to the Polyoma system on rat embryo cells.

Female rats of the inbred strain Lewis are sacrificed when 13 days pregnant. The embryos are removed aseptically; the head and the inner organs are removed. The inner organs were found to harbor an interfering virus of unknown nature, and in addition, some of the inner organs, particularly the liver and kidney, enter in infective interaction with Polyoma. The carcases are trypsinized. The cells are grown in Puck-Eagle's medium, which is supplemented with tryptose phosphate broth and 20 percent fetal calf serum. The cell type growing out is fibroblastic. After three days these cells are transferred to 60 mm dishes and 24 hours later infected with purified Polyoma virus Dishes seeded with 10^6 cells showed a multilayer felt of criss-crossing cells twelve days after infection. Dishes seeded with 10^5 cells had focal areas of piling up cells of equal size and distribution. 10^5 cells on a 60 mm dish appeared to be the ideal cell concentration and have been used since then. 10^5 cells cover only about 5 to 10 percent of the bottom area of the dish, and it takes about 4 to 5 days before a confluent layer is formed. Studies of the efficiency of cloning at different times after infection showed that cloning efficiency rose from 4 to about 40 percent 48 hours after infection, indicating that the malignant phenotype is expressed at that time. When at that time 2×10^6 noninfected cells were added, the expression of foci was completely interfered with, indicating that these newly transformed cells do still show "contact inhibition." From experiments in which normal cells were added, 72, 96, and 120 hours after infection it appears that accumulations of only 32 to 64 neoplastic cells are able to overcome the inhibiting effect of the surrounding normal cells to express themselves in a focus.

Besides the cell-concentration the nutritional conditions were found to be extremely important for the expression of the foci. It is generally known that neoplastic cells can multiply in rather poor nutritional conditions that do not support the growth of normal cells. The aim was therefore to find nutritional conditions that favor the selective outgrowth of neoplastic cells and slow down the nontransformed ones. After a long period of trial and error it was found that a tenfold reduction of the two basic amino acids, arginine and lysine, in the medium, and the replacement of 20 percent fetal bovine serum by 10 percent calf serum resulted in ideal nutritional conditions for the expression of the foci. At the present time we grow the primary cultures in Puck-Eagle's medium, designated PEM, supplemented by tryptose phosphate broth and 20 percent fetal bovine serum. The 10^5 rat embryo cells seeded on 60 mm dishes for the focus assay are kept for 24 hours in this rich medium and the plating efficiency is almost 100 percent. After infection the cells are overlaid with low concentration arginine-lysine PEM, supplemented with 10 percent calf serum and 10 percent tryptose phosphate broth. Three fluid changes are undertaken with this medium on the fourth, eighth, and tenth day. The foci are counted on day 12. The foci are at that time piles made up of about 2-5 $\times$ 10^3 cells, which are somehow brownish and contrast well with the white monolayer of normal background cells. The foci can be counted macroscopically.

Detailed investigations were undertaken to study the properties of the cells in foci and of focal lines at various times after isolation. As mentioned before, each focus contains about 2-5 $\times$ 10^3 cells at 12 days after infection. When such a focus or a greater number of them—cell numbers tested were in the range of 10^3-10^7—were transplanted subcutaneously into 15-day-old inbred rats, no tumors resulted at the site of inoculation. When foci were grown out to form focal lines, the transplantability (5 $\times$ 10^6) of the cells of the focal lines at early transfers was very low or absent and increased with later transfers. The cells of the focal lines were examined for two properties: the presence of infectious virus and the changes in the biological behavior (transplantability, cloning efficiency) and its relationship to chromosomal variation.

No virus was found in foci, early and late focal lines. Whereas these results made it unlikely that the Polyoma-induced neoplastic conversion was a consequence of the presence of a multiplying plaque-forming virus within the cells, they did not exclude the possibility that neoplastic properties depended on the presence within the cells of the virus in a defective state. Additional experiments were therefore carried out to test the following possible states of the virus in the converted cells:

A) The presence of a provirus having properties similar to those of prophage in lysogenic bacteria. X-rays and mitomycin, known to induce the formation of mature phage in lysogenic bacteria, and different conditions of starvation were applied. Since thymine deprivation induces the usually noninducible bacteriophage, the effect of aminopterin was also tested. The drugs mitomycin and aminopterin were removed after 12 to 24 hours, and the cultures were subsequently incubated in the presence of thymidine. In addition, focal lines have been superinfected with lp (large plaque) and sp (small plaque)

Polyoma DNA and SV40 DNA under hypertonic conditions in an attempt to rescue a defective genome. Seven days after these various treatments the cultures were harvested and assayed for plaque formation. No plaques were observed.

B) The possibility was tested that the neoplastic cells produced an oncogenic but noncytocidal virus. For this purpose, freeze-thawed cells and supernatant from several foci, early and late focal lines were tested with and without inducing treatment as mentioned before for the capacity to convert rat embryo cells to neoplastic cells. All trials were unsuccessful.

C) Attempts were undertaken to extract infectious nucleic acids from neoplastic cells after various inducing treatments. No DNA active for plaque or focus formation could be found.

Thus, all attempts to induce virus-synthesis in Polyoma-converted rat embryo cells and hamster embryo cells have completely failed (116).

The studies in the chromosome variation were prompted by the presence of an often unusually high number of dead cells in the focal lines at a time when no Polyoma virus could be detected. Many of the dead cells were doublets arrested at ana-telophase showing clearly anaphase bridges in the living state. Coverslip cultures were prepared at various transfer generations of the focal lines. They showed that the proportion of dead cells, as estimated semiquantitatively, correlated well with the proportion of mitosis which contained chromatid bridges. This proportion was very high in the early transfers (50 to 80 percent), at later transfers it decreased and progressively tended to that of the controls. These late transformed cells have a high transplantability, a very high cloning efficiency. The foci have a normal karyotype, the late transformed cells have a stable abnormal karyotype.

It appears from this that the neoplastic transformation of normal rat embryo cells caused by Polyoma virus occurs in at least two steps, and that the action of the virus is at least twofold: on the one hand, it causes the primary transformation of the cells, on the other hand it provides the mechanism for additional genetical variation of early transformed cells. The evolution of the early focal lines is probably one aspect of the phenomenon of tumor progression, which has been recognized as a constant property of cancers in animals. The finding of the chromosome breaks raises the question whether the progression observed in this system is due to gross chromosomal aberrations caused by the breaks. Such a view would be supported by the findings that most of the late focal lines are aneuploid. On the other hand, the chromatid breaks may not be directly involved in the progression, they could rather be a symptom of irregularities in the process of DNA replication in the transformed cells, able to cause several different consequences, including progression. The presented observations are relevant to the problem of the fate of the viral DNA in transformed cells. No virus nor viral DNA detectable by infectivity has been found. These results show that autonomously replicating Polyoma virus DNA is not present in the transformed cells; they do not, however, exclude the presence of an integrated viral DNA. Three points are in favor of this idea: (1) the relative to absolute immunity of these transformed cells to superinfection, (2) the presence of a new cell surface antigen in Polyoma-transformed cells which is not related to the Polyoma coat antigen, (3) the production of chromatid breaks in the focal lines, which continue to be produced after infectious virus has disappeared.

Functionally, the primary action of the virus in the transformation of rat embryo cells appears to be a release of the regulation of cell multiplication and contact inhibition. In cells in which the original change has taken place, some of the chromosomal aberrations subsequently produced acquire a selective value. A stepwise process, as it has been described for *in vivo* systems like the Shope Papilloma-Carcinoma sequence in rabbits by myself and others, leads thus finally to the fully malignant cell.

Szybalski: Do I understand correctly that there is neither infectious virus nor viral protein?

Bayreuther: There is no viral protein, no infectious DNA, and no infectious virus.

Szybalski: No infectious DNA?

Bayreuther: No, no infectious DNA.

Koprowski: Have you tried susceptibility to superinfections of Polyoma?

Bayreuther: Yes. The transformed hamster and rat embryo cells are immune to superinfection.

Eagle: How do you interpret the fact that the fetal calf serum does not permit this hyperplastic—

Bayreuther: Under fetal bovine serum the neoplastic cells do not pile up, the assay does not work.

Eagle: But is it that the biological change has not been produced or is it that you can't demonstrate it? Have the cells been, in fact, transformed by the virus?

Bayreuther: Yes, they are transformed, but they form a multilayer felt under fetal bovine serum instead of piling up.

DeMars: Is the number of foci formed in the hamster system proportional to the amount of virus?

Bayreuther: Oh, yes. When dishes with 10^5 rat embryo cells were infected with tenfold dilutions in the range 1 to 10^{-10} of a lp-Polyoma stock with 10^{11} PFU/ml, it was found that no foci could be induced when less than 10^6 were used for infection. At 10^6 PFU about 1 focus, at 10^7 PFU/ml about 10 foci, at 10^8 PFU/ml about 100 foci were counted. At higher inputs the curve levels off; when, however, 10^5 cells are seeded on a 100 mm dish and infected with 10^9 PFU/ml 800 to 1000 have been counted. The linearity established over three logs in the range of 10^6 to 10^9 PFU indicates that one single virus particle is directly responsible for the transformation. In contrast to the Rous-system, where the PP/FFU ratio was found to be in the order of 60:1 to 6:1, the PP/PFU/FFU ratio is $10^8 : 10^6 : 1$ for lp-Polyoma. For the two small plaque mutants the ratio PFU:FFU was found to be $10^5 : 1$, indicating that the small plaque Polyoma is ten times more efficient. This is a rather insane ratio of virus particles to cell.

Physical particle counts of virus populations of large and small plaque mutants with the same PFU titer showed, however, that the ratio PP:PFU for lp was $10^2 : 1$, that for sp $10^3 : 1$. This difference is also reflected in the difference of the ratio PFU:HAU for lp and sp which is $10^5 : 1$ for lp, but $10^6 : 1$ for sp. Thus, most likely the tenfold higher number of physical particles in the sp stocks, which is not expressed in the lytic interaction, accounts for the difference in transformation efficiency of these two mutants.

About the same viral efficiency was found for SV40 when focus-assayed on hamster embryo cells. SV40 is a latent passenger in Rhesus kidney, and was isolated from Sabin's and Salk's poliomyelitis vaccines. In physical and chemical properties it likens to Polyoma, and when tested it causes cancer in hamster cells *in vivo* and *vitro,* and in a variety of human cells *in vitro* (89, 90). We developed a plaque assay for SV40 on an established green monkey cell line, and can grow titers to 10^9 PFU/ml. SV40 forms in the cesium chloride density gradient three bands, the biological activity was found to reside at 1.29. The PP:PFU:FFU ratio was found to be $10^8 : 10^5 : 1$, for several stocks grown out from different plaque isolates.

Under the conditions described the cellular efficiency was found to be about 1 percent for both systems.

DeMars: Of course, the amount of virus may differ. You pointed out that the efficiency of the conversion in one system was about one per 100 cells. But this could represent the activity of one out of 10^6 or one out of 10^7 virus particles that you put in. As you pointed out, you are using what you said was an insane ratio of virus particles to cells. Now, did you discuss at all the question of whether you were dealing with a rare component of the virus population?

Bayreuther: Yes, it was our hope to find an agent in early foci that would have a high transforming capacity. All attempts failed. The other approach was to look for density mutants. Polyoma forms three bands in the cesium chloride density gradient. The biological activity resides only in one, which cannot be fractionated any further.

Szybalski: Could the system be somewhat analogous to the defective phage lamda dg? Since you do not superinfect the cells with a related functional virus you might have difficulties in releasing your "Polyoma dg," since they might be defective in some functions supplied only by the superinfecting virus.

Bayreuther: We tried to superinfect with Polyoma virus and Polyoma DNA, with negative results. It is quite possible, as you said, that the virus is defective and that the Polyoma DNA used for the rescue becomes defective upon entering a tumor cell. Polyoma seems to be a bad candidate for a helper, since it has only a weak cytolytic interaction with hamster heart and rat embryo cells. A more promising candidate could be the rat virus, which has a strong cytolytic interaction with both tissues.

It should perhaps be mentioned here that Winocour, Green, and Dulbecco are trying to use the DNA-RNA hybridization technique to test whether the Polyoma genome or parts of it are still present in neoplastic cells. So far they have worked out the conditions for the production of highly labeled RNA on the E. coli cell-free system, using Polyoma virus DNA as a primer.

DeMars: There might be another way of getting at the nature of these focus formers, even though the foci themselves do not produce virus. You say you grow this virus by infecting the animal. In kidneys?

Bayreuther: No, we grow only stocks in them.

DeMars: That's fair enough. You then take the infected kidneys out and put them in tissue culture?

Bayreuther: Yes.

DeMars: The indication here is that if it is a mutant, it is quite rare, and possibly only one cell in very many, perhaps, one cell in a quarter of a kidney, would liberate a clone of this mutant virus.

Wouldn't it be possible to infect the hamster in the usual way, and then to cut up the kidney, cultivating the cells from each portion separately?

Bayreuther: Oh, yes, that is a good idea.

DeMars: Different parts of the same kidney should yield virus populations of very different transforming ability.

Bayreuther: That would be a fluctuation analysis. We have thought of using the isolates from a greater number of plaques. The precondition for the success of such an approach would be, however, that the hypothetical mutant would have no selective disadvantage, otherwise we would select against it in the many multiplication cycles needed to grow high titer stocks.

Atwood: Another possibility is that the heterogeneity is in the cell somehow.

Bayreuther: Yes, that is quite true. We tried to synchronize the cells, with little success for primary or secondary cultures. There is not only physiological heterogeneity, we found genetical heterogeneity within litters, and in addition interfering viruses. It is surprising that it works at all.

Part 2

Neel: We will go on with the discussion of marker traits. Despite all of that furious discussion yesterday, we have made only a dent. We covered some aspects of biochemical, antigenic, and nutritional markers. We did not get into such topics as virus resistance as a marker, chromosome markers, and difference in culture morphology or in drug resistance. It seemed as if, in view of the work that Dr. Szybalski has done, it might be well to start this morning off with drug resistance.

Drug Resistance as a Genetic Marker

by Dr. Waclaw Szybalski

Szybalski: I should like to make one thing clear and I almost feel like apologizing for it. We are working with only one cell strain. It is a strain of human origin, an established cell line. I do not know

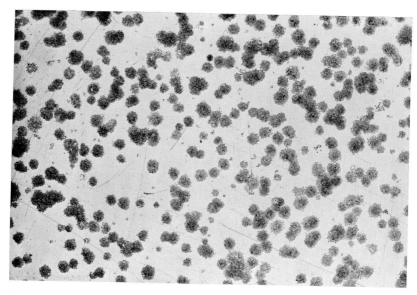

Figure 44. The projected image of methylene blue-stained colonies (clones) grown for 7 days (36°C, 5 percent CO_2 atmosphere, Eagle's medium supplemented with 10 percent horse serum) after seeding of a 60-mm plastic dish with 5000 D98S cells.

whether studies employing this cell line bear any relationship to the genetics of normal human traits, but at the time, our decision to use this cell line was based on its favorable cultural characteristics: it grew very well, plated with high efficiency, and in many respects we preferred it to the well-known HeLa cell line. As shown in Figure 44, this strain forms rather compact and uniform colonies which could easily be scored. It plates with an efficiency of 80 to 100 percent.

McKusick: What strain is this?

Szybalski: This strain was originally derived from a normal sternal human puncture by Berman and Stulberg (3), and was called Detroit-98 (D98). It is apparently of nonmalignant human origin. At present, it has a chromosomal complement of 63, plus or minus one, and this modal number is stable.

Now I would like to say a few words about the genetic markers that we have developed with this strain. However, before I discuss it I should perhaps tell something about the selective systems employed in this study.

The pathways of purine synthesis are illustrated in Figure 45. Inosinic acid (IMP) is the key intermediate. This compound can be

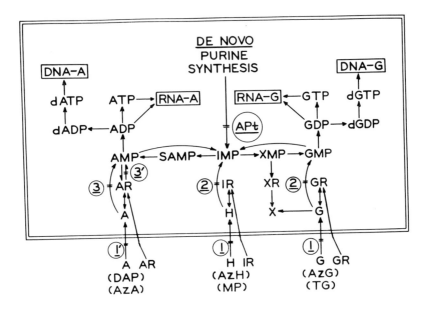

Figure 45. Abbreviated representation of the *de novo* and *preformed* pathways of purine metabolism in D98 mutant cell lines. A, H, X, G: adenine, hypoxanthine, xanthine, guanine; R: ribosides; MP, DP, TP: mono-, di-, triphosphates; IR: inosine; S-AMP: adenylosuccinic acid; d: deoxynucleotides; *1, 1'*: block in uptake of H, G, 8-azaH (AzH), 8-azaG (AzG), 6-thioG (TG), 6-mercapto-purine (MP), A, 8-azaA (AzA), 2, 6-diaminopurine (DAP), prior to ribophos-phorylation; *2*: block in ribophosphorylation of H, G, and their analogs; *3, 3'*: partial or complete block in ribophosphorylation of A and its analogs, and in AMP kinase activity, respectively; APt: aminopterin-imposed block of *de novo* pathway of inosinic acid biosynthesis (HAT medium). Mutation from D98S to D98/AG corresponds to blocks *1* and *1'*; from D98/AG to D98/AGR to partial block of *2*; from D98/AG to D98/AH to complete block of *2*; from D98/AH to D98/AH-R to partial restoration of pathway *2*.
Reproduced from Szybalski and Szybalska (99).

synthesized by two independent pathways: either through the long chain of reactions starting from PRPP (*de novo* pathway) or through direct ribophosphorylation of hypoxanthine (*preformed* pathway). This is a typical case of *convergent* biochemical pathways, and it is schematically presented in Figure 46. Usually, our cells use the *de novo* pathway, since there is no hypoxanthine in the medium. The *preformed* pathway, however, becomes very deleterious to the cell when hypoxanthine analogs are present in the medium, e.g., 8-azahypoxan-thine. The enzyme of the *preformed* pathway, IMP-pyrophosphorylase

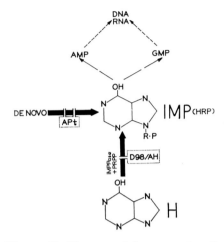

Figure 46. Diagram of "convergent pathways" leading to the synthesis of inosinic acid (IMP). For details cf. Figure 45.

(IMPPase) converts the innocuous 8-azahypoxanthine (AzH) to highly toxic 8-azainosinic acid (AzHRP). Thus the presence of AzH creates highly selective conditions under which IMPPase-deficient mutant cells are selected, which are immune to AzH, since they cannot convert it to the toxic nucleotide, AzHRP.

In this manner we isolated an AzH-resistant D98/AH cell line, which grows perfectly well and plates with close to 100 percent efficiency at AzH concentrations up to 500 μg/ml while the parental D98S line is partially inhibited even by 0.1 μg AzH/ml and all the D98S cells are killed and eliminated at concentrations above 0.5 μg AzH/ml with the exception of the AzH-resistant mutants.

This type of resistant mutant cell line has been developed also by several other research groups in the field, including Dr. Herzenberg, if my memory is correct.

Herzenberg: A number of people have found drug resistant mammalian cells, including Roosa and myself (85). Azaguanine as well.

Szybalski: We have listed most of the references pertaining to the *in vitro* isolation of analog-resistant mammalian cell lines in our more recent reviews on this subject (102, 100). In referring to the latter papers you would find also that the situation is much more complex than that presented hitherto by me. In addition to the parental line D98S and the highly AzH-resistant mutant line D98/AH we have a line D98/AG which was isolated from the D98S line by virtue of its

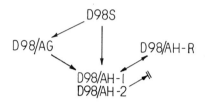

Figure 47. Origin of mutant lines referred to in this presentation and derived from the parental cell culture, D98S. The approximate inhibitory thresholds for purine analogs were as follows: D98S — 0.1 μg AzG/ml, 0.1 μg Azh/ml; D98/AG — 10 μg AzG/ml, 0.3 μg AzH/ml; D98/AH — 300 μg AzG/ml, 1500 μg AzH/ml; D98/AH-R — 100 μg AzG/ml, 20 μg AzH/ml. The following hypoxanthine (H) concentrations permitted growth in the presence of 0.02 μg aminopterin and 5 μg thymidine per ml of Eagle's medium: 0.1 μg H/ml — D98S and D98/AH-R; 0.5 μg H/ml — D98/AG; up to 500 μg H/ml did not permit any growth of D98/AH cells. For further details cf. references (102) and (100).

100-fold increased resistance to 8-azaguanine (AzG) when compared with the D98S parent (Fig. 47). Line D98/AG which is only two times more resistant to AzH than line D98S still retains full IMPPase activity. Complete tables of cross resistance of these and of other mutant lines are presented in the above-mentioned papers (102, 100). The chromosomal constitution of all these mutant lines seems to be identical.

Up to now I have discussed the selective systems for isolation of resistant cells. Let us turn now to the converse task, the selection of sensitive mutants. I have already stated that the D98/AH mutant lacks IMPPase and thus cannot form IMP from hypoxanthine (Fig. 46). This lack of the *preformed* pathway is harmless to the cell as long as the *de novo* pathway of IMP synthesis is operating. If, however, we block this *de novo* pathway, the growth of D98/AH cells is blocked and cannot be restored by addition of hypoxanthine, since the D98/AH mutants lacking IMPPase cannot utilize hypoxanthine. On the other hand, the IMPPase-producing parental lines, D98S or D98/AG, or the revertant, D98/AH-R, thrown off by some D98/AH sublines, can synthesize IMP by the *preformed* pathway and thus can overcome the biochemical block artifically imposed on the *de novo* pathway.

Eagle: How is the *de novo* pathway blocked?

Szybalski: We block the *de novo* pathway by the folic acid reductase inhibitor, aminopterin (APt) which, by the way, is an analog of folic acid. APt is a very efficient inhibitor of the *de novo* pathway, blocking two reactions. APt, however, inhibits several other "single carbon transfers" leading to the synthesis of thymidylic acid and a few amino acids. To offset these secondary inhibitory effects of APt we had to supplement the medium with thymidine; the required amino acids were already present in the standard Eagle's medium. Thus, our medium, which selects for hypoxanthine-utilizing "AzH-sensitive" cells, contains hypoxanthine (5 μg/ml). APt (0.02 μg/ml) and thymidine (5μg/ml) and is called HAT medium for short.

Herzenberg: Anything else in this HAT medium?

Szybalski: No. All of our IMPPase-producing cell lines (D98S, D98/AG, D98/AH-R) grow in this HAT medium just as well as in the normal Eagle's medium.

Herzenberg: Do you use whole serum in the medium?

Szybalski: Yes. We are using 10 percent horse serum. Hakala (35) in her studies on reversion of APt toxicity found it necessary, with her cell line, to add also glycine, which normally is not present in Eagle's basal medium (in addition to thymidine and a purine nucleoside). We did not find, however, any necessity for supplementation of HAT medium with glycine.

DeMars: There is a little question here that has never really been cleared up; that is, using dialyzed serum with HeLa cells, I found no requirement for serine or glycine in cells otherwise blocked with aminopterin, and those are the things that you might expect to be necessary, as you implied. They have never been necessary, so there must be some other way for the cells to make their glycine and/or serine, in this circumstance. They will grow without serine and glycine in the presence of aminopterin in dialyzed serum.

Szybalski: Aminopterin and amethopterin were used by other workers in this field to select for aminopterin-resistant cells. Both Dr. Herzenberg and Dr. DeMars have published papers on this subject. In addition, Dr. DeMars was using aminopterin for quite ingenious experiments involving selection of auxotrophic mutants (17). Some features of his system might, at first sight, appear similar to our selective procedure, but I would like to stress that his was based on quite a different principle and it was used for quite a different purpose.

Chu: Were your forward and reverse mutations induced by some agent, or were they spontaneous?

Szybalski: Those which we were discussing up to now were of spontaneous origin. I was supposed to talk only about genetic markers, but I could perhaps add just a few sentences about induced mutations. It is obvious that we have tried to apply our selective systems for the study of mutagenicity in human cells, and, to our great surprise we did not find up to now a single effective mutagen, although we tested at least 50 known mutagens, under many different conditions (102, 100). Worse than that, about half of our putative "mutagens" reduced the spontaneous mutation rates by a factor of 2 to 5. This could almost be called embarrassing.

Renwick: Can you tell us what the mutagens actually were?

Szybalski: UV, X rays, several nitrogen mustards, 5-bromodeoxyuridine, 5-iododeoxyuridine, colchicine, betapropiolactone, and many other alkylating agents, some antibiotics, which have shown cytotoxicity, etc. Once upon a time I studied extensively mutagenicity in bacteria, and I still have a large supply of different goodies (97).

Koprowski: Did you use carcinogens?

Szybalski: Yes, we did and, again, without success. We tried 2-acetylaminofluorene (AAF) and its more active natural metabolite, N-hydroxy-AAF, since Dr. James Miller at McArdle kindly supplied us with these compounds. These compounds were toxic to our cells, but we never had any success with increasing the mutation rate above the spontaneous level, under our experimental conditions, with our selective system. And I would like to stress that this system looked as if it should yield the type of mutation which is easiest to get, since we were selecting toward loss of enzyme function (loss of IMP-Pase activity). This is a forward mutation, usually caused by many types of damage in the proper cistron (DNA).

Patau: How high did you go with the X-ray dose?

Szybalski: From 90 percent survival down to as little as 1 percent survival.

Herzenberg: What is the spontaneous frequency of the mutations?

Szybalski: The mutation rate from D98S to D98/AG is $2\text{-}5 \times 10^{-4}$ per cell per generation; from D98/AG to D98/AH:- 10^{-6} per cell per generation; from D98/AH-1 to D98/AH-R:- approximately 10^{-4} per cell per generation; from D98/AH-2 to D98/AH-R:- less than 10^{-8} per cell per generation. D98/AH-1 and D98/AH-2 are AzH-resistant mutants of indepedent origin. These two lines represent extremes in the reverse mutation rate toward gain of IMPPase function. The spontaneous mutation, however, from loss to gain of the enzyme IMPPase is not a true reversion. The enzyme which the cell gains most probably is structurally somewhat different from the original one.

DeMars: That doesn't mean it is not a reversion, at the locus.

Szybalski: I mean that the cell does not regain the original parental phenotype.

Patau: You tested also the mutation with the highest mutation rate with X-rays, and didn't find any increase in that particular strain?

Szybalski: No. We did not test the mutagens on the D98/AH-1 to D98/AH-R reversions, in any systematic manner.

Lejeune: Do you have any proof of any chromosome change in the strain when the cells became sensitive or when they became resistant?

Szybalski: No. Dr. A. Levan spent some time with us, examining cytologically our parental and mutant cells. He did not find any clear-cut chromosomal differences between the mutants lines.

Patau: The fact that you got a sort of inverse mutation, even if not strictly the same, really speaks against a chromosomal rearrangement. With a rate of between 10^{-4} to 10^{-5}, I can't quite conceive that you would get with that frequency, any specific—

Lejeune: Well, you could, because you are dealing with a cell which is a hyperdiploid, which has many chromosomes, and the change has only to be in one particular chromosome.

DeMars: Even so, the fact that you do get these reversions would not speak against aneuploid variations without actual fragmentation or rearrangement of individual chromosomes, and Marguerite Vogt published some work in which two different types of mutants of hyperdiploids, HeLa cells, showed characteristic aneuploid changes accompanying the changes in phenotype. One of these changes was polio resistance, and the other was aminopterin resistance.

I think there is other work that has been published by people who work with mouse cells, where changes to aminopterin resistance were associated with changes in karyotype; so it is very important here not only to rule out rearrangements of chromosomes, but also changes in numbers of particular chromosomes.

Patau: But in Dr. Szybalski's case there was no change in chromosome number, so that makes it a bit more difficult.

DeMars: We are being forced closer to an acceptance of the idea that this might be, in some sense, a point mutation.

Szybalski: It is pleasant to think about it this way. There is, however, one very serious complication that everybody realizes: this forward mutation toward complete loss of an enzyme is obviously a mutation to a recessive state and should not be phenotypically expressed where the parental line consists of diploid homozygous cells. There is a way out, in our case, when we assume either that our aneuploid D98S cell line is haploid for the chromosome which carries the IMPPase determinant, or that D98S is heterozygous for the IMPPase marker.

Herzenberg: Isn't this in your experience one of the easiest kinds of resistance to get, and in the experience of others, that azaguanine or mercaptopurine resistance develops very quickly in any cell line you look at? From any sort of cells, whether it comes from a homozygous mouse, in which you wouldn't expect to have a heterozygous condition for a gene like this, in any cell you look at, the frequency of resistance of this sort varies from 10^{-3} to 10^{-6}.

Szybalski: Yes, I believe you.

Herzenberg: I don't know what this means, but it is a fact I would like to verify, to know if it is correct, in your experience.

Szybalski: I am afraid that I cannot answer this question in general terms since we have firsthand experience only with derivatives of one aneuploid cell line. Most of the other published work was done with tumor lines. I do not think any work was done with cell lines which could be safely classified as homozygous diploid for the IMPPase locus. I really don't know.

Herzenberg: The cells of the mouse fibroblasts all started from C3H mice. Aronow (109) has worked on this, and it seems to be a very common kind of resistance to obtain. None of this is very critical. It is just something that we ought, perhaps, to keep in the back of our minds.

Szybalski: Since the cells do not require the IMPPase-dependent preformed pathway, they could very easily become heterozygous for it, since there would be only minimal selective pressure to keep this double safeguard.

Herzenberg: In culture, you mean?

Szybalski: Yes, in culture. [Afterthought: But perhaps also *in vivo*. Maybe IMPPase is on the X chromosome. This is another possibility.]

Renwick: Would it be worth repeating some of these high mutagenic experiments with different oxygen tensions and low methionine concentrations?

Szybalski: You mean, with X rays?

Renwick: Particularly with X rays, yes.

Szybalski: No, we did not try to X-irradiate cells in methionine-free medium. We always irradiated them in Eagle's medium. But with UV, we used just the balanced salt solution, since Eagle's medium is UV-absorbing.

Renwick: But this is rather a strange situation, when you don't get any increase with any of these mutagens—

Neel: Is there any parallel situation known in which a metabolic variant which occurs in a measurable frequency such as this does not occur with an increased frequency, despite treatment with all of the known mutagens?

Szybalski: There are many so-called "mutagen-stable" mutants in bacteria, but these were studied mainly for reverse mutations to prototrophy.

Atwood: Sure, but they are a special class of mutants occurring in the same cistrons as the normally unstable mutants. It's quite different from this case in which every mutant you find is not revertable by mutagens. Is that right?

Szybalski: Yes, I agree with you.

Patau: Have any of your so-called inverse mutations a mutation rate as low as the original one? The one that first makes a block.

Szybalski: The mutation rate toward loss of IMPPase was about 10^{-6}, while the rate of gain varied from less than 10^{-8} to 10^{-4} per cell per generation. You should remember, however, that by the spontaneous "reverse" mutation we do not regain the original (parental) enzyme.

Patau: But is it possible that your initial mutation required several steps? You gave a spontaneous rate of 10^{-6}; could there possibly be two events that are required?

Szybalski: I think that mutation toward loss of IMPPase is a single-step mutation. We obtained these IMPPase-deficient D98/AH mutants both from D98S and D98/AG lines. Their frequency was constant both at barely inhibitory and 1000 times higher concentrations of AzH, which result argues for single-step mutation.

Herzenberg: May I ask, this is still a two-step process, actually, and when you start with D98S to get to AH, you can divide this into two steps. If you select with azaguanine at low concentration, you will get what I think is a permease or at least a permeability mutant of some sort. Then, the frequency from that, from your first step to your second step is about 10^{-3}, isn't it?

Szybalski: No, not 10^{-3} but 10^{-6}. The mutation rate is in the neighborhood of 10^{-6} independent of whether we select D98/AH mutants among D98/AG cells (our original D98/AH mutants were found that way), or among D98S cells.

Eagle: Does the D98/AH mutant obtained directly from D98S, also lack permeability to azaguanine?

Szybalski: We didn't determine it in any direct test. The only evidence indicating that there might be some permeability factor involved, which distinguishes D98S from the D98/AG mutants stems from the following two experiments: (1) The intracellular content of IMP.GMP-pyrophosphorylase is identical* in both the D98S and D98/AG cells, when assayed in cell-free extracts. (2) Intact D98S cells convert C^{14}-hypoxanthine, C^{14}-guanine, and C^{14}-azaguanine to the corresponding nucleotides several times more efficiently than D98/AG cells. These experiments were done in collaboration with Dr. R. W. Brockman (101).

Herzenberg: You could look for reversion in the presence of aza-guanine, but maybe we should go on.

Szybalski: In addition to guanine- and hypoxanthine-analog-resistant mutants we have a few aminopterin-resistant lines, but we did not study these in any detail. We have also some adenine analog-resistant mutants, but only with 2- to 3-fold increase in resistance. In the latter system the presence of the adenosine kinase (Fig. 45) makes it more difficult to isolate mutants. To eliminate two parallel path-ways of adenine to adenylic acid (AMP) conversion (phosphorylase + kinase and AMP-pyrophosphorylase) requires two mutations.

Renwick: Among your mutagens, did you try colchicine or colchi-cine-like agents?

Szybalski: Yes, we did try colchicine, but it was not mutagenic.

Eagle: Did you say that the 6-mercaptopurine resistance was anal-ogous to this, as a one-step resistance?

Szybalski: Exactly. 6-Mercaptopurine and 8-azahypoxanthine are interchangeable. The mutants which are resistant to azahypoxanthine are resistant to 6-mercaptopurine, and *vice versa.*

Lejeune: Do you have any idea of the use of this system in diploid cells?

DeMars: We have tried, with no success. We have tried 6-mer-captopurine, 8-azaguanine and aminopterin, and with hyperdiploid strains, mutants resistant to all three of these agents are very readily obtained. With several different strains of diploid cells, we were never able to obtain resistant mutants.

Szybalski: This may answer some earlier questions of Dr. Herzen-berg.

Eagle: To what extent was your inability to obtain such mutants referable to difficulty with the cloning of diploid cells?

DeMars: I can't give a satisfactory answer to that. I don't believe that was the problem. Our cells were growing well when we were carrying out these selection experiments.

---

* "GMP" stands for guanosine monophosphate.

Eagle: Growing well as single cells?

DeMars: Growing well as far as populations go. With HeLa cells, when these agents work, the cells quickly die and fall from the glass; they disappear, and then you are up against a cloning problem. With the diploid cells, however, the carcasses of the cells stay there forever. In a sense, they could act as a feeder layer.

Eagle: But not necessarily.

DeMars: Not necessarily, and that is why I said I can't give a satisfactory answer.

Gartler: Harris and Ruddle (37) have obtained resistant pig cell lines to 6-mercaptopurine from a parental line which is diploid in number but has at least one abnormal chromosome.

Koprowski: Could I ask for the definition of a normal diploid line?

Szybalski: Don't ask me, please.

Gartler: How about you, Dr. Lejeune?

Lejeune: I would consider as normal a cell which has an apparently normal karyotype. This is not saying that the genetic content is normal, because it's not the thing which is under test.

Koprowski: Can you have abnormal chromosomes?

Lejeune: No, not grossly [visibly] abnormal chromosomes.

Szybalski: Maybe I should proceed. We tried to regain the phenotype, that is, the production of IMPPase, not only by the reverse genetic step, but also by using fluorouracil along the lines proposed by Benzer, with his idea of changing the "messenger RNA" code. With the D98/AH mutants which we studied we were not able to detect the formation of any IMPPase when growing the cells of subinhibitory concentrations of fluorouracil. This will be all as far as the mutants and selective systems are concerned. More details could be found in our papers (102, 100).

Renwick: There is one mechanism for producing this forward mutation which might not be sensitive to any of these mutagens. That would be cell fusion. Is there any evidence that the nuclei are larger in the resistant lines?

Szybalski: I didn't see any morphologic differences, either on the cellular level or on the colony level or on the chromosomal level among all our mutants. If there are any, these are nondetectable.

Gartler: It seems to me, if it is out of order to talk about transformation, it is out of order to talk about cell fusion at this time. [Laughter]

Eagle: I don't want to harp on this, but in the extension of this kind of study to diploid cells, which would be both important and interesting, we are faced with the problem of cloning. It is possible that the inhibited cells may act as a feeder layer, but it is also possible that they are killed dead, so to speak, and do not act as a feeder layer. In that case, our ability to clone diploid cultures is central to the problem of getting this kind of mutations isolated from culture.

Lejeune: There is something I do not understand, really. Why are you obliged to clone? If you have cells growing, let's say, out of an explant, you just remove the explant. If you have medium that will kill every cell but not the mutant, you don't need to have any cloning. This cell will grow.

Herzenberg: That is a clone.

Eagle: You are cloning. If you have a mutational frequency in this situation, of 10^{-6}, this means that, roughly, as a million cells divide, you will get one cell which is capable of growing, and that is a cloning situation: unless the other million cells which are being killed can temporarily act as a feeder layer, which is an assumption which may not be valid.

Szybalski: Shall I go ahead?

Neel: Yes. We are going to make a gradual transition to the afternoon.

Szybalski: Since we had a selective system, we could not resist the temptation to use it for some good purpose; I mean to look for some rare genetic events. We hoped that we could study at least one sure thing, mutagenicity. We did not find, however, any active mutagens, which was quite a disappointment, as I discussed before.

Next, we looked for recombination between mutant cell lines, using two selective markers: one, resistance to azahypoxanthine (AzH), and the other, resistance to aminopterin. We looked for recombinants which would be resistant to both aminopterin and AzH, but we failed to find any (95). We realized, obviously, that the recessiveness of AzH would preclude a recovery of any chromosomal hybrids, since these would be still sensitive to AzH.

Next on our list was genetic transformation. The first time we employed a system composed of the D98S line as receptor and the AzG-resistant D98/AG line as the DNA donor. Mrs. Z. Opara-Kubinska tested this system as early as the fall of 1959, but we never succeeded in getting any AzG-resistant "transformants" in excess of the spontaneous mutation rate. We were also not successful in obtaining significant numbers of D98/AH-like cells, when treating D98S or D98/AG receptor cells with DNA extracted from D98/AH cells.

We realized that there are several problems involved in selection for a change depending on the loss of a "lethal" enzyme. There is the problem of phenotypic lag, since the cell not only has to lose the capacity to produce IMPPase but the preexisting enzyme must be completely diluted out. As long as the IMP pyrophosphorylase is present, it carries out a lethal synthesis, making a nucleotide out of the added analog, and this will kill even the genotypically transformed cells.

The second problem was the presence of spontaneous mutants, which made the demonstration of rare genetic transformation events very difficult.

We thus turned to another selective system, which looked much more favorable from our point of view. This was the already discussed system selecting for gain of the IMPPase, using the D98/AH-2 IMP-Pase-deficient mutant as the recipient, since with this particular strain we have never observed any so-called revertants. That means, if you plate any number of D98/AH-2 cells on the selective HAT medium (hypoxanthine + aminopterin + thymidine) no colonies appear. Now, since we grew them over a year and a half we must have tested a population close to 10^8, and we never saw a single revertant colony. But if this cell line (D98/AH-2) is treated—and I will supply the details in a moment—with deoxyribonucleic acid isolated from either the D98S line or the D98/AG line (it doesn't matter which) we get IMPPase-positive colonies appearing on the selective HAT medium.

DeMars: Could I get something straight there? In these cells, was pathway No. 1 intact, that is, the *de novo?*

Szybalski: In our mutants, the *de novo* pathway is always genetically intact. But we could block it phenotypically with aminopterin, in the presence of thymidine (Fig. 46).

DeMars: In other words, you could have found aminopterin-resistant mutants in this particular selective situation?

Szybalski: Yes.

DeMars: In the selective situation, nothing grew; is that right?

Szybalski: In the selective situation nothing grew. The aminopterin-resistant mutants, should such highly resistant cells appear, would grow in this system and would mimic the cells which have regained IMPPase.

DeMars: You can recover aminopterin-resistant mutants of the same cell strain?

Szybalski: Yes.

DeMars: Of the parent (D98S) strain?

Szybalski: Yes.

DeMars: And probably with a fairly reasonable frequency, probably, one in 100,000 cells or so, the first-step resistant?

Szybalski: Yes, only the first-step resistant.

DeMars: So there seem to have been two important changes in the D-98AH/2 mutants that you are dealing with here. One change is, it has become resistant to azahypoxanthine, and the other change is that it has suffered a great decline in the mutation rate to aminopterin resistance compared to the parent strain?

Szybalski: Not really, since we are using a comparatively very high aminopterin concentration in our HAT medium. To overcome aminopterin inhibition the D98/AH-2 cells would have to undergo three to four consecutive mutations, so we don't have to worry about it. In our system, we used aminopterin concentrations which are beyond the third or fourth steps, so we don't have to worry.

As I mentioned, aminopterin could be anywhere from .001 to 10 gamma. To tell you the truth, for other uses, we first used only ten-fold concentration, and we did isolate aminopterin resistant mutants, and that is how we got aminopterin, when we were purifying the line for mutational studies, because of this bad experience. Since then, we are using 0.1, just to save material, but we could just as well use 10 gamma of aminopterin. Then, the chances of getting four successive steps—well, we don't have to find them.

Eagle: You had aminopterin, thymidine, and hypoxanthine in your medium?

Szybalski: Yes. We call it HAT medium, for hypoxanthine, aminopterin, and thymidine.

Renwick: Am I correct in assuming that the reversion is not accompanied by a reappearance of IMPPase?

Szybalski: No. Spontaneous reversion (D98/AH ———→ D98/AH-R) is accompanied by the regain of IMPPase function. It is, however, a slightly different enzyme, since its ratio of affinities to bases and to their analogs is modified.

Renwick: If that altered enzyme which is present in the revertant cell contains, for instance, some peptide chain which is made by another locus, then, what you may be selecting for when you are selecting your reversion is a mutation of this third locus. Let's call it the no. 3 structural change.

Szybalski: I have no way to distinguish it.

Renwick: Now an AH/2 may have a deletion of this last structural gene, no. 3, so you may, in fact, by selecting an AH/2 to work on (in which reversion does not occur spontaneously)—be taking on a more complicated situation than in your main outline there.

Szybalski: Yes, but it is good, because I don't have any reverse mutants or any colonies appearing on the selective medium to bother me.

Renwick: Yes, but you are, in fact, moving into a field where you understand less, because you don't know anything about this mutation rate of the third structural gene.

Atwood: Well, is or is not the enzyme from the transformant the same as the donor enzyme?

Szybalski: Yes, it is the same (Table 4).

Atwood: O.K.! [Laughter]

Szybalski: You never gave me a chance to get to this "crucial" point. The enzyme from the transformant is indistinguishable from the original IMPPase of the donor. But we never got the original IMPPase by reverse mutation.

Atwood: That's very good. But when you transform with the DNA isolated from the D98/AH-R revertant, do you get then the other type of enzyme; is that right?

Szybalski: It would have been a nice experiment, but for some reason, it did not work. DNA extracted from D98/AH-R cells did not transform the D98S cells plated on HAT medium. I don't know why. But let's follow the main theme.

Most of our experimental evidence is summarized in Tables 3 and 4.

TABLE 3

DNA-mediated genetic transformation in D98 cells: transfer of capacity to utilize hypoxanthine from IMPPase-positive donors to IMPPase-negative D98/AH-2 recipient cells. Reproduced from Szybalska and Szybalski (95).

DNA donor	IMPPase activity of donor	Treatment of donor DNA	No. of transformants/ml‡			
			Donor DNA concentration (μg/ml):			
			0	1	10	100
D98S	+		0	1	32	128
D98/AG	+		0	2	19	62
D98/AH	−		0		0	0
D98/AH-2	−		0		0	0
D98/AG	+	RNAase*				65
D98/AG	+	DNAase†				0
D98/AG	+	Spermine omitted			0	0

* Treated with heated (10 min., 100°C) RNAase preparation (50 μg/ml for 30 min. at 37°C.

† Treated with DNAase preparation (2μg/ml) for 30 min. at 37°C in presence of 10^{-2}M Mg^{++}.

‡ Assayed under standard conditions, as described in the text, in presence of 50 μg/ml spermine HCl except where indicated.

TABLE 4

Characteristics of two transformant lines as compared with receptor strain, DNA donors, and spontaneous "revertant." Reproduced from Szybalska and Szybalski (95).

		Recipient	DNA donors		Spontaneous "revertant"	Transformants	
		D98/AH-2	D98S	D98/AG	D98/AH-R	D98/AH-TS (Donor: D98S)	D98/AH-TAC (Donor: D98/AG)
Sensitivity to	AzG	400	0.12	12	100	0.2	0.15
purine analogs:*	AzH	1800	0.12	0.28	80	0.13	0.09
	TG	12	0.006	0.12	8	0.01	0.008
Capacity to utilize hypoxanthine:†		500	0.08	0.5	0.1	0.15	0.07
IMPPase activity:‡		− (0)	+++ (100)	+++ (100)	+ (5)	+++ (100)	
Transforming	4 µg/ml	0	8	9		12	
activity of	40 µg/ml	0	102	48		92	
isolated DNA:§							

* Concentration permitting 50% survival (colony formaton); AzG=8-azaguanine, AzH=8-azahypoxanthine, TG=6-thioguanine.

† Concentration of hypoxanthine permitting 50% survival in presence of 0.02 µg/ml aminopterin and 5 µg/ml thymidine.

‡ Assayed with cell-free enzyme preparations in presence of hypoxanthine-C^{14} and PRPP, by Dr. R. W. Brockman and P. Stutts.

§ Transformants/ml, assayed under standard conditions, as described in the text.

Let me go rapidly through these. As could be inferred from Table 3, only DNA extracted from the IMPPase-positive strain produces "transformant" clones which grow on HAT medium. Increasing concentrations of DNA result in increasing numbers of "transformants" (Fig. 48). The "transforming principle" is immune to RNAase but easily inactiviated by DNAase. The transformation assay was carried out in the presence of spermine.

Atwood: You always have to put in spermine.

Szybalski: Yes. In the absence of spermine no transformants were obtained (Table 3). The spermine is claimed to protect DNA from nucleases. The transformation medium was also serum-free to avoid a possible source of nucleases.

Atwood: A wise precaution.

Szybalski: The details of the transformation procedure were as

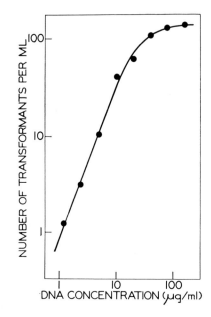

Figure 48. Number of IMPPase-positive transformants per ml of "reaction mixture," assayed in HAT medium, following treatment of IMPPase-negative D98/AH-2 recipient cells with increasing concentrations of DNA isolated from IMPPase-positive D98S donor cells, under conditions described in the text.

Reproduced from Szybalska and Szybalski (95).

follows (95): For the preparation of the recipient cell suspension, four- to five-day-old, heavily seeded cultures were grown up in 4-oz. prescription bottles. The cell sheet was rinsed twice with balanced salt solution (BSS) (8.0 gm NaCl: 0.4 gm KCl: 0.35 gm NaHCO$_3$: 1.0 gm glucose: per liter of water) and exposed for four to six min. to 0.25 percent pancreatin in BSS. The cells were detached from the glass by knocking the bottle against a hard surface and suspended in three ml (per bottle) of phosphate-buffered saline (PBS) (7.0 gm NaCl: 0.4 gm KCl: 2.75 gm Na$_2$HPO$_4$: 0.25 gm NaH$_2$PO$_4$H$_2$O: 1.0 gm glucose: per liter of water) supplemented with 50 μg/ml spermine HCl. The cell concentration of the combined suspension was then adjusted to 500,000 cells/ml by diluting with PBS.

To 1.5 ml aliquots of the recipient cell suspension the appropriate amounts of DNA solution and/or PBS were added, bringing the total volume to 2.0 ml/tube. After a 15-min. period (37°C), the contents of each tube were distributed between five 60 mm plastic petri dishes containing 5 ml of HAT medium (E_{90} medium + 5 μg/ml hypoxanthine, 0.1 μg/ml aminopterin, and 5 μg/ml thymidine). Following 12 to 14 days of incubation, with medium changes every two to three days, the plates were rinsed with PBS, and the colonies were fixed, stained, and counted (100). Cell viability (plating efficiency) during the DNA treatment was determined at intervals by plating 0.02 ml samples of the reaction mixture in E_{90} medium and scoring the colonies after seven days' incubation.

Krooth: I didn't get the way in which you extracted DNA.

Szybalski: DNA was extracted in the same way as for bacterial transformation, since we work also with bacterial systems in the next room. The donor cells were suspended in ten volumes of standard saline-citrate (SSC) (0.15 M NaCl + 0.02 M Na$_3$ citrate) and lysed with 2 percent sodium lauryl sulfate. After adjusting the NaCl concentration to 1 M, exhaustive deproteinization was carried out by repeated shaking with a 4:1 chloroform-butanol mixture and centrifugation. The nucleic acids were precipitated by addition of two volumes of 95 percent ethanol spooled on a glass rod and redissolved in 5 ml of 0.015 M NaCl + 0.02 M Na$_3$ citrate, after which the NaCl concentration was readjusted to 0.15 M. Some preparations were rendered RNA-free by treatment for two hours (37°C) with 50 μg/ml RNase (heated to 100°C for ten min.), followed by deproteinization and two more precipitations with ethanol and isopropanol (95).

Gartler: Did you try a hypertonic salt solution?

Szybalski: Yes, that was one of the first things we tried. The trouble is, if you use 1 molar sodium chloride, the treatment, although it gave slightly higher, or inconsistently higher results, produced so much cell killing and messy quantitativeness of the experiment that we discontinued it.

Lejeune: What does the spermine used alone do?

Szybalski: The spermine is not toxic to the cell at concentrations up to 100 μg per ml. We were using 50 μg/ml.

Lejeune: No, I mean on the transformation system.

Szybalski: The spermine alone has no effect.

Lejeune: It does not increase the rate?

Szybalski: No, it does not.

Gartler: Isn't there some evidence that spermine and protamine induce pinocytosis?

Szybalski: Spermine increases uptake of nucleic acid by a factor of tenfold or something like that.

DeMars: More serious than that, polyamines have a powerful effect on cells that are undergoing division: They cause bunching of chromosomes at anaphase.

Lejeune: With spermine?

DeMars: Spermine, cadaverine, and several polybasic compounds of this sort have been studied in plant cells in particular, so it is really a very important question, because what you said, Dr. Szybalski, is that the population as a whole was not inhibited or mistreated by the spermine concentrations that you used, but you get only one in 10,000 cells, roughly, showing this transformed property, and you might actually be attacking, with the polyamine, that small component of the population that is in some particular stage of division or some polyamine-sensitive stage. It is really a very important point.

Szybalski: This is a very well taken point, but we have no answer to it. As far as toxicity is concerned we have tried several polyamines and basic proteins. We found that other polyamines like spermidine or cadaverine were toxic. Since these are smaller molecules they might be entering the cell more readily, even when alone, while spermine might be entering only when associated with DNA. I don't know that. We tried basic proteins like protamine, and we found out the hard way what we should have known beforehand: protamine precipitates out the DNA when added to our standard transformation mixture.

As you can see, in Figure 48, increasing the concentration of DNA results in the appearance of higher numbers of transformed cells. The curve is very similar to that obtained with bacterial systems, but the DNA concentrations required are much higher. In the neighborhood of 100 μg DNA per ml the curve reaches a plateau.

Herzenberg: What is the final frequency there?

Szybalski: One to four transformants per 10,000 cells treated. It is a very high frequency, much higher than I would ever have expected.

We reasoned that one of the convincing proofs that it is really the deoxyribonucleic acid which is responsible for the transforming activity would be obtained by fractionation of the active material in the cesium chloride gradient. The results are presented in Figure 49, while the technical details were published in the meantime (95).

Ephrussi: Excuse me, but coming back to the design of the experiment, I just want to get it clear. You said that you washed these

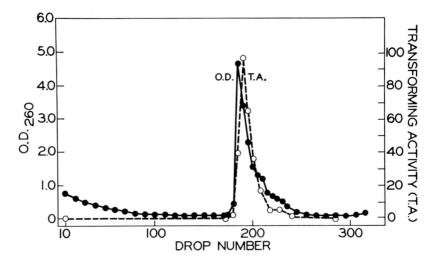

Figure 49. Distribution of human DNA (O.D.), measured as UV absorbance at 260 mμ, and of its transforming activity (T.A.), expressed as the number of IMPPase-positive transformant colonies per fraction, among 50 μl fractions collected after CsCl equilibrium density gradient centrifugation (35,000 RPM; 20°C.; 72 hours).
Reproduced from Szybalska and Szybalski (95).

cells and you described the preparation of the DNA. Then, the cells are exposed to DNA preparation in suspension?

Szybalski: We tried both, treatment in suspension and treatment of the washed cell while still attached to the glass. We now use routinely cell suspensions.

Ephrussi: For how long?

Szybalski: For about fifteen minutes.

Ephrussi: And then?

Szybalski: Then, we plate the cell in the selective HAT medium.

Ephrussi: Is the excess DNA removed or does it go together with the cells into the selective medium?

Szybalski: DNA is not removed, but it is over fifty times diluted in the plating step.

Eagle: What is the concentration of the cells in your reacting mixture?

Szybalski: In the reacting mixture we use 200,000 to almost 1,000,000 cells per ml, a quite concentrated suspension. One of the reasons for that was our desire to save the DNA; otherwise we would have to grow lots of donor cells. This is another reason why we use a suspension of recipient cells. With the surface-attached cells the waste of DNA is much greater.

Neel: Dr. Szybalski, was it possible to follow any other marker characteristics simultaneously in these experiments?

Szybalski: No. We were not successful with any other markers.

Neel: But can one exclude the remote possibility that something about this approach is increasing the mutation rate in general, and you are picking up this particular aspect of an increased mutation rate?

Szybalski: We can exclude the random "mutagenic" effect of DNA, since only the DNA which has the *specific* marker is active in our system.

Herzenberg: How general is that statement? Have you prepared DNA from other sources?

Szybalski: That is the next slide (Table 5). As I mentioned before, this was already on a slide, DNA from the strains which do not have the particular marker; that is, from donor cell, you get none.

Herzenberg: What are the figures on the left?

Szybalski: Table 5 gives some answers to this question. DNA from HeLa cells seems to have some traces of transforming activity at

TABLE 5

Transforming activity of heterologous DNA's and interference by nontransforming DNA's. Reproduced from Szybalska and Sybalski (95).

		No. of transformants/ml*					
D98S DNA Concentration	—	D98/AH DNA		HeLa DNA		Mouse L 60 DNA	Rat ML-2 DNA
		10 μg/ml	50 μg/ml	10 μg/ml	50 μg/ml	50 μg/ml	50 μg/ml
0 μg/ml	0	0	0	0	2	0	0
10 μg/ml	52	26	15	35	27	30	

*Assayed under standard conditions, as described in the text.

50 μg/ml. HeLa cells contain IMPPase. On the other hand DNA of mouse cells was inactive. Table 5 shows also that high concentrations of inactive DNA's, both homologous and heterologous interfere with the transforming activity.

Herzenberg: There is just a little technical question. One would expect offhand that the HeLa DNA might be able to transform. It is human, again; it has got the enzyme. What are the conditions under which you grow your cells? For example, these things must always be kept in the back of your head. Is there a possibility that your culture is contaminated with PPLO and that HeLa is not? This would account for this kind of conversion. Are you getting mammalian transformation or bacterial? Do you have anything which would absolutely rule it out for us?

Szybalski: The only thing I could say is that when PPLO became fashionable we were carrying our cells for a while in the presence of tetracycline.

Herzenberg: That was years ago, though.

Szybalski: Yes. This was a good two years ago.

Herzenberg: You could exclude it again, presumably, by just putting these cells in tetracycline and getting the effect. Since this is, obviously, a very important and interesting discussion we were having, could we ask questions about it? A question was asked before, and you mentioned one trial that you had done, Dr. Szybalski, to transform with DNA from the spontaneous "revertants" from a somewhat different line, and you didn't get any transformation in that case.

Szybalski: Yes, we did once, and in that particular experiment we didn't get any transformation.

Gartler: Were your transformed cells checked cytologically [for chromosomes]?

Szybalski: No.

Renwick: Do I understand that you did not try fragmented DNA?

Szybalski: No, we did not study the effects of shear on human transforming DNA. But we did quite a bit along these lines with bacterial DNA for several markers. Obviously, there are many experiments which still remain to be done.

Herzenberg: Do you pick up your clones of transformed cells and grow them again in selective medium?

Szybalski: The clones of transformed cells are formed in the selective HAT medium.

Herzenberg: How big is such a clone?

Szybalski: Fifty to several hundred cells.

Ephrussi: Dr. Szybalski, several of us were puzzled by the difference in incidence of transformation that you got with your D98AG, on the one hand, and the HeLa cell, on the other. In this connection, the question arose, what are the karyotypes of your donor cells, in this case, as compared with the HeLa karyotype? What we are really interested in is whether there could be a total amount of irrelevant DNA (irrelevant to your particular transformation), so different that the difference in enzymes would be accounted for by interference.

Szybalski: I don't have data on it. I know that in the case of the karyotype of D98S, you really would want to know the total amount of DNA per cell.

Ephrussi: You would want to know the total amount of DNA per cell because, for one thing, the variation in quantity of relevant DNA could hardly be much beyond, say, a one to three range; I mean, the gene dose could be say, three in the extreme. That is what I would expect, and not much more. On the other hand, the irrelevant DNA could vary very much more. What is the total DNA content? Do you know?

Szybalski: Both HeLa and our D98 cells contain about 10^{-5} μg DNA per cell. Our data on P^{32} killing (84, 98, 7) indicate that a very high fraction of this DNA is irrelevant to cell function under laboratory growth conditions.

Herzenberg: This HeLa could be fortuitously resistant to these drugs, since the frequency is not astronomically low?

Chu: May I just add a little information on the question of karyotype of HeLa and D98?

Szybalski: Yes, since you did it. [Laughter]

Chu: As everybody knows, HeLa lines are heterogeneous populations with the chromosome numbers varying from one time to another and from laboratory to laboratory. In the early 1950's, the modal chromosome number was in the 80's. Even the clonal HeLa cell lines cannot be said to be pure. So it is very difficult to say what the DNA content of the HeLa cells is, although some average value of a particular line at a particular time can be expressed.

Several years ago I also examined the karyotypes of the original D98 cell line. At that time, the modal chromosome number was much higher, in the 90's, I believe.

Ephrussi: In which cells?

Chu: In the D98.

Ephrussi: Are you speaking in terms of chromosome number or chromosome arms?

Chu: In terms of chromosome number. D98 was originally a heterogenous line. When Levan examined your clonal line, I think he found a modal number of 63. You said the line is now stable. The situation today is much better for determining the DNA content.

Ephrussi: The DNA content is much more relevant.

Chu: That's right, in the D98S.

Szybalski: Where did you get your original D98? I wonder whether there is a possibility of some mixup of the cell lines. We got our D98 line from Dr. H. Moser of the Cold Spring Harbor Laboratories.

Chu: I doubt it. At one time we surveyed the chromosomes of many human cell lines of normal origin in order to find suitable material for radiation studies. Detroit lines were among the candidates. Since almost all the lines we examined were heteroploids, we finally gave up and instead began establishing euploid cells from primary cultures.

Patau: Did you find any chromosomes with definitely too long arms in the D98?

Chu: I did not carefully analyze the karyotypes of D98 cells.

DeMars: You could make a guess as to be amount of nonspecific DNA here. You wouldn't imagine it to be much more than twice the diploid amount of DNA, and, in that case, you can compare what happened when Dr. Szybalski mixed, say, equal amounts of transforming DNA and nonspecific DNA, such as mouse. In those cases, he mixed in appreciably equal amounts. The depression in transforming ability was one-half to maybe one-fourth the full amount. In this case, roughly comparable amounts of the two kinds of DNA were mixed, and he got, at best, one-twentieth or one-thirtieth; so it may be not only nonspecific DNA. This is rough guesswork.

Ephrussi: I quite agree with you. I just wanted to see if there were some more precise data. On the rough guess, though, I completely agree with you. The conclusion would be that, on this basis alone, you would hardly account for the disproportion that you have between the incidence of HeLa and the other transformation.

Krooth: One wonders whether it is fair to attempt to estimate, on the basis of the total DNA content or on the basis of the karyotype, the percentage of the total DNA in these cells which is relevant for transforming activity. I am thinking, for example, of the findings of Pavan and Brewer (79) and Pavan (78), where they showed that in the giant chromosomes of the larvae of a certain tropical fly (*Rhynosciara angelae*), the quantity of DNA per band depended upon the particular tissue from which the chromosome came. This fly had giant chromosomes in a number of tissues, and they measured the quantity of DNA at a specific band in different tissues. They found that this quantity varied quite sharply from tissue to tissue. If you compare the transforming activity of several different cultured cell lines, it need not follow that this will vary as a simple function of the karyotype or of the total DNA content.

Patau: I would be somewhat skeptical as to whether you can transfer observations on polytene chromosomes, in which you may find differences from tissue to tissue in very specific regions, to ordinary chromosomes. As far as one can tell, there seems to be no difference in DNA content between metaphase chromosomes from different tissues.

Ephrussi: I agree with Dr. Patau, and, moreover, my main emphasis was really not on the relative amounts of total DNA, but precisely on the irrelevant.

Krooth: The ratio of the irrelevant to the relevant is what I should think is crucial for predicting the amount of interference. I think it is perfectly true that one cannot extrapolate by inexorable logic from the polytene chromosomes of a Dipteran insect to human cells. However, in view of their findings, one must admit the possibility that different cell lines may have different transforming activities for a specific enzyme, which are not revealed in their karyotype or total DNA.

Ephrussi: Another question which is connected with this one: Do you by any chance know, Dr. Szybalski, what the activity of your enzyme on a per-cell basis is for the HeLa and your D98AG?

Szybalski: No, this particular ratio was not determined for HeLa cells.

Herzenberg: Just a technical point, again. Have you added DNAase after the incubation period of the cells, to see what effect it has on transformation?

Szybalski: We had difficulties with this type of experiment, since, for some reason, our DNAase preparation was quite toxic to the cells.

Herzenberg: How do you avoid that problem in the incubation of DNA with DNAase before adding it to the cells? It was a very much lower concentration?

Szybalski: Yes, the concentration was much lower.

Gartler: It seems to me that under these conditions, that is, with spermine possibly inducing pinocytosis, that the cells may actually take up DNAase.

Herzenberg: What was your (to Gartler) experience when you added DNAase? It was not in the published report, if you added DNAase. Do you take out all the DNA left?

Gartler: No, DNAase treatment did not remove all the labeled DNA. However, we noted that if the DNAase treatment was carried out for 20 to 30 minutes that we could no longer extract any polymerized DNA from the treated cells. I interpreted these results as indicating possible penetration of added DNAase into the cells. I might mention that Wilczok (118) has reported work on the uptake of DNA by Novikoff hepatoma cells, and he has shown that DNAase treatment does not remove all the labeled DNA.

Neel: It is apparent that we have made the transition from the topics of Day 2 to the topics of Day 3. But, without formally transferring the baton of leadership, maybe, at this point, we could turn it over to Dr. Eagle.

Eagle: Well, this is obviously *pro forma.* It does strike me that we have discussed a wide variety of markers which are available in cultured cells. The specific ones have ranged all the way from chromosomal markers to the antigenic markers which have been sorted out by Dr. Herzenberg; biochemical markers deriving from patients with hereditary disease, as well as in different cell strains in serial culture; markers introduced by virus, either morphologic or malignant transformations caused by virus; and, this morning, we have had drug-resistant markers typified by the experiments of Dr. Szybalski. But even this galaxy of markers by no means exhausts the total which are available for genetic studies. We have not discussed the virus-resistant markers; we have not discussed what I think is the important and complicated problem of the so-called malignant transformation in culture, which is in some cases debatable and in others quite real; and there is also the reverse transformation which has recently come to our attention, in which cells deriving from malignant tissue and which have for years retained this biological property of malignancy, have in some laboratories apparently lost their malignant character.

We have also not discussed other biochemical variants which can be selected out of the serially propagated cell lines; for example, the variants isolated by Chang (12, 6), which can use xylose and which might be useful as a marker. Our inability to repeat these experiments does not reduce the usefulness of the isolated variant.

If time permits, Dr. Neel, perhaps this afternoon, we can come back to markers. But I do think it is important that we address ourselves to the question of what can be done with these markers, and this is typified by the very exciting and important work that Dr. Szybalski has just described.

I would now like to ask Dr. Ephrussi if he would like to discuss a different type of experiment with marker cells, the ones which he has described on chromosomal recombination.

Chromosomal Markers

by Dr. Boris Ephrussi

Ephrussi: Well, alone, I cannot discuss. I can make a few statements. [Laughter] I really don't know if what we are doing with cell mating is of interest to this audience. I think, if I make some statements about what we know and where we are at this time, a number of questions could be asked. I am afraid these are the questions to which I myself would like to have the answers, but I don't. What I propose to do, therefore, is to say very briefly where we stand. I shall be very brief, because those who are interested probably have seen the two short communications that we made some twelve and six months ago, respectively.

The first thing I would like to say is that the process I am going to talk about as "cell mating" or "cell fusion" could be most adequately referred to as "vegetative hybridization." I avoid this term for the obvious reason that it has been proposed and used in a very different context; and because I am not quite sure whether by adopting this term, I will please those who insisted on the occurrence of vegetative hybridization, or disappoint them by showing that the rigorous demonstration of vegetative hybridization is based on the constancy of the chromosomes which they like to consider as variable products of changing metabolism. Be this as it may, the thing I want to emphasize is that the phenomenon I am going to talk about was discovered, not by me, but by Dr. Barski, working at the Cancer Institute, in Paris, who undertook mixed cultures of two lines of "fibroblasts," produced years ago in Earle's laboratory at NIH, the so-called high- and low-cancer-inducing lines. I will call them, for brevity, N-1 and N-2. Their real numbers are NCTC 2472, for the high line, and NCTC 2555 for the low line.

Dr. Barski had these lines in his laboratory for some time and, in 1960 or 1961, started mixed cultures of the two lines, which are very readily recognizable by their very different, but equally abnormal, karyotypes. After a few months of mixed culture, Dr. Barski and his coworkers discovered karyologically the appearance of a new cell type, characterized essentially by a total number of chromosomes roughly corresponding to the sum of the karyotypes of the parental

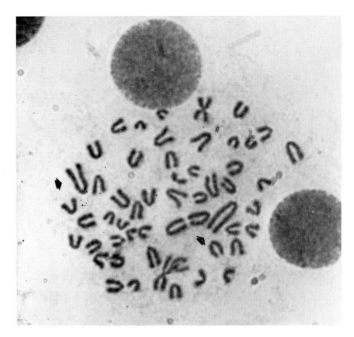

Figure 50. Cell of line NCTC 2472 (N-1). Arrows indicate the two extra long chromosomes.
Reproduced from Ephrussi and Sorieul (27).

strains, and the simultaneous presence of the characteristic markers of the two strains.

Very soon after Dr. Barski discovered this phenomenon and published his first paper on it, we decided to repeat these experiments, and we got hold of the original strains. I would like to point out that both of these strains are derived from a C3H mouse.

Incidentally, there is some confusion in the literature; lots of people confuse this particular family of clones or lines with the famous L cells. The only common trait of these lines is that both families of strains are derived from C3H mice, but there is a several-year interval between the isolation of the two groups of lines. The lines I am calling N-1 and N-2 are actually two clones ultimately derived not only from the same individual mouse but, moreover, from a single cell. This single cell gave rise to a clone which was multiplied in several bottles, and these were kept as separate lines and underwent, obviously, very different chromosomal changes, and, in addition,

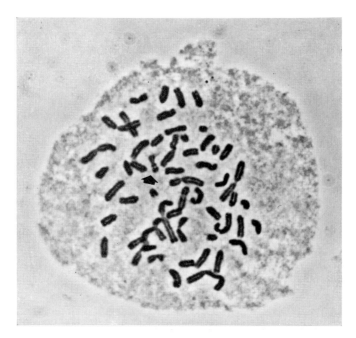

Figure 51. Cell of line NCTC 2555 (N-2). Notice the numerous biarmed chromosomes. Arrow indicates a characteristic short metacentric marker.
Reproduced from Ephrussi and Sorieul (27).

became neoplastic or at least tumor-inducing: N-1 with high frequency and N-2 with low frequency.

Well, we got hold of these two strains from Drs. Earle, Sanford, and Barski, and our first experiments were essentially a repetition of Barski's, with one difference: his first crosses involved at least one line which was recently passed through the animal and produced a tumor, and from it was recovered the new cell line, which had essentially the same characteristics and was used in the experiments. We, on the other hand, used the *in vitro* lines, which have not undergone animal passage, and we soon reproduced Barski's results. I don't know whether lantern slides will add very much to my account, but maybe you would like to see what the things look like.

The first three slides concern our first cross. Figure 50 shows a cell of line N-1, the high cancer-inducing line. This line shows a good deal of variation in karyotype, but with a good distribution. I can give you the variation extremes, if you are interested. It has a

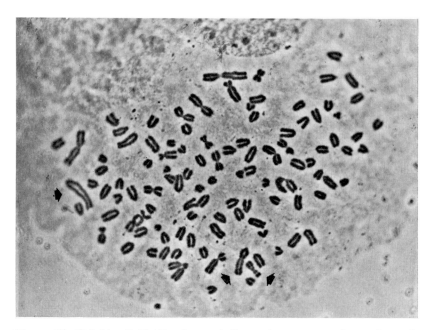

Figure 52. Hybrid cell H-109t. Arrows indicate the two extra long telocentric chromosomes, markers of line N-1, and the short metacentric marker of line N-2. Reproduced from Ephrussi and Sorieul (27).

modal number of 55 chromosomes. It usually has one or two metacentrics. You can see two here. Its characteristic feature, however, is the presence of an extra long chromosome, an acrocentric, which is very considerably longer than any normal telocentric in the normal mouse. It also has a second long chromosome with a secondary constriction: this is not very clear on this slide, but you can probably see an indication of the constriction. These are what we consider the markers of line N-1.

Figure 51 shows a cell of line N-2, which has a modal number of 57 chromosomes. It has usually 14 to 15 metacentrics. You can recognize many of them here, even though this is not a very good slide. It has one very characteristic, small metacentric, with constrictions on both sides of the centromere, which is poorly but, nevertheless, somewhat visible here. This is a very characteristic marker.

Figure 52 is a photograph of a cell of a hybrid clone. I don't remember the total number of chromosomes here, but it is almost exactly what is expected from the fusion of modal cells of the two lines. You can recognize easily the extra long chromosome and the other long chromosome coming from N-1, with the secondary constriction here. As expected, you have many metacentrics coming from the N-2 parent, including the small metacentric that I tried to show you on the previous slide.

Well, this is, then, the first hybrid. I may add simply that we have obtained this hybrid in many independent experiments, either using both original strains or clones therefrom. Incidentally, N-1 and N-2 clone very poorly, but we did succeed in extracting some clones and testing the ability of the clones to mate.

The only sort of quantitative information that I can supply at the present time is that every bottle of mixture we set up independently gave us, ultimately, a hybrid population. This was detected sometimes after three weeks and sometimes after three months. All I am trying to point out is, since so far we have no method for quantitation (and the establishment of such a method is our main purpose right now)—that the event cannot be astronomically rare, because, in fact, every bottle we set up did end up with hybrid formation.

Patau: May I ask one question? No doubt, you sometimes found spontaneously occurring tetraploid cells?

Ephrussi: Yes.

Patau: Can you give the order of magnitude of the frequency of spontaneous tetraploids in your hybrids? I am asking for the reason that if the event of hybridization in normal human cells were of comparable frequency as spontaneous polyploidization, then it should be possible to demonstrate hybridization in a culture of, let's say, a sex chromosome mosaic. We know that spontaneous polyploidization occurs because we sometimes see diplochromosomes. Can you give any information on this?

Ephrussi: Very little, but I can say something about it, very briefly. Two strains are concerned here. N-2 contains a very low number of what we call "doubles" or higher multiples of the modal number. I would not really like to give quantitative data, but the order of magnitude, I would say, is 3 to 5 percent.

Now, N-1 is the one I made a few remarks about a day or two ago. I shall remind you of what I said then. This line always contains a somewhat higher proportion of "doubles" or even higher types. Their frequency used to be somewhat between 5 and 10 percent. We had the impression, and some data, that there were very few or no intermediates between the cells with the modal number of 55 chromosomes and the doubles. Then, as I said the other day, suddenly, the doubles in this strain started increasing, and finally, about two months ago, we ended up with a strain in which the cells with the 55 mode represented, roughly, only 20 percent of the population, and all the rest of the cells contained approximately 85 to 90 chromosomes. This situation, as I mentioned the other day, recently reverted spontaneously.

The only thing I want to add, which I did not say the other day, is that when we noticed this reverse trend, due, no doubt, to some sort of spontaneous selection, and when the two karyotypes were about 50/50 we decided to make another cross with N-2, asking simply this question: all we had observed so far was mating of the 55 type with N-2. Would the 90 type, which now was one-half of the population, mate, also?

We were very lucky, because we got many hybrids within three weeks, and, clearly, some of them were products of fusion of the 55 type with N-2, and others of N-2 with the 90 type. That is all I can say about this.

Patau: Don't these data suggest that the frequency of hybridization is comparable with that of spontaneous polyploidization?

Ephrussi: I really hate to express an opinion because I don't know.

Patau: What is a reasonable guess? I mean, if hybridization were a hundred times rarer—

Ephrussi: Let's say you cannot go very wrong. [Laughter]

Patau: If it were a hundred times rarer, I would hate to start looking for hybridization in human cells. But it seems that an attempt might be worth while.

Ephrussi: Yes, I would say so.

DeMars: I think that this event has to occur through cell fusion. Is that fair?

Ephrussi: Which?

DeMars: The production of these hybrids.

Ephrussi: Oh, sure. I don't see what else it can be. Obviously, there must be cell fusion. What happens next, we don't know. Do interphase nuclei fuse? Or overlapping spindles? This, we don't know. I may add just a brief comment which may not be totally uninteresting.

As soon as we repeated Barski's experiment and satisfied ourselves that mating does occur, the following question immediately became of great interest to us: is the ability to mate a particular characteristic of the two cell lines used or can any two cell types mate?

The first thing I did was a purely paper job. I went through all the papers, by the NIH people, who created these strains, describing their different properties. Finally, in one of the papers published some seven or eight years ago, which describes the origin of N-2, I ran into a sentence which shows that N-2 has a very peculiar feature in its history. When the culture from which N-2 is derived was cloned and the cell was fished out, which is the origin of the N-2 clone, Sanford noticed that this cell was binucleate. The next day, there was still a single cell, but it had a single nucleus.

I must say this greatly alarmed me, because I wondered whether we were facing a situation similar to that in which the *E. coli* people were for a long time, when K-12 was the only "mater." The question was: Is N-2 a "mater," so that, unless we use that line, we shall get no mating?

Unless there are other questions, I will just go on with this problem. Before I do that, however, I would like to point out that, once this hybrid appears in this population, it has a tremendous selective advantage and, in no time, it takes over the culture.

Usually, the hybrid is detected when N-2 is a very small minority already. Whether or not this is significant, I don't know. But it so happens that N-1 usually overgrows N-2, and when there is just 2 to 3 percent of N-2 left, then the first hybrid cells are detected. Then, they start shooting up and eliminate everything else.

Chu: Are you going to make any statements about the mechanism of fusion?

Ephrussi: No.

Chu: May I ask you to speculate on what has happened: either (1) the engulfment of one cell by another, (2) intrusion of one into another, or (3) pinocytosis?

Ephrussi: The answer to all those questions is I don't know. I wish I knew, but I don't.

Renwick: Is there contact inhibition in your cells? There shouldn't be.

Ephrussi: Well, yes, I know that. [Laughter] I think there is little.

DeMars: What do you mean by "contact inhibition?"

Ephrussi: Well, really, when they say that, they don't mean contact inhibition as it was discovered by Abercrombie, when he saw the cells coming together and then retracting. If I understand correctly or interpret the question correctly, what they mean is: Does it grow in a monolayer, or do the cells climb on top of each other? Isn't that what you mean by "Is there contact inhibition?"

Renwick: I would like to have included both types in the question.

Ephrussi: Strictly, the notion of contact inhibition was deduced from moving pictures showing the movement and retraction of cells.

However, today, we say, for example, that neoplastic cells have no contact inhibition, not because we made the same type of observation but because we see there is no longer a monolayer.

Renwick: Yes. Thank you.

Ephrussi: Well, anyway, these cells have a distinct selective advantage. Actually, we don't know very exactly the generation time of N-1 and N-2. I would say, it is of the order of 24 to 28 hours in the medium in which we culture them. Now, the hybrids grow faster. Here I can give the generation time, which may be even a maximal estimate, because I have watched these cells in microdrops under oil: they clone beautifully, contrary to the two "parental" strains. They have a very high cloning efficiency. Just by observing single cells, in microdrops I saw that they systematically divide every 16 to 17 hours; so they have a distinctly better generation time and, as a result, obviously, this selective advantage.

Once they appear, they overgrow the whole culture in a very short time, and you hardly need cloning, really, to be able to say you have a practically pure population.

Are there any questions?

Lejeune: I would like to ask a question. After this hybrid cell overgrows the culture, can you by cloning sometimes get back to one of the parent strains, or does it definitely stabilize as a hybrid?

Ephrussi: May I come to that a little later?—because I think I want to treat that after I go on to the next point. It will save time.

Thus, the first question we asked was: Was there a special "mater?" But you could also widen the question. You see, as I pointed out before, both cell lines were derived not only from the same histocompatibility type (the C3H inbred line) but from the same animal, and, moreover, from the same cell. We, therefore, asked several questions and set up several mixtures with lines we got from different people. The mixtures had these characteristics: both lines from C3H, but from different animals, or from the same animal but not the same cell. We even had that. Then, of course, we had different inbred lines.

We set up a number of crosses. I will not describe all of them because the result is very simple. Every one was negative except one, and that brings me to the second hybrid. In a way, this was the best one to answer the whole complex of questions that I just presented, because the next hybrid we succeeded in making was between N-2, which is derived from C3H, and a cell derived from a Swiss mouse.

This is, as you will see in a different connection, rather unfortunate,

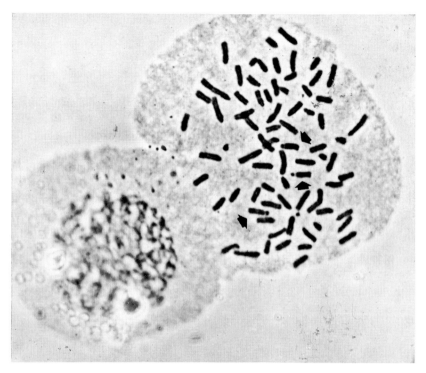

Figure 53. Cell of line Py 198-1. Arrows indicate the acrocentric chromosomes used as markers.

Reproduced from Ephrussi and Sorieul (27).

but, you know, we are all for economy in experimentation now, and so we combine several questions into one. The reason for the choice of this Swiss mouse-derived cell was a specific one. It is what Dr. Bayreuther talked about yesterday—a Polyoma converted cell. It is one of Dulbecco's converted nonvirus-releasing but tumor-inducing cells.

As I said, this hybrid was between N-2, which you already saw, with its many metacentrics. Here (Fig. 53) is the Polyoma line of Dulbecco's. This is a cell with a modal number of 74 chromosomes, and a variation range of, roughly, 72 to 76. Here, all chromosomes are telocentric, and there is no gross abnormality, but there is a normal feature which is no longer present in N-2: the normal mouse has several short acrocentrics, with the very short arms. They were called by Hungerford "heterochromatic differentiations." Maybe Dr.

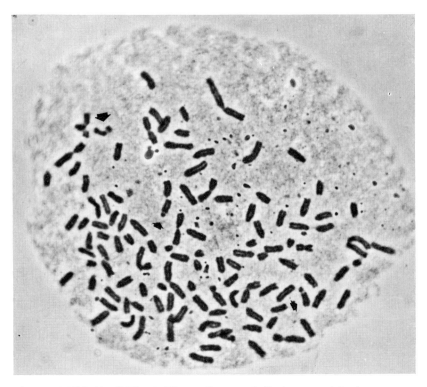

Figure 54. Hybrid cell M-109. The small arrows indicate acrocentric chromosomes of line Py 198-1; the large one indicates the small metacentric marker of line N-2. Reproduced from Ephrussi and Sorieul (27).

Bayreuther or Dr. Chu could tell me what to call them. Anyway, you can see one here and another one there.

Chu: That is in the normal?

Ephrussi: These chromosomes are present in the normal mouse karyotype. N-2 does not have them any more. We successfully crossed this cell, as you will see in Figure 54, with N-2.

This cell (Fig. 54) has, I guess, 132 chromosomes, as expected from the fusion of modal cells. Somewhere here are the 15 metacentrics coming from the N-2 parent. You have, very clearly, the chromosome coming from the Polyoma cell, and, also, somewhere is the little metacentric, which is not very clear here, that I showed you in the N-2 cell. It is curled up here, the one with the constriction.

This hybrid cell, like the other, immediately overgrew the whole population. But when the hybrids were at the 10 percent level, we cloned the population, and every one of the clones we got was a clone of hybrids, because, again, the two parental lines which we used, under the conditions which we used for cloning, clone very poorly, while the hybrids clone extremely well.

That settles one question, then: obviously, cell fusion can cross histocompatibility barriers.

Now, the question of whether a specific mater gene was involved was still not settled, because the mater gene, if it were present, was suspected to be present in N-2, and N-2 is involved in this cross, as well as in the first one. However, I learned in June, at the Cold Spring Harbor meetings, from Leo Sachs, that in his laboratory they recently succeeded in producing a hybrid with the L cell—I don't know which particular line of L. We worked a lot with L and did not get any place, so far. But he succeeded, apparently, in producing a hybrid between L and a Polyoma converted cell derived from some inbred line. I forget whether it is DBA or something like that. Do you remember with what he worked?

Billingham: No.

Ephrussi: Dr. Bayreuther, do you remember?

Bayreuther: DBA, I think.

Ephrussi: That's what I thought.* Leo Sachs's hybrid then, is the first hybrid which does not involve N-2 and it was N-2 that, we thought, could be a mater.

From this, I draw the optimistic conclusion that, presumably, very distant genotypes can be crossed, can produce hybrids, and that a closer relationship is not required.

DeMars: Every cross so far involves a tumor-forming cell?

Ephrussi: Well, that is another common characteristic. I discussed this in a paper in press which will apparently appear very shortly.† Jim Neel can tell us about it. It was a series of lectures last winter at the University of Michigan. In it I gave the first detailed account of all these experiments, and I pointed out that there is another common feature to all these crosses. They all involve cells suspect, at least, from the neoplastic point of view. One of the things we are most anxious to do, of course, is to make crosses with normal cells, and this is one of the things we are working on.

Well, this is the essence of what we really know. Maybe, the only thing that I will add is an answer to Dr. Lejeune's question. As soon

---

* Actually it is SWR.

† B Ephrussi and S. Sorieul (27).

as we got this out, people started asking: "Do you have segregation"? My answer usually was: "I don't know." In fact, I don't know whether I should expect four-spored or eight-spored asci! But we started following a number of hybrids. I can't give you any details, but, very clearly, all these hybrids lose chromosomes very easily and very soon. By now, they have gone down considerably. They must have lost—well, I have forgotten the percentage—percentage of chromosome number really does not mean very much—but they must have lost, within a couple of months, something on the order of 10 percent of their chromosomes.

Chu: Is it possible to combine a cell with 130 chromosomes and another with more or less 50 chromosomes?

Ephrussi: I'm sorry; I didn't get that.

Chu: Suppose you call this a N-1-N-2 hybrid. Can this hybrid be backcrossed to N-1 or N-2?

Ephrussi: No, we haven't done that. But you know more about chromosomes than I do. You know that when you get to very high numbers, it is quite a problem to make proper preparations, and count, and all that. It is not easy.

Patau: Some of your clones are losing chromosomes quite rapidly, you say. You must have clones which differ in their chromosomal constitution. Have you found any differences in growth rate between your clones?

Ephrussi: No, we have not had time to study that.

Patau: Is there any evidence of selective difference?

Ephrussi: Maybe, but we just have not done this. I want to add one thing. I can show you this on a slide (Fig. 55). The upper graph gives the chromosome distribution in our second (Polyoma) hybrid established within, say, the first month or six weeks after we detected the hybrid cells, i.e., when they represented about 10 percent of the population. The estimate in terms of percentage of mitoses is, as you know, a very poor estimate because it is affected by the relative growth rates and so on. But it is a rough measurement.

Anyway, this was the distribution. The fusion of modal cells should have given a value of about 131 chromosomes (or 146 chromosome arms). These, actually, are the first 24 mitoses studied, and they are in accord with expectation. The interesting point is the grouping of the first six mitoses observed—when the hybrids were first detected at the one per 1000 level—they are here in black. This gives the impression that they all arose in this particular bottle, from a single event.

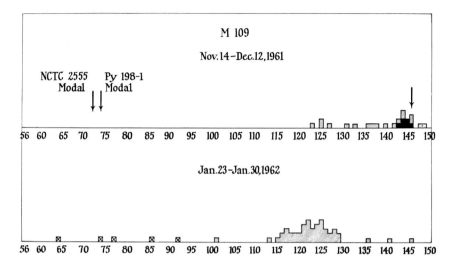

Figure 55. Distribution of numbers of chromosome arms in hybrid M-109 at various times.
Reproduced from Ephrussi and Sorieul (27).

We made a calculation. Given this total distribution, there is only one chance out of 700 for this grouping of the six first mitoses to be an accident; so we have the strong impression that the whole hybrid population may have come from a single fusion event, followed by chromosome loss.

The upper distribution represents the situation in November to December, and about a month later, in January (lower graph), the whole population had shifted to the left. The mode has gone down. So this represents the chromosome loss that I was talking about.

The thing I want to point out is that I have a certain number of cells here with very low chromosome numbers which are marked with a cross. They are marked distinctly to show clearly that while the proportions of the other karyotypes in the histogram truly reflect (with the above reservation, of course) their frequency in the population, this is definitely not so for the "very low karyotypes." These cells were deliberately looked for. I don't know exactly what their frequency is, but I do know they are very low in number. They have the markers of the two strains. We are now trying to extract these cells, even though they are very rare. We don't know what the cloning efficiency of these cells could be.

Patau: Have you looked at the mitoses themselves, without hypotonic treatment? Were there any tripolar divisions?

Ephrussi: No, we have not looked. That is one of the things we were aware of and interested in. But I can't say.

Stern: I wanted to ask the same question, because, when the initial fusion occurs, you bring two chromosomes into one cell, and you would expect, unless there is a control of one centrosome over the other, to start out with a tetrapolar spindle, wouldn't you?

Ephrussi: It is entirely possible. I just don't know, Curt.

Stern: These last single low-numbered individual cells, do they occur in a strain which was cloned from a plated cell?

Ephrussi: The very small ones?

Stern: Yes. Did they occur in a clone of the mated cell or in a culture in which mated cells had occurred?

Ephrussi: Both in the initial culture, from the initial culture uncloned, and also in several clones extracted from this population. We have, in several of them, very low cells, but with a very low frequency.

Stern: In the initial not-cloned mixture, I would expect them.

Ephrussi: But they are present also in the clones.

Stern: But what are the relative proportions, do you know?

Ephrussi: No, I have no idea. It is very low.

Szybalski: Do you know whether they are viable?

Ephrussi: All I can say is that they can, obviously, undergo one mitosis.

Patau: With too few chromosomes, of course, the question is always whether the small number might not have resulted from accidental loss. How confident are you that all these numbers are real? It might have happened, let's say, that the hypotonic treatment exploded the cell and you got an artefact.

Ephrussi: No, these are cells. The contour of the cells is clearly preserved.

Patau: Yes, but we have seen the following thing at least once: The cell was very little squashed and well rounded, but attached to it was a little plasma bubble, and this contained a chromosome. I think a cell in the hypotonic medium might well round off again after having expelled part of its content.

Ephrussi: This, obviously, is entirely possible. I can't say. The solution to this is not a microscopic observation, but cloning. That is what we want to do.

Eagle: Does the hybrid of the high and low malignancy strain of the N-2 and the Polyoma behave biologically like the high malignancy or low malignancy, or does it behave like the Polyoma cell?

Ephrussi: Well, insofar as the hybrid between N-1 and N-2 is concerned—maybe we should, but we didn't do anything about it. Dr. Barski has a paper on this, and he claims, and I think the evidence is good, that the hybrid gives high incidence. So, apparently, the N-1 frequency is the dominant one.

The other hybrid, between N-2 and the Polyoma line, poses quite an interesting problem and, in fact, this is one of the reasons why the Polyoma line was chosen.

One of the reasons we undertook the cross with the Polyoma line (Py) should be evident from the statement of the present position of the Polyoma problem, made yesterday by Dr. Bayreuther. I might just briefly repeat it.

Dulbecco observed that when the cytocidal reaction of mouse cells is over, the growth of the survivors gradually and very slowly accelerates during a period of a month or two. The cultures thus obtained release extremely small amounts of virus. Dulbecco cloned these cultures and found that the great majority of cells do not release any virus, and these are the converted cells. The Py line I am talking about is one of these Polyoma converted lines.

Then came the search for the presence of the virus in some form in the Polyoma cells, and this, Dr. Beyreuther outlined yesterday. The first question asked was: Is there any virus antigen present in the converted cells? The fluorescent antibody technique gave a negative answer. Then, after DiMaiorca discovered the infectivity of viral DNA, and a highly sensitive assay system was worked out, an attempt was made to extract the DNA of converted cells and to reveal the presence in it of the viral genome. According to Dulbecco the experiment was performed under conditions such that the viral DNA would have been detected even if there were only one viral molecule present per cell. Well, that assay was completely negative, and so were, as Dr. Bayreuther mentioned yesterday, all the attempts at inducing virus production. (They were playing for a while with the prophage idea).

After these results were obtained, Dulbecco stated the problem in the following form, which is, perhaps, a little simpler than things could be in reality, but I think very useful. He pointed out that we are now faced with this alternative. We can imagine, on the one hand, that in a Polyoma cell a part of the viral genome is integrated in the normal mouse genome. This part of the viral genome is sufficient to make the cell cancerous, but it is defective enough to be noninducible, and not to be able to reform the complete virus.

The other possibility corresponds, in fact, to the oldest hypothesis of carcinogenesis. In the olden days, when it was discovered that carcinomas could be induced with tars (that nobody imagined to be self-reproducing), the idea was that carcinogenic agents altered some cell element indispensable for the normal functioning of the cell. On this view, the virus is really not carcinogenic at all. It is not necessary for cancer. It is a tool which knocks out a normal constituent.

In genetic terms, the first hypothesis postulates a gain of genetic material, the second a loss. This has one corollary. If the first hypothesis is correct, the fusion of a Polyoma converted cell with a normal cell should produce a hybrid which should be neoplastic, because it still has the extra genetic material. On the contrary, if the loss hypothesis is correct, the hybrid between the Polyoma cell and a normal cell would compensate for the deficiency and should cure the Polyoma cell of cancer.

That is one of the reasons why we tried to hybridize the Polyoma cell. Well, naturally, you want to know the answer. The answer is that, unfortunately, we have all sorts of troubles. The main source of trouble is that at the time Dulbecco started this work, he didn't know what we would need. He picked the Swiss mouse. Had he picked an inbred mouse, we would have an answer by now.

The histocompatibility situation interferes with a rigorous test (by inoculation) of the neoplastic or normal character of this hybrid which we do have. We are trying, nevertheless, to get some idea about it from inoculations into X-rayed and cortisonized mice and so on. We are also planning to try to detect the Habel antigen.

Now the question, where are we going? What can we do with cell mating? I think in the first place, this is a puzzling phenomenon in itself. Nobody knows what role this kind of phenomenon can play, whether in cancer or anything else. But I look at it also from another angle. I personally am not terribly interested in mapping, say, human chromosomes; nevertheless, it is an important problem. Some people like to do it. As you know, Pontecorvo insisted very much on the fact that, especially in species which have a long generation time or where, for other reasons, we cannot undertake experimental breeding, mapping could be done by means of parasexual phenomena, i.e., of mechanisms which are substitutes for the usual meiotic recombination, such as somatic crossing over, nondisjunction and chromosome loss.

In our hybrids, chromosome losses occur, obviously, with an increased rate. I say "obviously," because, first, it should be expected that lots of chromosomes in such hybrids should be dispensable. They are present in triplicate or more. The other thing is simply the evidence that I showed—and I could have shown you more—of the rapid chromosome loss. Hybridization, then, apparently *is* a tool for formal genetic studies on somatic cells.

Yesterday, I think, the question was raised as to whether the prophage situation is ever realized with oncogenic viruses. Well, this is a matter of debate, as Dr. Bayreuther pointed out. I think that Dr. Temin has some experiments with Rous sarcoma which convince him that he is dealing with a situation similar to the prophage situation in lysogeny. I think the question is somewhat debatable, but it cannot be excluded altogether from consideration in the Rous sarcoma case. The situation is obviously very different in the case of the Polyoma.

If you do have a prophage-like or lysogeny-like situation, you may ask the question, for example, whether, mating results in a phenomenon equivalent to what in bacteria is known as zygotic induction. This, again, from certain angles, presents a certain interest.

To me, personally, the most interesting aspect, but one which will require ability to mate normal cells, is the problem of cell differentiation. As you know, the usual view is that, whatever cell differentiation consists of (and we really don't know much about it), it is a kind of exclusive process; in other words, it is assumed that, once a cell has started differentiating in one direction, it cannot at the same time follow another path of differentiation. The different developmental states are apparently mutually exclusive. The only and very recent evidence against this classical view, is to be found in the recent papers by Charles Wilde of the School of Dentistry at the University of Pennsylvania, who claims that he can obtain, by certain treatments, what he calls "confused" cells which start simultaneously in two directions, that is, the two ends of the cell differentiate in two different directions. However, this statement relies on criteria so subjective that I would not put too much weight on it. I still think that there is something very fundamental about this exclusiveness of directions of differentiation.

I am rather puzzled, therefore, to see what we could do with such a system. If we could mate normal cells, which have preserved their differentiations *in vitro*, or even take from the animal typically differentiated cells which will preserve their characteristics for a certain time, and fuse them and see what happens, we could possibly get some idea of the mechanisms involved.

Now, to make all these things possible, what is most urgently needed, I think, is to make our system into a quantitative system. We would like to be able to induce mating, or at least to increase its incidence.

But to be able to increase the incidence, we have to be able to measure its frequency. This, in turn, requires markers. We have a certain number of projects under way along these lines.

One of them consists precisely in taking the three systems here, N-1 × N-2 and N-2 × Py, which we know can mate, as model systems, and in trying (in cooperation with Dr. Swim at Western Reserve) to make them into selective systems by introducing a number of markers into the parental lines.

Then, because antigenic markers are of interest in themselves and may eventually serve a practical purpose, we have also undertaken a piece of work, chiefly done by Drs. Amost and Hauschka, which is aiming essentially at the description of these same three cell lines, of the two hybrids and their "segregants," in terms of H2 antigens and its correlation with their karyotypes. This work is proceeding now. It is far from finished, but it looks encouraging, in the sense that apparently we are going to get rather clearcut results.

Well, that's it. I think I have brought you up to where we stand today. Of course, if you have any questions, I will be pleased to answer them — mostly by "I don't know."

Szybalski: I wonder whether you consider feasible the following experiments. To prepare a hybrid line between your cells, but with one parental line which was made azahypoxanthine resistant. I would predict that this hybrid would still be sensitive to the drug since AzH sensitivity should be dominant. I assume that your AzH resistance would depend on the loss of IMPPase, as in our D98/AH mutants.

This system would also permit positive selection for AzH segregants from your hybrid lines. It would be a relatively simple experiment, since all that is required is to put the AzH-resistance marker on one of your lines which should be an easy task. The actual mating procedure would not be different from what you are doing now.

Ephrussi: Yes, but we need more than that. We need more markers, really, to be able to detect the hybrids very early; that is, only by wiping out both parents, really, and having the hybrids survive. We are trying to do something of this sort, but we are just at the beginning.

Szybalski: I was really proposing a less sophisticated experiment. To use AzH resistance not as a selective marker in your usual hybridization procedure, but only at the next stage: to select for the AzH-resistant segregants among a phenotypically sensitive hybrid population. Obviously, you could select also for hybrids using two selective markers, one for each parental strain. AzH resistance, however, would not be suitable for this purpose since it must be a recessive trait.

Aminopterin resistance should be all right as one of the markers, since increase in folic acid reductase is most probably a dominant property.

Atwood: Could you tolerate some comments rather than questions?

Ephrussi: Oh, sure! I welcome them, rather than tolerate them. [Laughter]

Atwood: One is that in view of the history of these lines—

Ephrussi: Which lines?

Atwood: That were successfully mated. In view of their history, the neoplastic or normal character of the fusion products would not be interpretable, even if it could be demonstrated.

Ephrussi: Oh, yes. I am quite aware of that. The other difficulty, as you see here, is that the N-2 line, as I myself said, is a low cancer line.

Atwood: The impression this story gives is that fusion is detected because occult markers are already present in these lines, which give a tremendous selective advantage to the hybrid. The limitation of the phenomenon to certain pairs of lines may have nothing to do with the incidence of fusions, but may depend only on which pairs of lines give heterosis when fused. The Polyoma line and N-1 can be thought of as genetically complementary, in some respects, to N-2. I take it you have tried many times to combine the Polyoma line and N-1, but no fusion product was found.

Ephrussi: No, we have not obtained it.

Atwood: Probably, with known complementary selective markers, you would find that fusion is a ubiquitous phenomenon and there is no such thing as a mater.

Ephrussi: We gave up the idea that N-2 may be a unique mater, since Leo Sachs claims that he obtained a hybrid between an L cell and a Polyoma cell.

Crow: There is an observation from the immunogenetics group at Wisconsin that suggests that it might not be entirely fruitless to search for mating in somatic cells. I don't know the full details, but there was a mosaic calf that was born as a twin and showed erythrocyte chimerism during the early part of its life. Later, a third type of cell was found which had some combined antigenic properties of the other two types and which had become the predominant cell type.

DeMars: Another possible point about ubiquitousness is that I think many people who have worked with HeLa cells have readily found tripolar spindles. I have always found them, and in quite a few different strains. One reason for taking this seriously, with regard to the possibility of segregants, is that in the laboratory at NIH, Dr. Eagle's laboratory, starting with the strain S3 HeLa, which had a modal number of close to 80, a strain was obtained by the random isolation of clones, which subsequently was named S3R1. This strain had a modal chromosome number of 55 and was altered in at least two properties that we looked at.

It is the strain that was unable to grow readily in the absence of glutamine. This strain was also relatively resistant to polio virus. It was the first one found by Darnell. But it was unaltered in its level of aminopterin resistance, so there was some big accident at mitosis there that led to an alteration in two properties of the cells.

Herzenberg: Do you see very many binucleate cells in either one of the parental lines used for the fusion?

Ephrussi: Yes.

Herzenberg: This is not something which could be correlated easily with the matability or nonmatability?

Ephrussi: I really don't know.

Patau: It doesn't mean too much because you will find, I would guess, in any tissue in which you search long enough a mitosis that is not followed by cytokinesis.

Herzenberg: I was just wondering whether those strains which happen to mate might have 20 or 10 percent binucleate cells, as compared to—

Ephrussi: No systematic study has been done. I was rather impressed by recent papers by Roizman from Johns Hopkins, on the formation of polykaryocytes, and, in fact, I wondered whether it was not frequently resulting in nuclear fusion and hybridization. Of course, he could not have discovered it because what he did to produce polykaryocytes was chiefly to mix virus-infected cells with nonvirus-infected cells of the same line. Since the cells that fused were karyologically identical, "hybrids" could not be distinguished from tetraploids formed otherwise. We did take this up for a while and tried to see whether polykaryocytosis could be used as a screen for the occurrence of hybrids, and, secondly, whether polykaryocytosis would promote hybrid formation. Unfortunately, all the known means producing polykaryocytosis seem to interfere with further cell division.

Renwick: May we ask Dr. Billingham if he sees any way around the histocompatibility problem in this hybrid?

Billingham: I gathered from what Dr. Ephrussi said that he is exploring several possible approaches. I'd like to suggest two additional ones.

In the first place if you simply inoculate homologous cells into newborn mice of most strains the cells will probably enjoy at least a 15-day period of exemption from an effective immunological attack on the part of their hosts because of their immaturity. If a fairly high dosage of cells is inoculated intraperitoneally, perferably intravenously, then some measure of tolerance may be induced in the hosts, assuring the inoculated cells and their descendants even more security of tenure.

The second approach involves trying to make some Swiss mice tolerant of a high proportion of the histocompatibility factors segregating in the noninbred stock employed. This could be done by selecting parents at random, to produce hybrid offspring. Then, in a cell suspension prepared from the pooled bone marrow of about ten such animals a broad isoantigenic spectrum should be represented. If newborn Swiss mice are then injected intravenously with a dosage of about 20 million cells from such a bone marrow "cocktail" there is a very good chance that "polyvalent" tolerance would be induced, enabling them, when they grow up, to accept cellular homografts from many different mice in the stock. Dr. Silvers and I have established the feasibility of such an approach in experiments conducted upon a large closed but noninbred population of Wistar rats (4). Bone marrow cells should be used to avoid the possible occurrence of graft-versus-host reactions leading to "runt disease."

If Dr. Ephrussi used either of these possible approaches on a fairly large scale to test his cells and failed to get tumors, then it would seem reasonable to conclude either that his cells were not malignant, or that they are malignant but possess some completely extraneous antigen unrelated to a histocompatibility factor.

Bayreuther: It should be added here that there are Polyoma virus transformed lines from inbred mice available by now. They have been developed by R. Weisberg.

Neel: Is there any further discussion of Dr. Ephrussi's contribution?

Stern: I would just like to ask Jim Crow whether the story of the mosaic cow that he told us about has been published?

Crow: No, it has not. I just heard about it a week ago in a casual conversation with W. H. Stone, and I told you all I know.

Neel: Perhaps this is the time for Dr. Koprowski to give us his criteria for a temperate mammalian virus.

Criteria for the Proof of Virogeny
in Mammalian Cells

by Dr. Hilary Koprowski

Koprowski: This is essentially an assignment in semantics. The first difficulty is to find a suitable term to describe a parallel condition to the temperate phage in an animal cell-virus system. I use the term "virogeny," but I do not like it. I have attempted to make a list of four criteria which have to be met before we can consider that there is a "virogeny."

"Virogeny," in a nonlysing mammalian cell culture can be accepted if the following criteria can be met:
1. Induction of appearance of the infectious virus.
2. Induction of appearance of an infectious nucleic acid.
3. Presence of virus antigen.
4. Resistance of the cell to superinfection, provided a cell of similar origin, treated in the same way as the exposed cell, is fully susceptible to the same infective dose of virus.

Eagle: Now, Hilary, do you mean that any one of these four would establish the condition, or that all are necessary? Are these four co-partners?

Koprowski: Either of the first two; I have not made up my mind whether the third and fourth criteria should be considered together or whether either one would be satisfactory.

Atwood: To the fourth criterion, you would have to add "regularly reproducible" and "virus-induced" to exclude mere selection of virus-resistant cells.

Bayreuther: I just wonder whether one could not replace the word "induction" by something else, perhaps "activation."

Koprowski: Yes, I know. I told you this was an assignment in semantics.

DeMars: I think it would be important to qualify all these statements by applying them to single cells. Dr. Koprowski began by discussing a nonlysing culture of cells. Many of these phenomena could be simulated in a culture, but, by working and emphasizing work with single cells, you might make these decent criteria.

Atwood: That's right.

Eagle: The release of the virus itself under appropriate stimulation is, of course, conclusive. On the other hand, to take the last criterion, the fact that a cell cannot be superinfected may have other explanations: the virus may have had a permanent effect on the genome of the cell, without, however, persisting as virus or even as a segment. This is not equivalent to the question that was asked about temperate phage.

Koprowski: I agree with you. For example, it would be difficult to make up our minds about the presence of Polyoma antigen in mouse tumor cells which do not yield virus at all and yet do not grow when implanted in adult mice immunized against Polyoma. Except for this single observation, there is no indication whatsoever that these cells differ "immunologically" from other mouse cells. Do we consider this "virogeny?"

At the present time one could speculate along two lines in regard to the genetical basis of the Polyoma virus induced antigen in tumor cells. (1) Presence of the Polyoma genome or part of it in a nonextractable, noninducible, probably defective form. (2) Polyoma acts as a mutator via early protein, to alter a specific gene site, and that the new antigen is due to something like a "cis-trans effect." We do not know if a genetic fragment of the virus did not express itself in altered cell surface antigens. However, it is possible that we should only establish the first and second criteria and disregard the third and fourth completely. However, does not a situation exist where phage infection can only be traced through superinfection of the bacterial cell?

Atwood: Well, no, I think not.

Koprowski: There is no such situation?

Atwood: No, because, in every case where you can demonstrate it that way, you can find other ways of demonstrating it as well. Wouldn't you say that was so?

DeMars: Yes.

Koprowski: The defective phage?

DeMars: Yes. You also run into some borderline cases; for example, there are some examples of transducing phages, where the genetic fragment established in the bacterium lacks the genetic elements that confer immunity on the bacterium; nevertheless, these genetic elements have been introduced with a transducing phage, and partake of some of the properties of a virus genome; so there is an element of ambiguity there, and this applies, also, to the Polyoma antigen, which can be related in a general way to what has been called lysogenic conversion. Often enough, infection with a temperate virus or establishment of a prophage leads to a phenotypic alteration that has no obvious connection with the phage at all. An example is the toxin produced by lysogenic Clostridium. Nevertheless, these are integral genetic elements of virus genome and you could imagine their establishment under conditions where other important elements of the virus genome would be lost. Therefore, your criteria do most of the job, but, as always, they leave vague areas.

Koprowski: Dr. Ephrussi, did you want to comment?

Ephrussi: No. I just wanted to be reminded of what the exact phrasing of the question yesterday was, that you tried to answer.

Koprowski: Maybe Dr. Herzenberg should rephrase his question. My interpretation was to provide a definition of essential criteria for the acceptance of certain conditions as temperate virus.

Ephrussi: In a bacterial cell?

Koprowski: No, this is all related to mammalian cells.

Ephrussi: Well, the best-known system is, of course, the lysogenic system and your fourth criterion is based on the situation in bacteria, where lysogenic integration of the phage genome leads to what we call immunity. It seems to me that there is a great deal of suspicion that immunity need not necessarily accompany integration.

I think that Bob DeMars said something about it. I have particularly in mind a case which is much less known, but about which I think we know enough to make what I am going to say rather probable. This is L'Héritier's case of CO_2 sensitivity in Drosophila, where definitely, a virus intervenes, the transmission of which indicates some kind of integration, but at what level one does not know. He has a number of situations with mutants of the virus which can be accounted for only by assuming, on the one hand, that there is in the cell an integrated virus and, on the other, that this does not prevent vegetative reproduction in the cytoplasm of the same cell; in other words, there seems to be integration not leading to immunity.

Eagle: That is why I mean that the fourth criterion is neither necessary nor sufficient.

Ephrussi: That's why I asked how the question was phrased—whether you were asked to define exactly what a situation similar to prophage, say, lambda in bacteria would be, or as a general proposition for any virus-carrying cell. My conclusion would be that there are obviously a number of examples which suggest that an integration which, in itself, is similar to that of prophage is not necessarily conducive to immunity.

Szybalski: Which really means that we have to define specific experimental criteria which must be satisfied when the problem of possible viral lysogeny is considered. At least four or five specified experiments should be executed and the results presented. With these results on hand it would be possible to decide whether true lysogeny or some borderline case prevails. So let's better specify exact experimental requirements, instead of worrying about semantics.

Koprowski: Let me give you a hypothetical example which may serve as an illustration of the fourth criterion. A Polyoma-induced tumor of a mouse has been grown in tissue culture and cloned. In order to provide adequate statistical support, let us say that 500 clones were obtained and all were investigated for presence of infective virus, infective DNA, and for virus antigen by appropriate immunological means. Results were all negative. However, all clones were resistant to superinfection by Polyoma virus. Progeny of 500 other clones obtained from tumors induced in the same mouse strain either by chemical carcinogens or other viral agents support growth of Polyoma. How should we classify the condition prevailing in the Polyoma-induced clones?

Atwood: It sounds very promising. [Laughter]

Koprowski: How would you know? By what would you go?

Atwood: I would say it suggests that such a virus genome might be there, perhaps. [Laughter]

Koprowski: Which is the fourth criterion.

Eagle: You say they can be superimposed?

Koprowski: Yes, they can.

Atwood: I would like to add a fifth criterion; that is, the demonstration of renatured hybrid nucleic acid, in which one of the participating strands is of viral origin and the other from the tumor in question.

Szybalski: With the experiment properly done. Especially since in the mammalian system the heterogeneity of DNA requires eliminating all nonspecific types of interaction. You know exactly, Kim, what I mean since this type of work is being done in your department.

Atwood: This can easily be done.

Herzenberg: I am confused now about what we are doing, again, because it seems that you say, Kim, if we meet only condition 4, the resistance of the cell to superinfection, then we can consider this very promising for being a virogeny situation?

Atwood: Yes, promising.

Herzenberg: I don't think it is—well, do you also think it is very promising for the idea that, perhaps, we simply selected a Polyoma-resistant variant in this way, with the selecting agent being the Polyoma virus?

Atwood: It has heuristic value. Then, you can explore that possibility afterward.

Herzenberg: And your exploration of it would be No. 5?

Atwood: Yes, that would be a very good way.

Herzenberg: So long as you are making hypothetical examples, one could certainly think of only a very small portion of the viral genome being incorporated here, and it might be that just random coincidences of reasonably small nucleotide sequences would then allow you to conclude that you do, indeed, have 1 percent of the total virus.

Atwood: One of the controls is an uninfected cell, whose nucleic acid should not significantly base pair with the virus.

DeMars: I can think of one case where a prophage, whose presence was unsuspected, was detected exactly through superinfection with a related virus, and many of the viruses that emerged from these bacteria had mutant properties. It turned out that there resided in the bacteria a defective prophage, which did not confer immunity but contained markers of a related prophage, different from those of the superinfecting phage, and this does present a good opportunity for detecting even small fragments of a virus genome, provided that you have a superinfecting phage that has enough different markers on it. "Marker rescue," this would be called.

Atwood: In the case of Polyoma virus, what markers could be used? The large and small plaque?

Bayreuther: We have got some temperature mutants of Polyoma by now. They have been developed by M. Fried.

Atwood: I don't know how you could rescue those.* [Laughter]

Szybalski: A propos your last criterion, perhaps you could refresh my memory, since I have some faint recollection that a virulent lambda virus which does not establish the lysogenic relationship still pairs with *E. coli* DNA. If this is correct, how would this modify your fifth criterion?

Atwood: I don't know.†

Szybalski: Anyway, I believe that the experimental criteria of molecular hybridization experiments should be clearly outined, especially for those virologists who are not quite familiar with these partly physico-chemical techniques.

Atwood: They are quite easy to work with.

Szybalski: You do not have to convince me. We use these techniques almost every day and I believe they are grand.

---

* Afterthought: Actually, temperature mutants might be very good for marker rescue.

† Afterthought: Evidence (1, 39) has appeared that lambda and P1 phages regularly possess host-homologous sequences adjacent (in the host) to the transducible gal and lac loci.

Herzenberg: We are now left with the conclusion that resistance to superinfection is a necessary criterion for virogeny in mammalian cells.

Szybalski: It is always useful but only accessory information in a case where you suspect virogeny.

Herzenberg: It is correct, I think, that we have not left that impression on the record at this point.

Koprowski: Do you agree to the presence of virus antigen?

Herzenberg: As being necessary?

Atwood: No.

Herzenberg: No.

Szybalski: If the viral antigen appears only after infection, this must have some meaning. It would indicate that some fragments of the viral genome are responsible for the production of new virus-associated proteins.

Neel: This question originated because of the discussion about the possible role of latent virus infections of cells, in cell transformation, and, as one entirely outside the field, I wondered what kind of criteria could be applied to pinning down the validity of this concept. I gather that criteria one and two would have wide acceptability around the table. If, after many cell generations, you get either the virus back or infectious DNA, this would satisfy everybody.

Atwood: Well, so far, in the few cases where the pairing method has been used, with virus versus host, except where criteria such as 1 and 2 would show that the host has some viral material, none has been found. For example, T2 and T4 have no squences in common with the host, and the RNA phage has no such sequence (18, 36).

Neel: So you feel pretty strongly about No. 5, too?

Atwood: Well, if viral nucleic acid paired with that of the tumor cell, but not the untransformed cell, it would show that some of the viral genome had persisted. If no pairing was found, an upper limit could be set on the amount that could have persisted. If viral nucleic acid paired with that of the untransformed cell, or with both, that would be interesting, but I would not know what to make of it.

Herzenberg: How about RNA virus? Is it possible to conceive of that being incorporated into the "genome" of the cells which have semiautonomous information? In other words, cytoplasmic particles of some sort which might not contain DNA. Or does this complicate it too much?

Atwood: The RNA bacteriophage has been explored more completely in the year and a half that it has been known than even TMV (19, 67), and it looks as though it does not go through any DNA stage of transcription; that is, it uses an enzyme which makes RNA on an RNA template. Infected *E. coli* usually lyse, the entering viral RNA being conserved through the lytic cycle. In the cells that do not lyse, the phage RNA is broken down. In other systems perhaps viral RNA could persist.

Herzenberg: So you also have to do annealing experiments?

Atwood: With RNA virus?

Herzenberg: Yes, with RNA as well as the DNA of the cell. DNA virus develops RNA virus. I think I could see the possibility at least of the reverse; that is, the DNA virus being incorporated with an RNA part of the genome. Is this too antidogmatic?

Atwood: In *E. coli*, the enzyme which makes RNA on RNA template cannot be found in uninfected cells (31, 123).

Herzenberg: But there are other cells besides *E. coli*. Mammalian cells may be somewhat different.

Atwood: In *E. coli* cells, the enzyme which does this RNA on RNA template cannot be found in the uninfected cell. I understand it has been found in some other cell, though; I can't remember what.

Renwick: How sensitive at the experimental level is this pairing technique? What proportion of the virus there would have to be labeled to be able to pick it up?

Atwood: It is extremely sensitive. I think it would detect the whole genome of even the very smallest virus, but I can't give you a proper answer.

Eagle: I would like to say, Jim [Neel], we spent a long time at this meeting discussing a wide variety of markers. There are a number of others which could be discussed, which, obviously, we will not get to. We have had two examples of how these markers can be used fruitfully, one by Dr. Ephrussi and one by Dr. Szybalski. Are there any other experimental situations in which these markers can be helpful, in terms of genetic analysis of somatic cells?

Neel: You are asking what we would do with markers if we had them?

Eagle: Yes.

Discussion on the Applications of
Somatic Cell Genetics

Atwood: I think this might be the time to put into the record the practical application about which I have talked to a number of people. If we accept as being highly probable the transformation story, and if we see that what is required to get a transformant is extremely strong selection for it, it becomes evident that it is worth a try to cure people who have orotic aciduria by transforming some of their cells, and this might be done *in vivo* by injecting them with transforming DNA, or it might be done on some cells you take out, transform, and put back very quickly, before anything else can happen to them.

One reason for thinking that it might succeed, aside from the transformation seeming to succeed, is that it is possible for the bone marrow to be repopulated by a very small surviving number of cells. The evidence is that some unique karyotype, which serves as a marker, is sometimes present after sublethal irradiation in up to 20 percent of the bone marrow cells.

This means that the number of cells present at the low point, just before recovery started, must have been very small; and so the transformation of a very small number, perhaps even one cell, out of all the cells of that individual, might effect a cure, at least so far as his bone marrow goes. You would have to rig up the situation properly to apply to selection; that is, first, feed in uridine and cytidine, so that the number of cells is built up to a large number. Then, right after the transformation, starve him so that only a transformed cell would grow, and then await results.

Lejeune: The only problem is to keep the individual alive during this time. [Laughter]

Atwood: Well, if the situation which Dr. Krooth described is the usual course, the patient has had many narrow escapes before. [Laughter]

Krooth: In theory, in this disease—and this is the only such disease that I can think of—it would be possible to carry on selection experiments *in vivo*, and to protect the patient by *weaning* him off his dietary cytidine and uridine, rather than by abruptly stopping them. You would gradually cut back on the quantity, and this might give transformed cells of rapidly growing tissues such as bone marrow, an advantage if they had been transformed to the point where they could now biosynthesize these compounds.

I think, if one reflects about this business, and I am sure everybody has, there are complicated problems, and the art does not appear to be advanced to the point where one has to grapple with them as yet. We know that, just to cite three very obvious ones, the serum is rich in deoxyribonuclease. We know, from certain disease states, that the human reticuloendothelial system can on occasion make powerful antibodies against DNA. Third, we know that many of the organs whose cells one would like, perhaps, to get infectious DNA into, are protected by physiologic filters which closely monitor the macromolecules that go across them. Of course, the cells that man would like most to transform probably do not divide. [Laughter]

Szybalski: Yesterday, we discussed this question and thought, perhaps, it would be possible to carry transformation outside of the body and then replant it back. But I am worrying now about another complication: If this is a point mutation which produces this clinically deleterious block, with the large cell population and the selective pressures which you expect in a large animal, you would think that some reverse mutations would occur and thus the needed function would be spontaneously restored. The irreversibility of the hereditary deficiencies about which we are talking now seems to indicate that a loss of a whole chromosome might take place, and this deficiency would be a little hard to restore by DNA-mediated genetic transformation.

Atwood: Yes, perhaps the cases that can revert in bone marrow are not ascertained, so the disease may be more common than we suppose.

Motulsky: Maybe, some experiments should be mentioned in relation to abnormal hemoglobins in tissue culture. There are two papers that report that a different variety of hemoglobin was gotten out of a tissue culture following attempts at transformation with "DNA." One of them, apparently, was achieved by incubating normal hemoglobin with DNA from marrow cells from a patient with sickle cell anemia (117). The culture produced an abnormal hemoglobin which was not sickle cell hemoglobin. It turned out that contaminating RNA rather than DNA had this effect. The new hemoglobin had an ill-defined structure which was not normal or abnormal hemoglobin; yet, something happened under these conditions.

Another set of experiments was published by Kraus, in which, apparently, she claimed that she got a different kind of hemoglobin, again (57). The full circumstances are not quite clear.

However, there are at least two experiments showing that something is happening. Would anybody care to comment on these hemoglobin experiments by Weisberger and Kraus?

Bearn: The nonspecific alterations do not seem to be of particular interest. One has to show, it seems to me, that a new hemoglobin has been formed, that it behaves like sickle hemoglobin electrophoretically, and, finally, that the only structural alteration is the substitution of a valine for a glutamic acid in the β tryptic peptide I, and that the change is abolished by DNAase.

Szybalski: This was not a hereditary change, but, even if it were, it could not be tested in the system they studied. This was something analogous to protein synthesis under influence of the proper messenger, with nondisrupted cells.

Neel: But, surely, there are a few less spectacular uses of markers than this. Jim Renwick, you must have thought a great deal about using markers for linkage studies?

Renwick: This has already been referred to, actually, by Dr. Ephrussi. I am sure that everyone is familiar with Professor Pontecorvo's ideas about using these markers, mainly depending on detection of monosomics rather than of somatic crossing over. But the only real comment I would like to make is that to be useful in mapping the loci which we know already and are interested in in man, we must find not only markers, but we must also find at least a few *common* markers which are already polymorphic in the population, and we must be able to detect these at the cell level, in culture.

Neel: How do the prospects look?

Renwick: I am fairly confident that somebody will do it some time. [Laughter]

Szybalski: Tell me whether there are, at present, any good markers which you could detect both in human populations and in cultured cells?

Renwick: I think that the G-6-DP locus is the only polymorphic one which is really promising at the moment.

DeMars: There are two related currents that have run through the entire session. Both of these deal with accidents in karyotype. One of these currents applies directly to the markers that have been discussed here and, also, most of the markers that have not been discussed.

There is a real question of whether the genetic variants that arise in tissue culture *de novo* are karyotype accidents, in the sense of being aneuploid variations, or whether they are what we would call, in a general sense, point mutations. In very few cases have the genetically determined phenotypic alterations been clearly associated with or dissociated from such aneuploid variations. This problem has not really been tackled and solved.

The related current that, I think, is very clear is that aneuploidy in man constitutes a serious load, when you add up the accidents that occur in mongolism, D-trisomy, chromosome No. 18 trisomy, and the other sorts of aneuploid variations that have been discussed here. It seems that we should pay very careful attention to trying to use these cultures to study nondisjunction in an organized way. The reason why these cultures would be good is that the prevalence of mosaicism in man indicates that a lot of the nondisjunction that disturbs man is mitotic nondisjunction, the kind that we can study in the cultured cells.

I was hopeful of hearing during this session somebody who had had a bright idea on how to go about studying one of these basic processes of genetic variation with cultured cells. I think that is one of the things for which they are especially fine. It is a question and a hope.

Herzenberg: Just to add one bit of information there, Bob, it doesn't really get to the crux of your point, which I think is a very well-taken one, but if drug-resistant mutations or variations which you get in culture are due to point mutational changes, there should be no a priori reason why it should be more difficult to get them in diploid cells than within the animal itself, provided that one has a system in which the animal itself has not put intervening complicating factors in the way.

We did try very hard but completely unsuccessfully to induce or to select for mutations in intact animals: to resistance to azaguanine, aminopterin, fluorodeoxyuridine, and fluoridine. The idea was to give just sublethal doses of these compounds to mice, repeatedly, over many months. Since most of these are toxic agents to the bone marrow and lymphoid system in general (the immediate toxicity is supposedly due to hemorrhagic difficulties) we might have selected, by this means, a cell which would be somewhat resistant to these agents, if such a cell did exist. We were unsuccessful.

Perhaps, the design of these experiments could be improved in some way, and any suggestions would be very gratefully applied.

DeMars: Didn't Law some years ago succeed in selecting for aminopterin-resistant leukemic-type cells in mice?

Herzenberg: Oh, yes, with tumors, you can do it all the time. I'm talking about normal cells, not tumor.

Szybalski: How would you detect the normal resistant cells in the animal? There are so many different replicating tissues in the animal. You don't mean that the animal as a whole would be more resistant to the drug, do you?

Herzenberg: Several things were done. The assumption was that the animal might be more resistant to 6-mercaptopurine, for example, or azaguanine, because the deaths were due to hematological difficulties. If you did induce a change in the bone marrow cell, the animal would be somewhat more resistant, the intestinal problems would not arise for quite a while, and the other dividing cells in the body are not so important; at least, in the first stages. This was one possibility.

It was checked, though, simply by giving slightly supertoxic levels and transplanting bone marrow and spleen isologously from one animal of inbred strain to another animal of inbred strain, and carrying this on through a couple of such transfers, trying, again, to up the level of resistance of the animals.

There was also, although this is not very good work at this point, some attempt to see whether freshly explanted cells of the lymphoid organs were somewhat more resistant to these two agents in primary culture.

Eagle: I have two questions here. What advantage does this have over the isolation of resistant mutants from diploid cultures *in vitro?*

Herzenberg: None. Well, I shouldn't say none, but I haven't heard of it being done as yet, either, with a diploid culture. I don't know of these things existing.

Eagle: I think this is a very promising area. I wanted to ask Dr. Renwick, would not a series of such mutants obtained in diploid cells give you material for the kind of mapping you were talking about?

Renwick: Yes, it would.

Herzenberg: You need an indefinitely propagable cell. So far, we do not have such a diploid cell.

Eagle: This is something we do not now have, so that we can, indeed, carry on the culture long enough to be able to do this. There is one technical trick, however, which does make these cells indefinitely propagable; that is, to freeze them very early, so that you always have a stock of the parent culture and can come back to it.

Herzenberg: Yes, but you have to induce your mutation.

Eagle: Yes, you get your mutation, and the mutation can be—

Herzenberg: I suggest that an animal, particularly the mouse or the rat, where you have inbred strains, does allow you, perhaps, to have an indefinitely propagable cell. It might be possible to maintain a cell diploid in culture for a while, then get rejuvenation back in the animal, where the nutritional needs might be more adequately satisfied, and then put it back in culture again. Only a genetically identical (histocompatible) animal will do.

Eagle: The trouble is, if you put back a diploid cell in a normal animal, it usually disappears.

Herzenberg: If you can pick the right kind of cell, it might not; for example, a lymphoid cell, again, which does divide continually. Certain ones certainly do divide continually.*

Eagle: I began to say that there are two technical problems which are, perhaps, not insurmountable. Even if it were true that, for reasons which are not now clear, the life span of a diploid cell is limited, freezing away the parent culture and the mutants does greatly prolong the total length of time over which one can operate, even though all of us have had problems in the restitution of such frozen cells; so that this really is not a problem.

The second technical problem, as was mentioned this morning, lies in our ability to clone these cultures, because the mutant must be isolated under essentially cloning conditions. This is, I think, not insuperable. By definition, these cells in small populations require something that they do not require in large populations.

Renwick: If I might modify my previous answer, there is an additional difficulty in Dr. Eagle's idea of using induced markers as linkage tools. If you find that one marker, induced in culture, is linked, say, with a rare marker gotten from the whole organism, say galactosemia, there is the difficulty that, if you repeat this in another strain and show that another induced marker is phenotypically identical with the first induced one, is linked with some other rare disease marker, then, you still have to show that the two induced mutants are identical. If we have no crossing, it is not easy.

To get around this, we might have to go to an amino acid sequence of a particular protein to show that a particular induced mutation affected a specific peptide, and this might be an adequate criterion that the two mutants are located in the same cistron without the crossing experiment. I don't know whether this would be acceptable to other people as a criterion.

Szybalski: This looks like a lot of work.

Renwick: It all is.

Neel: If we can go back to Dr. Herzenberg's experiment, how would

---

* Afterthought: An additional unselected (neutral) marker would be useful here. The gamma globulin isoantigens (allotypes) would serve well here. We are currently producing two pairs of mouse strains in which each one of a pair would carry a distinct gamma globulin antigen but be histocompatible (coisogenic) with the other member of the pair. Then cultures could be started with plasma cell precursors. The cultures, or hopefully, cloned subcultures could be introduced into the second strain and the fate of these cells easily traced by the gamma globulin marker.

you interpret the apparently well-established phenomenon of the emergence of resistance to the purine and pyrimidine antagonists in a patient with leukemia being treated with these drugs?

Herzenberg: You mean, how would I distinguish that result from the result with normal cells?

Neel: Yes, and is that, possibly, a manifestation of the phenomenon you are looking for?

Herzenberg: That is exactly the question, I think. It is very easy to induce resistance to antimetabolites either in culture or in tumors *in vivo,* but so far it has not been done with normal cells. I would like to know the reason for this. Perhaps, as Dr. DeMars indicated, the possibility still remains that there is some connection between aneuploidy and the development of resistance, or some chromosomal rearrangement and the development of resistance.

The best experiments, I think, which, apparently, give the most hope for throwing some light on this question, are the ones Dr. Szybalski described this morning; that you can, indeed, restore enzyme activity—in this case, it happens to be in a drug-resistant strain—with DNA, and show this is true transformation, in every sense of the word. Then, it is not due just to chromosomal rearrangement, but to a change in the DNA sequence, presumably.

Eagle: Or even simpler, producing the mutation in a diploid culture.

Neel: But, in leukemia, there is an increase in the mass of proliferating white cells, so there is a bigger population at risk. Has anyone done the simple experiment of sampling white cells from a patient with leukemia at various stages in therapy, setting up cultures and then testing for resistance?

Herzenberg: Law (62) has done this, essentially, with a fluctuation test in mice, with the subsequent development of resistance to, I think, aminopterin, in mouse leukemia, and he has some estimates of the mutation rate. I don't recall what they are. Perhaps, Dr. DeMars does. But they are not astronomically low, at all.

DeMars: They were about what you would want them to be.

Szybalski: Is this leukemia essentially diploid?

Neel: Yes. Has he controlled the chromosome counts at the same time?

Herzenberg: Essentially, not diploid, no, because they are either diploid or they are not. I think they are essentially not diploid, in the sense that they do have some small chromosome changes which, to the cytologist, are enormous with respect to the cell.

Neel: But is this known?—aside from the Philadelphia chromosome, again.

DeMars: You've got to remember what happens when you grow cells from marrow, Dr. Neel. We started to do your experiment, hopefully, and, I guess, this is Dr. Herzenberg's experiment, too. We can readily grow cultures from marrow, but the cells that grow are not members of the hematopoietic system. It is very unlikely that the altered phenotypes of the blood cells will be manifested in the cultures that grow from marrow. But I wouldn't rule out that possibility. It is just possible that some of these other nonblood-type cells in the marrow would express the mutant phenotype.

Krooth: I think we often assume, because of Law's work, that when a human patient with leukemia ceases to respond to a drug, it is because of a change in the biochemistry of the leukemic cell. But this may not be so. It is possible that if one took a normal individual and gave him some of these antimetabolites, normal bone marrow would also, in time, become resistant, by the same kind of systemic pharmacologic mechanism that confers resistance to huge doses of morphine in a person who is addicted. Admittedly, this did not happen in Dr. Herzenberg's mouse experiments.

Do we really have direct evidence in man that the acquisition of resistance by a malignancy is due to the biology of the malignant cell?

Szybalski: I know Jack Davidson at N.I.H. has found biochemical differences between drug resistant and sensitive human tumors.

Herzenberg: In some cases, you are probably right. Unfortunately, in the experiment I described, we did not have that complication. I say "unfortunately," because that would have been quite an interesting finding in itself, but it was not found, either.

DeMars: One point to make is that if this is some kind of systemic response, for instance, of other cells or tissues in the body, these changes are persistent. Once the child's leukemia becomes resistant to the antifolic or to the purine analog, even when he is put for several months, maybe six months, on other drugs, the resistance to the antifolic or whatever agent he first became resistant to persists.

Lejeune: It can vary. It is not absolute.

DeMars: You mean?

Lejeune: Sometimes, you will find sensitivity that differs from patient to patient. It is not general.

Herzenberg: Is it the rule or is it uncommon? So far as I know, they start them on methotrexate, aminopterin, 6-mercaptopurine, the steroids, and that's the end, because when they start mixing them or trying to go back to the beginning, in general, the leukemia resists everything that has been tried.

Lejeune: That's right, of course, but sometimes they do find, again, another type of sensitivity. It is not a general rule, I would say.

Neel: I have the impression, on the basis of empirical experience and some theoretical reasoning, the clinician now tends to use mixed therapy from the beginning.

Lejeune: Oh, no!

Neel: Maybe not in France, but in the United States, yes. I believe this is true, that the trend has been toward mixed therapy.

One can argue that if resistance is due to mutational events, then the probability of getting two simultaneous mutations conferring resistance to two antagonists is so much smaller than the probability of getting one that mixed therapy would seem to be a wise approach. This is the same argument as the one for using mixed antibiotics, which has been waged.

Crow: It isn't bad there, or not as bad as it is here.

Eagle: I'm sure that one would find no unanimity among a group of qualified physicians as to the value or lack of value of combined chemotherapy. As a matter of fact, I do know that this is under experimental and clinical study at the present time.

Szybalski: At least since 1950.

Eagle: There is a tremendous program under way, both at the NIH and in satellite laboratories, on just this matter of combined use of agents in the treatment of leukemia in man.

Motulsky: And this has been going on for some time, and the results are still not very clear.

Neel: That is correct, but the point is, whereas, originally, a treatment with one agent at a time seemed indicated, now there is very active investigation of the desirability of treating with two effective agents from the beginning, which is all I wanted to establish.

Eagle: But the results as of now are uncertain. However, even the premises on which this is undertaken are debatable.

Neel: What are the premises on which it is undertaken?

Eagle: One of them is, as you said, that we are dealing with mutations which grow out selectively, and if one uses combined agents, the possibility of having a mutant resistant to both is correspondingly reduced. There are, however, other possible explanations, including the one which was mentioned earlier, that resistance involves not necessarily the presence of a mutant cell, but an alteration in the host response to the drug.

Crow: If the system is complicated enough so that a polygenic model is appropriate, you can argue the other way around; simultaneous selection of two drugs is the most efficient way of accomplishing combined resistance. The animal breeder knows that if he wants to select for two traits, he can accomplish this more effectively by simultaneous selection than by doing them in series.

Eagle: I think this may be a very good example of the danger of extrapolating from a rigorous science to what is at the present time still a complex art.

Neel: What about the approach to mixed antibiotics on the treatment of a staphylococcal infection right now?

Eagle: The problem of combined antibiotic treatment, again, is not as simple as one might think. It is not just the prevention of the selective multiplication of a mutant. Resistance to a drug is usually due, not so much to the fact that you are supplying the drug in a concentration insufficient to kill off any possible one-step mutant, but that the organism is resistant to the antibiotic in *any* concentration, because of the very special conditions of *in vivo* growth. For example, an organism in a locus in which it is not multiplying will not be killed by penicillin, even though that same organism is rapidly killed by penicillin in culture, and at concentrations which are a small fraction of those which are achieved *in vivo*. It is therefore not a simple situation at all.

Neel: Let me phrase the question so we can get a yes or no answer. Given an effective drug, given in effective concentrations against the susceptible organism, then, what would be your position on mixed antibiotic therapy?

Eagle: In general, yes.

Krooth: I don't think that's a fair question, because it is put in such generalities. Many of these antibiotics, and many similar drugs, have quite significant toxic side effects, and there is often a very good argument that if you can do the job with just one adequately, why use two? Very often, by combining them, you may increase the risk of serious side effects and add the danger of clinical superinfection, infection with a resistant organism.

Neel: Yes. This is what I have told medical students for years. Yet, I think there is a broad tendency now to reexamine the philosophy of using two effective antibiotics, and perhaps two effective chemotherapeutic agents in high concentrations simultaneously; at least, it is being actively investigated, whereas, some years ago, we had accepted the idea that one agent at a time was the way to do it. Wouldn't you agree with that?

Eagle: No, I wouldn't.

Koprowski: I believe there is now a tendency to use one antibiotic which has been found effective against the specific organism causing the infection. I think that antibiotic cocktails are in disrepute and the clinicians are quite satisfied with the "one drug—one bug" approach. The staphylococcic infection is another story; this is a letdown of normal sterility precautions and has little to do with antibiotic therapy.

Eagle: I would go one step further. An antibiotic failure is rarely due to the failure to provide the active drug at the site of the infection in concentrations sufficient to kill off all the organisms, but it is due to other factors which have no relevance to the problem of drug resistance as considered by, e.g., Szybalski. For example, in the treatment of many staphylococcic infections, the problem is not one of killing the sensitive organism, but its replacement by other resistant organisms from the environment. Your conclusion is valid if you are faced with the simple situation on the basis of which you made your suggestion; but the therapeutic situation is much more complex than this.

Neel: Let's go back to where we got off on the antibiotics, which was the chemotherapeutic agents. It is correct, is it not, that there is now a widespread program of testing whether or not combined chemotherapeutic agents have a greater efficiency than a single agent, given until you exhaust it, and then switching over to another one?

Eagle: In cancer, yes.

Neel: And it has much of the rationale of the emergence of resistant mutations and the lesser probability of a double mutant?

Eagle: That is one element, yes.

DeMars: I can imagine situations where double chemotherapeutic treatment will actually give a higher survival of leukemic cells than the use of either agent alone. For instance, aminopterin or methotrexate apparently kills mainly by creating a thymine starvation, but chemotherapeutic agents that block RNA synthesis or protein synthesis will impede the killing effect of aminopterin. Together, these agents might create a stalemate situation, which prevents the actual multiplication of the cells, but does not lead to their death, which is really what you want to achieve in leukemia—not a stasis, but actual cell death. The double agent that you choose, therefore, has to be very carefully chosen.

Szybalski: Anyway, the principle is very sound. It was applied several times with great success, and the best example is tuberculosis. Each time, the combination of drugs should be carefully evaluated (96).

Lejeune: I would like to come back to something which has to do with the genic content of cell lines. Maybe I could suggest as a general statement that it is useful to possess a great number of pure lines which are very stable, of a normal karyotype. With the mongol, we are dealing with thousands or billions of cells which have a given karyotype. Don't you think it would be wise to try to know what is the biochemical effect of this given deviation, and that would be, possibly, a wise way to try to map this extra chromosome? It could perhaps also be done with the sex chromosomes and other aberrations. I don't know.

For the moment, it has been suggested that one of the ways to do this mapping with human cells would be to look at the special biochemistry that those people should have, or not have. Quite certainly, they will show a change because if they did not, they would be normal.

DeMars: I hate to end, or almost end, this meeting on a depressing note, but we have been trying to do this quite hard with the various trisomies that Dr. Patau and the pediatrics group at Madison have been working with. I can give you flat "noes" to the question of biochemical variation.

Gartler: What have you done?

DeMars: Careful enzyme determinations.

Gartler: Of what?

DeMars: Of acid phosphatase; an ill-defined enzyme entity, beta-glucuronidase; gamma-glutamyl transferase. Those three are carefully done so far. D-trisomy, chromosome 18-trisomy, and the mongoloid trisomy have failed to affect significantly these three enzymes.

Motulsky: Why should they, a priori? There are so many enzymes, and quite a few chromosomes.

DeMars: That is why I didn't want to end on a depressing note. We have no idea what to look at and, in just a simple-minded way, we proceeded with one at a time.

Neel: Do we have any other use for markers to put in the record before we adjourn?

Krooth: Yes, sir. I should like to comment on just one, in view of the data that Dr. Szybalski presented today. It has been pointed out here by several people that one cannot grow specialized cells in culture, as a rule. Although one cannot show that cultured cells resemble their tissue of origin, one can, of course, get highly polymerized DNA from a great many differentiated organs.

We know, for example, that there are certain enzymes which have very low activity in some tissues and very great activity in others. If one could transform cultured cells with regard to such an enzyme, one could bioassay the DNA from different tissues with regard to its transforming activity. Thus, one could see whether tissues with a higher concentration of enzyme had more transforming DNA for the enzyme than tissues with a lower concentration of the enzyme.

I think that one of the most exciting possibilities, if one can readily transform human cells in culture, is that it might prove a key for unlocking whatever genetic secrets may reside within the nucleus of the differentiated mammalian cell.

Neel: We stand adjourned.

REFERENCES

1. ATTARDI, G., NAONO, S., GROS, F., BRENNER, S., and JACOB, F. Effet de l'induction enzymatique sur le taux de synthèse d'un RNA messager spécifique chez *E. coli. C. R. Acad. Sci.,* **255**: 2303-5 (1962).

2. BEERS, R. F., and SIZER, I. W. A Spectrophotometric Method for Measuring the Breakdown of Hydrogen Peroxide by Catalase. *J. Biol. Chem.,* **195**: 133 (1952).

3. BERMAN, L., and STULBERG, C. S. Eight Culture Strains (Detroit) of Human Epithelial-like Cells. *Proc. Soc. Exp. Biol,* **92**, 730-35 (1956).

4. BILLINGHAM, R. E., and SILVERS, W. K. The Induction of Tolerance of Skin Homografts in Rats with Pooled Cells from Multiple Donors. *J. Immunol.,* **83**: 667-79 (1959).

5. BOYER, S. H., PORTER, I. H., and WEILBAECHER, R. Electrophoretic Heterogeneity of Glucose-6-Phosphate Dehydrogenase and Its Relationship to Enzyme Deficiency in Man. *Proc. Nat. Acad. Sci.,* **48**: 1868 (1962).

6. BRADLEY, S. G., and SYVERTON, J. T. *Proc. Soc. Exp. Biol. and Med.,* **103**: 215 (1960).

7. BRYSON, V., and SZYBALSKI, W. Microbial Drug Resistance. *Adv. in Genetics,* **7**: 1-46 (1955).

8. BUONASSISI, V., SATO, G., and COHEN, A. I. *Proc. Nat. Acad. Sci.,* **48**: 1184-90 (1962).

9. CAHN, R. D., KAPLAN, N. O., LEVINE, L., and ZWIL-
ING, E. Nature and Development of Lactic Dehydrogenase. *Science*, **136**: 962 (1962).

10. CANN, HOWARD M., and HERZENBERG, L. A. *In
vitro* Studies of Mammalian Somatic Cell Variation. I.
Detection of H-2 Phenotype in Cultured Mouse Cell
Lines. *J. Exp. Med.*, **117**, 2: 259-65 (1963).

11. CANN, HOWARD M., and HERZENBERG, L. A. *In
vitro* Studies of Mammalian Somatic Cell Variation. II.
Isoimmune Cytotoxicity with a Cultured Mouse Lymphoma and Selection of Resistant Variants. *J. Exp. Med.*,
117, 2: 267-84 (1963).

12. CHANG, R. S., and LIEPINS, H. *Proc. Soc. Exp. Biol.
and Med.*, **96**: 818 (1957).

13. COHEN, E. P., and EAGLE, H. *J. Exp. Med.*, **113**: 467-74
(1961).

14. COX, R. and PONTECORVO, G. Induction of Alkaline
Phosphatase by Substrates in Established Cultures of
Cells from Individual Human Donors. *Proc. Nat. Acad.
Sci.*, **47**: 839 (1961).

15. DeMARS, R. *Biochem. Biophys. Acta*, **27**: 435-36 (1958).

17. DeMARS, R., and HOOPER, J. L. A Method for Selecting for Auxotrophic Mutants of HeLa Cells. *J. Exper.
Med.*, **111**: 559-72 (1960).

18. DOI, R. H., and SPIEGELMAN, S. An Analysis of
Homology Between the Nucleic Acid of an RNA Virus and
the DNA in its Host Cell. *Science*, **138**:1270-72 (1962).

19. DOI, R. H., and SPIEGELMAN, S. Conservation of a
Viral RNA Genome During Transcription and Transla-
tion. *Proc. Nat. Acad. Sci.* (in press, 1963).

20. DRAY, S. Effect of Maternal Isoantibodies on the Quantitative Expression of Two Allelic Genes Controlling Gamma Globulin Allotype Specificities. *Nature*, **195**: 667
(1963).

21. DULBECCO, R., and FREEMAN, G. Plaque Production
by the Polyoma Virus. *Virology*, **19**: 396-97 (1959).

22. EAGLE, H. Amino Acid Metabolism in Animal Cell Cultures. *Science*, **130**: 432 (1959).

23. EAGLE, H., and PIEZ, K. *J. Exp. Med.*, **116**: 29-43
(1962).

24. EAGLE, H., PIEZ, K. A., and OYAMA, V. I. *J. Biol.
Chem.*, **236**: 1425-28 (1961).

25. ELDER, T. D., SEGA, S., MAXWELL, E. S., and TOP-
PER, Y. J. Some Steroid Hormone-like Effects of Menthol. *Science*, **132**: 225 (1960).

26. EPHRUSSI, B. *Virology*, **11**: 547 (1960).

27. EPHRUSSI, B., and SORIEUL, S. Mating of Somatic
Cells *in vitro*. *Univ. Michigan M. Bull.*, **28**, 347 (1962).

28. FALLON, H. J., LOTZ, M., and SMITH, L. H. Congeni-

tal Orotic Aciduria. Demonstration of an Enzyme Defect in Leukocytes and Comparison with Drug Induced Orotic Aciduria. *Blood,* **20:** 700 (1962).

29. FRANKLING, R. M., and BALTIMORE, D. Patterns of Macromolecular Synthesis in Normal and Virus-Infected Mammalian Cells. *Symp. on Quant. Biol., Biol. Lab.,* Cold Spring Harbor, **27:** 175-99 (1962).

30. GERBER, P. An Infectious Desoxyribonucleic Acid from Vacuolating Virus (SV 40). *Virology,* **16:** 96-98 (1962).

31. GIACOMONI, D., and SPIEGELMAN, S. Origin and Biologic Individuality of the Genetic Dictionary. *Science,* **138:**1328-31 (1962)

32. GREENFIELD, R. Personal communication.

33. HABEL, L. Resistance of Polyoma Virus Immune Animals to Transplanted Polyoma Tumors. *Proc. Soc. Exp. Biol. and Med.,* **106:** 722-25 (1961)

34. HAFF, R. F., and SWIM, H. E. *Proc. Soc. Exp. Biol. and Med.,* **93:** 200 (1956).

35. HAKALA, M. T. Prevention of Toxicity of Amethopterin for Sarcoma-180 Cells in Tissue Culture. *Science,* **126:** 255 (1957).

36. HALL, B. D., and SPIEGELMAN, S. Sequence Complementarity of T_2 DNA and T_2-specific RNA. *Proc. Nat. Acad. Sci.,* **47:** 137-46 (1961).

37. HARRIS, H., and RUDDLE, F. H. Clone Stains of Pig Kidney Cells with Drug Resistance and Chromosomal Markers. *J. Nat. Cancer Inst.,* **26:** 1405-11 (1961).

38. HAUGHTON, G., and DAVIES, D. A. L. Tissue Cell Antigens: Antigens of Mouse Tumor Cell Ghosts. *Brit. J. Exp. Path.,* **43:** 5, 488-95 (1962).

39. HAYASHI, M., SPIEGELMAN, S., FRANKLIN, N., and LURIA, S. E. Inducer Function and Cistron Transcription. *Proc. Nat. Acad. Sci.* (in press, 1963).

40. HAYFLICK, L., and MOORHEAD, P. S. The Serial Cultivation of Human Diploid Cell Strains. *Exptl. Cell Research,* **25:** 585-621 (1961).

41. HERZENBERG, L. A. Steps Toward a Genetics of Somatic Cells in Culture. Part I. *J. Cell Comp. Physiol.,* **60,** Supp. I: 145-57 (1962).

42. HERZENBERG, L. A., and HERZENBERG, Leonore. Association of H-2 Antigens with the Cell Membrane Fraction of Mouse Liver. *Proc. Nat. Acad. Sci.,* **47:** 762-67 (1961).

43. HÖGMAN, C. F. Blood Group Antigens on Human Cells in Tissue Culture: The Effect of Prolonged Cultivation. *Exp. Cell Res.,* **21:** 137-43 (1960).

44. HOLMES, R. 1963. Personal communication.

45. HUGULEY, C. M., BAIN, J. A., RIVERS, S. L., and SCOGGINS, R. B. Refractory Megaloblastic Anemia

Associated with Excretion of Orotic Acid. *Blood,* **14:** 615 (1959).

46. HÜLSMAN, W. C., OEI, T. L., and VAN CLEVALD, S. V. Phosphorylase Activity in Leucocytes from Patients with Glycogen Storage Disease. *Lancet,* **ii:** 581 (1961).

47. ISSELBACHER, K. J. Evidence for an Accessory Pathway of Galactose Metabolism in Mammalian Liver. *Science,* **126:** 652 (1957).

48. ISSELBACHER, K. J. Galactosemia. In *The Metabolic Basis of Inherited Disease,* ed. J. B. Stanbury, J. B. Wyngaarden, and D. S. Fredrickson. New York: McGraw-Hill Book Co., Inc., 1960. P. 1477.

49. KALCKAR, H. M. Biochemical Genetics as Illustrated by Hereditary Galactosemia. In *Biochemistry of Human Genetics,* ed. G. E. W. Wolstenholme (Ciba Foundation Symposium). London: J. A. Churchill Ltd., 1959. P. 347.

50. KALCKAR, H. M., KURAHASHI, K., and JORDAN, E. Hereditary Defects in Galactose Metabolism in *Escherichia coli* Mutants. I. Determination of Enzyme Activities. *Proc. Nat. Acad. Sci.,* **45:** 1776 (1959).

51. KELUS, A., GARNER, B. W., and COOMBS, R. R. A. Blood Group Antigens on Hela Cells Shown by Mixed Agglutination. *Immunology,* **2:** 262-67 (1959).

52. KIDSON, C., and GORMAN, J. G. Mechanisms Underlying Glucose-6-Phosphate Dehydrogenase Deficiency: Heterogeneity of Response to Stromal Activation in Erythrocytes. *Biochem. Biophys. Res. Comm.,* **7:** 268-71 (1962).

53. KIRKMAN, H. N. Electrophoretic Differences of Human Erythrocytic Glucose-6-Phosphate Dehydrogenase. (Abstract) *Am. J. Dis. Children,* **104:** 566 (1962).

54. KIRKMAN, H. N., RILEY, H. D., Jr., and CROWELL, B. B. Different Enzymic Expressions of Mutants of Human Glucose-6-Phosphate Dehydrogenase. *Proc. Nat. Acad. Sci.,* **46:** 938-44 (1960).

55. KLEIN, EVA. Studies on the Mechanism of Isoantigenic Variant Formation in Heterozygous Mouse Tumors. I. Behavior of H-2 Antigens D and K: Quantitative Absorption Tests on Mouse Sarcomas. *J. Nat. Cancer Instit.,* **27,** 5, 1069-93 (1961).

56. KODANI, M. *In Vitro* Alteration of Blood Group Phenotypes of Human Epithelial Cells Exposed to Heterologous Blood Group Substances. *Proc. Soc. Exp. Biol. and Med.,* **109:** 252-58 (1962).

57. KRAUS, L. M. Formation of Different Hemoglobins in Tissue Culture of Human Bone Marrow Treated with Human Deoxyribonucleic Acid. *Nature,* **192:** 1055 (1961).

58. KROOTH, R. S., and WEINBERG, A. N. Properties of Galactosemic Cells in Culture. *Biochem. Biophys. Res. Comm.,* **3:** 518 (1960).

59. KROOTH, R. S., and WEINBERG, A. N. Studies on Cell Lines Developed from the Tissues of Patients with Galactosemia. *J. Exp. Med.,* **113:** 1155 (1961).

60. KROOTH, R. S., HOWELL, R. R., and HAMILTON, H. B. Properties of Acatalasic Cells Growing *in vitro. J. Exp. Med.,* **115:** 313 (1962).

61. LAGUNOFF, D., and BENDITT, E. P. *J. Exp. Med.,* **112:** 571 (1960).

62. LAW, L. W. Origin of the Resistance of Leukemic Cells to Folic Acid Antagonists. *Nature,* **169:** 628 (1952).

63. LeBOUVIER, G. 1962. Personal communication.

64. LICHTENSTEIN, J., BARMER, H. D., and COHEN, S. S. The Metabolism of Exogenously Supplied Nucleotides by *Escherichia coli. J. Biol. Chem.,* **235:** 457-65 (1960).

65. LIEBERMAN, I., and OVE, P. Enzyme Activity Levels in Mammalian Cell Cultures. *J. Biol. Chem.,* **233:** 634 (1958).

66. LOCKART, R. Z., Jr. Personal communication.

67. LOEB, T., and ZINDER, N. A Bacteriophage Containing RNA. *Proc. Nat. Acad. Sci.,* **47:** 282-89 (1961).

68. McCOY, T. A., MAXWELL, J., and NEUMAN, R. E. *Cancer Research,* **16:** 979 (1956)

69. McFALL, E. and MAGASANIK, B. *J. Biol. Chem.,* **235:** 2103-8 (1960).

70. MAIO, J. J., and RICKENBERG, H. V. *Science,* **134:** 1007 (1961).

71. MELNICK, J. L. Papova-Group. *Science,* **135:** 1128-30, (1962).

72. MÖLLER, ERNA, and MÖLLER, GÖRAN. Quantitative Studies of the Sensitivity of Normal and Neoplastic Mouse Cells to the Cytotoxic Action of Isoantibodies. *J. Exp. Med.,* **115:** 3, 527-52 (1962).

73. MÖLLER, G. Demonstration of Mouse Isoantigens at the Cellular Level by the Fluorescent Antibody Technique. *J. Exp. Med.,* **114,** 4, 415-34 (*1961*)

74. MORRIS, C. C. Quantitative Studies in the Production of Acid Mucopolysaccharides by Replicate Cell Cultures of Rat Fibroblasts. *Ann. N. Y. Acad. Sci.,* **86:** 878 (1960).

75. NISHIMURA, E. T., HAMILTON, H. B., KOBARA, T. Y., TAKAHARA, S., OGURA, Y., and DOI, K. Carrier State in Human Acatalasemia. *Science,* **130:** 333 (1959).

76. NOMURA, M., MATSUBARA, K., OKAMOTO, K., and FUJIMURA, R. Inhibition of Host Nucleic Acid Synthesis by Bacteriophage T_4: Its Relation to the Physical and Functional Integrity of Host Chromosome. *J. Mol. Biol.,* **5:** 535-49 (1962).

77. PAUL, J., and FOTTRELL, P. Tissue-specific and Species-specific Esterases. *Biochem. J.,* **78:** 418 (1961).

78. PAVAN, C. Morphological and Physiological Aspects of

Chromosomal Activities. *Proc. of the Xth International Congress of Genetics,* Toronto: University of Toronto Press, 1959. I: 321.

79. PAVAN, C., and BREWER, M. E. Differences in Nucleic Acid Content of the Loci in Polytene Chromosomes of *Rhynohosciara angelae* According to Tissue and Larval Stages. In *Symposium on Cell Secretion,* ed. M. G. Belo Horizonte, Brazil: Instituto de Biologia la Faculdade de Filosofia da Universidade de Minos Gerais, 1955. P. 135.

80. PESCH, L. A., SEGAL, S., and TOPPER, Y. J. Progesterone Effects on Galactose Metabolism in Prepubertal Patients with Congenital Galactosemia and in Rats Maintained on High Galactose Diets. *J. Clin. Invest.,* **39:** 178 (1960).

81. PHILIP, J., and VESELL, E. S. Sequential Alterations of Lactic Dehydrogenase Isozymes During Embryonic Development and in Tissue Culture. *Proc. Soc. Exp. Biol. and Med.,* **110:** 582 (1962).

82. PRICE, V. E., and LEVINTOW, L. Sodium Pyruvate. In *Biochemical Preparations,* ed. E. Ball. New York: John Wiley and Sons, Inc., 1952. 2: 22.

83. RACE, R. R., and SANGER, R. Blood Groups in Man. 4th ed. Oxford: Blackwell Scientific Publications, 1962.

84. RAGNI, G., and SZYBALSKI, W. Molecular Radiobiology of Human Cell Lines. 11 Effects of Thymidine Replacement by Halogenated Analogues, on Cell Inactivation by Decay of Incorporated Radio-phosphorus. *J. Molecular Biol.,* **4:** 338-46 (1962).

85. ROOSA, ROBERT A., BRADLEY, T. R., LAW, L. W., and HERZENBERG, L. A. Characterization of Resistance to Amethopterin, 8-azaguanine and Several Fluorinated Pyrimidines in the Murine Lymphocytic Neoplasm. *J. Nat. Cancer Inst.,* p. 109 (1962).

86. SCHINDLER, R. *Biochem. Pharmacol.,* **1:** 323 (1958).

87. SCHINDLER, R., DAY, M., and FISCHER, G. A. *Cancer Research,* **19:** 47 (1959).

88. Schlesinger, R. W. Vagaries of Adenovirus Cell Complexes. *Perspectives in Virology,* Minneapolis: Burgers Publishing Co., 1960. 2: 69-77.

89. SHEIN, H. M., ENDERS, J. F., and LEVINTHAL, J. D. Transformation Induced by Simian Virus 40 in Human Renal Cell Cultures. II. Cell-Virus Relationship. *Proc. Nat. Acad. Sci.,* **48:** 1350-57 (1962).

90. SHEIN, H. M., ENDERS, J. F., LEVINTHAL, J. D., and BURKET, A. E. Transformation Induced by Simian Virus 40 in Newborn Syrian Hamster Renal Cell Cultures. *Proc. Nat. Acad. Sci.,* **49:** 28-33 (1963).

91. SHENG, T. C. A Gene That Causes Natural Death in Neurospora Crassa. *Genetics,* **36:** 199-212 (1951).

92. SJÖGREN, H. D., HELLSTRÖM, I., and KLEIN, G. Resistance of Polyoma Virus Immunized Mice Against Transplantation of Established Polyoma Tumors. *Exp. Cell Res.*, **23**: 204-8 (1961).

93. SMITH, L. H., SULLIVAN, M., and HUGULEY, C. M. Pyrimidine Metabolism in Man. IV. The Enzymatic Defect of Orotic Aciduria. *J. Clin. Invest.*, **40**: 656 (1961).

94. STOKER, M., and ABEL, P. Conditions Affecting Transformation by Polyoma Virus. *Symp. on Quant. Biol., Biol. Lab. Cold Spring Harbor*, **27**: 375-86 (1962).

95. SZYBALSKA, E. H., and SZYBALSKI, W. Genetics of Human Cell Lines. IV. DNA Mediated Heritable Transformation of a Biochemical Trait. *Proc. Nat. Acad. Sci.*, **48**: 2026-34 (1962).

96. SZYBALSKI, W. Theoretical Basis of Multiple Chemotherapy. *Tuberculology*, **15**: 82-85 (1956).

97. SZYBALSKI, W. Observations on Chemical Mutagenesis in Microorganisms. *Annals N. Y. Acad. Sci.*, **76**: 475-89 (1958).

98. SZYBALSKI, W., and BRYSON, V. Origin of Drug Resistance in Microorganisms. In *Origin of Resistance to Toxic Agents*, M. G. Sevag, R. D. Reid, and O. E. Reynolds, eds., New York: Academic Press, 1955. Pp. 20-41.

99. SZYBALSKI, W., and SZYBALSKA, E. H. A New Chemotherapeutic Principle for the Treatment of Drug-Resistant Neoplasms. *Cancer Chemotherapy Reports*, **11**: 87-89 (1961).

100. SZYBALSKI, W., and SZYBALSKA, E. H. Drug Sensitivity as a Genetic Marker for Human Cell Lines. *Univ. Mich. Med. Bull.*, **28**: 277-93; and in *Approaches to the Genetic Analysis of Mammalian Cells*. Michigan Conference in Genetics, D. Merchant, and J. V. Neel, eds. Ann Arbor: The University of Michigan Press, 1962. Pp. 11-27.

101. SZYBALSKI, W., SZYBALSKA, E. H., and BROCKMAN, R. W. Biochemical Basis of Sequential Mutations Toward Resistance to Purine Analogs in Human Cell Lines. *Proc. Amer. Assoc. Cancer Res.*, **3**: 272 (1961).

102. SZYBALSKI, W., SZYBALSKA, E. H., and RAGNIE, G. Genetic Studies with Human Cell Lines. In *Nat. Cancer Instit. Monog.*, **7**: 75-89 (1962).

103. TAKAHARA, S. Progressive Oral Gangrene Probably Due to Lack of Catalase in the Blood. *Lancet*, **ii**: 1101 (1952).

104. TAKAHARA, S. Progressive Oral Gangrene Probably Due to Acatalasemia. *Laryngoscope*, **64**: 685 (1954).

105. TAKAHARA, S., HAMILTON, H. B., NEEL, J. V., KOBARA, T. Y., OGURA, Y., and NISHIMURA, T. Hypocatalasemia: A New Genetic Carrier State. *J. Clin. Invest.*, **39**: 610 (1960).

106. TAKAHARA, S., OGATA, M., KOBARA, T. Y., NISH-

IMURA, E. T., and BROWN, W. J. The "Catalase Protein" of Acatalasemic Red Blood Cells, an Electrophoretic and Immunologic Study. *Laboratory Invest.,* **11:** 782 (1962)

107. TEMIN, H. M. Mixed Infection with Two Types of Rous Sarcoma Virus. *Virology,* **13:** 158-63 (1961).

108. TING, R. Virus Release from Clones of Rous Sarcoma Cells. *Annual Report,* Division of Biology, California Institute of Technology, 142 (1962).

109. TOMIZAWA, W., and ARNNOW, L. Studies on Drug Resistance in Mammalian Cells. II. 6-Mercaptopurine Resistance in Mouse Fibroblasts. *J. Pharmacol. Exper. Therapeutics,* **128:** 107-14 (1960).

110. UZMAN, L. L. The Intrahepatic Distribution of Copper in Relation to Wilson's Disease. *A.M.A. Arch. Path.,* **64:** 464 (1957).

111. UZMAN, L. L., IBER, F. L., CHALMERS, T. C., and KNOWLTON, M. The Mechanism of Copper Deposition in the Liver in Hepatolenticular Degeneration. (Wilson's Disease). *Amer. J. Med. Sci.,* **231:** 511 (1958).

112. VESELL, E. S., and BEARN, A. G. Localization of Lactic Dehydrogenase Activity in Serum Fractions. *Proc. Soc. Exp. Biol. and Med.* **94:** 96 (1957).

113. VESELL, E. S., and BEARN, A. G. Isozymes of Lactic Dehydrogenase in Human Tissues. *J. Clin. Invest.* **40:** 586 (1961).

114. VESELL, E. S., PHILIP, J., and BEARN, A. G. Comparative Studies on the Isozymes of Lactic Dehydrogenase in Rabbit and Man. Observations During Development and in Tissue Culture. *J. Exp. Med.,* **5:** 797 (1962).

115. VOGT, M., and DULBECCO, R. Virus Cell Interaction with a Tumor-producing Virus. *Proc. Nat. Acad. Sci.,* **46:** 365-70 (1960).

116. VOGT, M., and DULBECCO, R. Studies on Cells Rendered Neoplastic by Polyoma Virus: the Problem of the Presence of Virus Related Materials. *Virology,* **16:** 41-51 (1962).

117. WEISBURGER, A. Induction of Altered Globin Synthesis in Immature Erythrocytes Incubated with Ribonucleoprotein. *Proc. Nat. Acad. Sci.,* **48:** 68 (1962).

118. WILCZOK, T. The Absorption of Heterologous Desoxyribonucleii and by Novikoff Hepatoma Cells. *Neoplasma,* **8:** 453-62 (1961).

119. WILLIAMS, H., and FIELD, J. Leucocyte Phosphorylase in Hepatic Phosphorylase-deficient Glycogen Storage Disease. *J. Clin Invest.,* **40:** 1841 (1961).

120. WILLIAMS, H. E., JOHNSON, P. L., FENSTER, F. L., LASKER, L., and FIELD, J. B. Intestinal Glucose-6-

Phosphatase in Control Subjects and Relatives of Patients with Glycogen Storage Disease. *Metabolism,* **12:** 235 (1963).

121. WINOCOUR, E. Purification of Polyoma Virus. *Virology,* **19:** 158-68 (1963).

122. WYNGAARDEN, J. B., and HOWELL, R. R. Acatalasia. In *The Metabolic Basis of Inherited Disease,* ed. J. B. Stanbury, J. B. Wyngaarden, and D. S. Fredrickson. New York: McGraw-Hill Book Co., Inc., 1960. P. 1477.

123. YANKOWSKI, S. A., and SPIEGELMAN, S. The Identification of the Ribosomal RNA Cistron by Sequence Complementarity. II. Saturation of and Competitive Interaction at the RNA Cistron. *Proc. Nat. Acad. Sci.,* **48:** 1466-72 (1962).